W9-CDS-231

AGRICULTURAL GEOGRAPHY

BELL'S ADVANCED ECONOMIC GEOGRAPHIES

General Editor

PROFESSOR R. O. BUCHANAN

M.A.(N.Z.), B.Sc.(Econ.), Ph.D.(London)

Professor Emeritus, University of London

A. Systematic Studies

AN ECONOMIC GEOGRAPHY OF OIL
Peter R. Odell, B.A., Ph.D.

PLANTATION AGRICULTURE
P. P. Courtenay, B.A., Ph.D.

NEW ENGLAND: A STUDY IN INDUSTRIAL ADJUSTMENT
R. C. Estall, B.Sc.(Econ.), Ph.D.

GREATER LONDON: AN INDUSTRIAL GEOGRAPHY
J. E. Martin, B.Sc.(Econ.), Ph.D.

GEOGRAPHY AND ECONOMICS
Michael Chisholm, M.A.

B. Regional Studies

AN ECONOMIC GEOGRAPHY OF EAST AFRICA
A. M. O'Connor, B.A., Ph.D.

In Preparation

THE GEOGRAPHY OF RURAL LAND USE
Professor J. W. Birch, B.A., Ph.D.

AN ECONOMIC GEOGRAPHY OF JUGOSLAVIA
Ian Hamilton, B.Sc.(Econ.), Ph.D.

AN ECONOMIC GEOGRAPHY OF CARIBBEAN AMERICA
Peter R. Odell, B.A., Ph.D.

AN AGRICULTURAL GEOGRAPHY OF GREAT BRITAIN
Professor J. T. Coppock, M.A., Ph.D.

AN ECONOMIC GEOGRAPHY OF BRAZIL
J. D. Henshall, M.A., M.Sc. & R. P. Momsen, A.B., M.A., Ph.D.

AN INDUSTRIAL GEOGRAPHY OF THE BRISTOL REGION
John N. H. Britton, M.A., Ph.D.

AGRICULTURAL GEOGRAPHY

LESLIE SYMONS

B.Sc.(Econ.), Ph.D.

Senior Lecturer in Geography,
University of Canterbury,
Christchurch, New Zealand

LONDON
G. BELL AND SONS, LTD
1967

York House, Portugal Street
London, W.C.2

Printed in Great Britain by
NEILL & Co. LTD., EDINBURGH

TO

My Wife,

Alison and Jennifer

Contents

Tables

Maps and Diagrams

Acknowledgements

My first acknowledgement must be to Professor R. O. Buchanan for encouragement to write this book and for reading and commenting on the whole script. Moreover, to him and to the late Sir Dudley Stamp I owe my own introduction to the systematic study of agricultural geography and land utilisation at the London School of Economics. Many others deserve mention but it would be impracticable to acknowledge all the help and ideas that have contributed to this book. Numerous colleagues have read parts of the script and to all I am deeply grateful, though responsibility for any errors and all omissions is entirely my own.

I am pleased to acknowledge the co-operation of the following authorities for permitting me to use their material: C.S.I.R.O. Australia (Division of Soils), U.S. Department of Agriculture and Messrs. Edward Arnold (Figure 1); Messrs. George Allen and Unwin Ltd. (Figure 2), The University of London Press, Ltd. (Figures 4 and 15), The Association of American Geographers (Figure 6), The Editor, *Journal of Tropical Geography* (Figure 12), The Editor, *Economic Geography* (Figures 13, 14, 16 and 17) and Messrs. Routledge and Kegan Paul Ltd. (Figure 11 and associated material). Extracts from maps of the Land Utilisation Survey of Great Britain and the second Land Utilisation Survey of England are reproduced in Figure 19 by permission of the late Sir Dudley Stamp and Miss Alice Coleman respectively. The sources of other maps indicate the authorities who have kindly given permission for their use in this volume.

For their co-operation at all stages of preparation of the book I wish to thank the technical staff who have re-drawn and photographed maps and diagrams, and my wife who has devoted many hours to preparing the index, proof-reading and other tasks.

Introduction

This book makes no pretence at being a comprehensive geography of agriculture; such a treatment would be far beyond its scope. In teaching geography, and more particularly economic geography, however, it has become apparent that there is need of a short study in which the emphasis is on the approach to the unravelling of questions about agricultural distributions rather than on the detail of the distributions themselves.

Agriculturalists and agronomists are increasingly concerning themselves with the world-wide distributions of crops, animals and types of rural economy and the problems associated with them. It is hoped, therefore, that this book will be of interest to specialists in the agricultural sciences as well as to geographers, whose primary concern is the investigation and understanding of the spatial patterns of human and physical phenomena on the earth's surface, and their interrelationships.

If it be felt that the term agricultural geography does not in itself adequately define the subject, this may be better understood by recourse to a definition of economic geography. Some authorities regard economic geography as a discipline in its own right, or at least a primary division of geography.[1] More widely, however, it is considered as a part of human geography, which alone is placed with physical geography to constitute two primary divisions. Many definitions of economic geography have been attempted, but none has the merit of combining adequacy and brevity better than 'the geography of man's work'.[2] Agricultural geography fits into this definition as the geography of man's husbandry of the land.

Modern economic geography is not merely the geography of production or even of production and exchange, recognition being given to the geography of consumption. In those aspects

[1] See for example the Russian view expressed by Konstantinov (1962).
[2] R. O. Buchanan (1951).

of the subject which may be grouped under the title 'agricultural geography' there is necessarily an emphasis on the pattern of production, with consumption or, more immediately, effective demand, as the necessary stimulus which calls forth production.

Hunting and collecting are not here regarded as agriculture unless there is conscious effort to improve, or at least modify, the hunting or collecting grounds beyond their natural state. Modification of the natural environment is the essence of agriculture. It may be argued that every hunter or collector modifies the environment by limiting the spread of his prey, be it animal or fruit, but a reasonable interpretation of agriculture would seem to be deliberate effort to modify. Thus, when the hunter deliberately burns the range or selectively culls animals, he is on the verge of becoming a pastoralist, and for practical purposes we should include pastoralism in agriculture. When man follows fire by scattering seeds of desired species in the ashes, he is an agriculturalist, even if he does not so much as turn the soil with a digging stick.

Whether or not to include forestry in agriculture is a question not susceptible of easy solution. In parts of Scandinavia and central Europe, for example, forestry is an important part of the agricultural economy. Forest lots form an integral part of the overall and long-term management of the individual farm. Even so, the day-to-day integration of use of the forest and farm is usually limited to pasturing stock in the woodland, and this only where it can be done without serious harm to the trees. More generally, farmers see forests as competitive rather than complementary with their activities, though scientists and foresters may interpret the relationships otherwise.[1] On balance, and having regard to the moderate length imposed on this book, I have excluded forestry from direct consideration.

Geographers have been much occupied during the development of the subject in this past half-century with the extent to which the environment is responsible for the forms of man's occupation of the earth. 'Determinism' viewed the natural environment as closely controlling man's activities, to the extent that the organisation of his life was a response to the

[1] See for example 'Agriculture and forestry', *International journal of agrarian affairs*, II, 1955.

restrictions imposed on him by relief, soils, climate and other manifestations of the physical surroundings. Revolt against the acceptance of such limitations produced the 'possibilist' school of thought, which holds that the environment offers certain possibilities which man may or may not exploit. Determinism is generally discredited but 'probabilism' offers a compromise position.[1] It may appear to the reader at times that my thought verges on the deterministic when dealing with the more severe environments. I justify such nearness to heresy by reference to the oft-repeated instance of growing bananas at the North Pole. It may be accepted that it would be possible to grow bananas at the North Pole (or more likely in this century at the South Pole, as it has a more satisfactory base for permanent establishments) but this is unlikely to have any practical significance, at least in economic geography. It will always be so much cheaper, in the world as we know it and within the changes that we can visualise, to grow bananas in the tropics, that for practical purposes we may say that polar climates are unsuitable for the cultivation of the banana, and that climatic considerations set limits to the zone within which it is possible, i.e. economically possible, to cultivate the banana. New and hardier strains of the banana may be evolved, which will enable it to be cultivated beyond the present limits, but the limits at any one time will be those set by climate, in relation to the current stage of technological advance.

The plan of this book implies a proposition that climate and weather set broad limits to the types of agriculture that man may pursue in any region. Within these limits, relief factors impose further limitations or, to express the same idea in a positive instead of negative way, offer certain possibilities. The relief controls operate partly through the climate they create, high altitudes being in some respects similar to high latitudes, and partly through angle of slope and irregularity of surface. The soil reflects both these major factors (climate and relief) as well as the nature of vegetation, which is itself an expression of the interaction of climate, relief and soil. Also in the character of soil, partly through his effect on the vegetation, but also directly, is found the impact of man.

[1] Space precludes more than brief reference to this philosophical argument. Lewthwaite (1966) provides a recent and readable guide to the debate.

Given these limitations, man's response in modifying the environment will depend on the stage of his development—the science and technology at his command, the possession of suitable economic and social institutions and organisations and his initiative in making use of these attributes. These, in turn, will be affected by the historical background of his race, nation and local community, and by his religious and other personal convictions.

Finally, response will be conditioned by economic forces—the revenue he will get for his products, the prices he must pay for the goods and services he wishes to purchase, and the cost he incurs in production. Cost is not to be evaluated solely in terms of monetary outlay, for, as the economist teaches, the cost of something is what is gone without to achieve that thing. The cost to a farmer of spraying his wheat to kill a particular insect may be the construction of a new shed to protect valuable livestock in winter—the cost of not spraying may be the loss of the wheat. Unfortunately, true costs of this kind are difficult to evaluate, but they must influence the policy of the individual and of governments.

In this book there is consideration of these forces and their effects in particular instances. Following this analytical treatment in Part I, synthesis is attempted in Part II through the portrayal of certain types of agriculture selected both for their importance in the world and for the principles they illustrate.

It was thought better to treat of only a small number of types of agriculture in some detail, rather than briefly to survey the whole range. Such a general survey is available in many textbooks of economic geography but the relationship of the selected types to the general field of farming may be judged from the introduction to Part II (Chapter 4). Furthermore, in selecting the types of agriculture to be discussed, and the regions to illustrate these types, I have chosen those with which I am most familiar. Between them, they cover a wide enough field to illustrate and develop the principles advanced in Part I. Chapter 5 deals with mixed crop and livestock farming in temperate latitudes, with examples from the British Isles and New Zealand. The former region provided the setting for much of the technological development of this type of farming, while the latter illustrates its adaptation by people of the same culture to a different environment in a newly-settled country, and to greatly differing market conditions. The two following chapters emphasise the geographical and economic importance of the form of organisation adopted in farming. Chapter 6 takes one example of plantation agriculture, rubber production in Malaya, to illustrate this form of organisation and a type of farming largely conducted by this means. It is the shortest chapter of the book, because a complete volume on plantation agriculture has already appeared in this series.[1] Chapter 7 examines agriculture in the U.S.S.R. as an example of collective and state farming. Opportunity is taken in this chapter to stress the importance of historical perspective in evaluating a system of agriculture and its successes and failures. A decreasing proportion of the world's farmers is engaged in subsistence farming, at least in its purer forms. In considering farming in which production for the market is still unimportant, the emphasis in Chapter 7 is placed on shifting cultivation, and one example which is well documented is treated in some detail. A brief resumé of a contrasting aspect of subsistence farming is also given for comparative purposes, and the selection here again of the Malayan scene permits maximum economy of space as it connects with the earlier chapter on plantation agriculture.

A distinctive contribution that geography makes to scientific knowledge is its study of the regions of the earth's surface. Part of the task of the agricultural geographer is the delimitation and assessment of the regional characteristics of agriculture. Regional variations are obvious to the most casual observer but their complexity is such that their resolution presents a continuing challenge of an academic, and more latterly, a practical significance. The attention given to planning for economic and social development since the world-wide economic depression of the nineteen-thirties, and more especially since the Second World War, has brought to the fore the practical necessity to recognise regions for development programme purposes. In order that measures applied to deal with the problems of any particular area shall be applied as widely as required, and yet shall not obtrude into neighbouring areas where different problems exist and different remedies are

[1] Courtenay (1965).

needed, an area of study must be broken down into regions. Some of the concepts and techniques that have been used to delimit and describe agricultural regions are summarised in Chapter 9, while some of the methods used in assessing the productivity of regions and their relevance for development programmes receive attention in Chapter 10.

We end, then, with attention to concepts which may be of value in assessing future trends and in planning to meet the problems of the future. No better beginning, however, can be found than in a reminder of the inheritance of agricultural science from the past and the depths of the roots of man's cultivation of the soil, so we first briefly consider some important theories regarding the origins of agriculture and some aspects of its historical development.

PART I

THE PHYSICAL AND SOCIAL ENVIRONMENT

CHAPTER 1

The Origins and Development of Agriculture

The origins of agriculture provide a rich field for investigation by archaeologists and anthropologists in co-operation with botanists, zoologists and other specialists in the physical sciences. Before man's earliest attempts to control or influence vegetation, plants provided him with some food directly and some through the insects, animals and birds they supported. Use of fire-culture in some deliberate form, such as clearing forests and driving game, may take us back hundreds of thousands of years, but almost certainly tens of thousands.[1] The setting of fire to improve pasture is both old and widespread, and selection of plants, some to be encouraged, some to be destroyed by fire and other means, undoubtedly preceded the beginnings of agriculture proper.

The domestication of plants and animals probably began about 8000 B.C. The relationships between early agriculture and pastoralism are controversial:

> One theory favours the view that, from a common cradle of mixed farming, which is to be located in the lands of the Fertile Crescent, the new food-producing economy spread in different directions. One of these led into the steppes of Eurasia, where the culture was altered into a completely pastoral and nomadic one—a process which was furthered by environmental factors. A second theory hinges on different origins of plant cultivation and stock-raising, respectively. Spreading into the other continents of the Old World, the two economies met each other and inter-

[1] Stewart (1956).

mingled in the region of the Fertile Crescent or adjacent countries, thus giving rise to mixed farming.[1]

The theory, handed down from the Romans, that agriculture had developed by direct sequence from collecting through hunting and pastoralism is now rarely voiced. Similarly, evidence weighs against origins in the great river valleys, where water control was required. Investigation has given evidence of earlier cultivation among the foothills and upland country of easily worked soils. As one widely accepted view of the origins of agriculture, Sauer's basic premises[2] may be summarised:

(*a*) Agriculture did not originate in communities desperately short of food, but where there was sufficient freedom from want to experiment.

(*b*) The hearths of domestication are to be sought in regions of marked diversity of plants or animals.

(*c*) Primitive agriculture began not in the large river valleys, subject to lengthy floods and requiring protective dams, drainage or irrigation, but in hill lands.

(*d*) Agriculture began in wooded lands which have soils easy to dig.

(*e*) The inventors of agriculture had previously acquired special skills, but hunters would be least inclined towards domestication.

(*f*) Above all, the founders of agriculture were sedentary folk. Growing crops require constant attention. Unless constantly guarded, the crop will be lost.

To Sauer, the most likely people to begin agricultural practices were 'some well-situated, progressive fishing folk living in a mild climate along fresh waters'. He proposed south-east Asia as the cradle of earliest agriculture. 'No other area is equally well situated or equally well furnished for the rise of a fishing-farming culture.' He argued that the earliest domesticated animals—dog, pig, fowl, duck and goose—originated there as animals of the household, in contrast to the

[1] Narr (1956), 136.
[2] Sauer (1952), 21.

herd animals of south-west Asia. Here also is the major centre of planting techniques and vegetative reproduction which, he accepted, man learnt before he learnt the growing of crops from seeds.[1]

Diffusion of these cultures, in Sauer's view, occurred in the Pacific region, northwards to China, round the Indian Ocean to Africa and through the Mediterranean lands to Europe. Similar reliance on vegetative reproduction is found in tropical America. He favoured the north-western extremity of vegetative planting, that is, the Mexican-Central American border, as the hearth of the principal seed plants. In the Old World, Sauer recognised three centres of seed domestication—one in north China, a second in western India, extending to the eastern Mediterranean and a third in Ethiopia. 'In all three, vegetative reproduction was made difficult, annual seed growing facilitated by climate.'[2]

Earlier, Vavilov[3] had listed eight independent centres of origin of the world's most important cultivated plants, based on expeditions he and other Russian scientists made throughout the world between 1916 and 1934:

I China. 'The earliest and largest independent centre . . . consists of the mountainous regions of central and western China, together with the adjacent lowlands'. Vavilov credited this region with important millets, buckwheat, soya beans, legumes and fruits and listed 136 endemic species.

II India, including Burma and Assam, excluding north west India. 'India is undoubtedly the birthplace of rice, sugar cane, a large number of legumes and many tropical fruit plants, including the mango and numerous citrus plants. . .' Pulses, gourds and vegetables including cucumber, lettuce and radish were among the 117 listed species.

(IIa) The Indo-Malayan centre, including Indonesia and the Philippines. 55 species were listed by Vavilov.

[1] Sauer (1952), 23–29.

[2] Sauer (1952), 72–73.

[3] Vavilov (1935, 1949–50). See Hutchinson (1965) for a collection of recent essays on crop plant evolution.

III Central Asia, including north west India, Afghanistan, Tadjikistan, Uzbekistan and western Tian-Shan. To this region were attributed a range of wheats, important legumes including peas, lentils and beans, and cotton. 42 species were listed.

IV The Near East, including the interior of Asia Minor, Transcaucasia, Iran and the highlands of Turkmenistan. Nine botanical species of wheat and rye, the grape, pear, cherry, fig, walnut, almond and alfafa were among the 83 species listed.

V The Mediterranean centre, home of the olive and many vegetables, was an important secondary source, in which man's part in selecting the more promising varieties for cultivation is particularly notable. 84 species were listed.

VI Ethiopia. Vavilov's expedition in 1927 established the importance of this area as an independent centre of origin, important especially for varieties of wheat, barley, sorghum and millet. 38 species were listed.

VII South Mexico and Central America (including the Antilles). Here was placed the primary centre of maize (corn), the sweet potato and upland cotton, and 49 endemic species were listed.

VIII South America. The Russian expedition of 1932–3 stressed the importance of the high mountainous area of Peru, Bolivia and part of Ecuador, remarkable for its endemic plants, notably numerous species of potato. Other centres distinguished were the island of Chiloe (VIIIa) and the Brazilian-Paraguayan area (VIIIb). A total of 62 species were listed.

In each of the old world hearths of seed agriculture it would seem that cultivation included grasses for grain, legumes for protein and fat, and usually some additional oil and perhaps fibre plants. The distinctiveness of the agricultural complex that developed between the eastern Mediterranean and south-central Persia is the combination of seed growing with herding of animals—cattle, sheep and goats—in which we find the origins of modern mixed farming.

More than a thousand years elapsed between this early mixed farming of the Near East, which was certainly established before 5000 B.C., and the establishment of agriculture in Europe, at least at known sites. The Danubian sites of central Europe reveal an economy based on the cultivation, on easily-worked loess soils, of barley, one-grained wheat (Einkorn), beans, peas, lentils and flax. Cultivation was by primitive hoes, and was probably of a shifting kind, if only because of the lack of manure. Stock raising seems to have been limited to small numbers of oxen, sheep and pigs. In the later Neolithic economy of northern Germany and southern Scandinavia, however, cattle played an important part. Settlements became more permanent.[1] Clearance of the forests was beginning to outstrip their regenerative capacity, a condition that extended to the Rhineland and the Netherlands by the beginning of the Bronze Age. Throughout the Neolithic Age the diffusion of agriculture continued and settlements dated to as early as 2500 B.C. show that the grain and animal economy had extended to Ireland.

The Bronze Age, approximately 1500 to 500 B.C., saw the introduction in northern Europe of a light plough, the ard, which would not have been capable of breaking in new ground but would have permitted more efficient tillage of land already in cultivation. The succeeding Iron Age was the period in which the heavier soils came under cultivation with the development of the iron ploughshare.[2] Iron tools did not begin to affect cultivation in Britain until about 300 B.C., but were part of the civilisation of southern Europe by 1000 B.C.

About 800 B.C. the Greek *polis* or city settlement was developing, based on the improved agriculture possible with the use of iron. Hills were terraced for the vine and olive, and these fruits together with grains and Greek breeds of the principal domestic animals were sent to the colonies, which extended from Egypt and the Crimea to the Iberian peninsula. In return Greece acquired other plants and animals, including the domestic fowl from the East. By the fourth century B.C. Greek agriculture and its administration were treated as a fine art.

[1] Clarke (1952), 97.

[2] Evans (1956).

During the following centuries many agricultural treatises appeared and the science acquired its Roman name.

During the period of Greek and Roman colonisation and supremacy, agricultural products and ideas were exchanged throughout the great region of their influence, and beyond it through intermediate traders. New scientific devices, such as the Archimedes screw, made possible new approaches to irrigation and other aspects of land improvement and cultivation. All this development was stimulated by the growth of a monetary economy and the abandonment of subsistence agriculture in favour of production at least partly for a market. Estates organised by government agencies became dominant in large areas of the classical world. The *latifundia*, great estates based on slave labour, took the place of peasant settlements in much of the Roman world. As the supply of slaves diminished in the changed conditions of the *pax Romana* of later centuries, there was some reversion of organisation of these estates to a type of peasant tenantry, and subsistence farming became again more common.[1]

The second century A.D., however, in spite of a decline in farming for the market, saw the spread of techniques, tools, plants and domestic animals beyond the Roman world as far as Ireland, Scandinavia and western Siberia. As in Rome in the fourth and fifth centuries, the feudal system bound the peasant or serf to the estate in much of Europe. In the Byzantine east freeing of the peasantry began in the sixth century, but this movement was not paralleled in western Europe. The monasteries which developed in Egypt in the fourth century were, however, followed in the west during the succeeding centuries by the growth of the strong religious communities which kept alive scientific agriculture and land development.

The Middle Ages

In the millenium that preceded the agrarian revolution of the eighteenth century and the development of commercial farming as we know it today, developments in the techniques and administration of agriculture came at long intervals. The feudal system, in which the vassal owed allegiance to his lord in return for a measure of security, was expressed on the land

[1] Heichelheim (1956).

by manorial organisation. The vassals supplied the lord with a portion of their produce and also had to work on the desmesne lands farmed for the lord's benefit. The system was partly a response to an economy in which money was scarce, as in western Europe, which was drained of gold and silver by the shift eastward of economic and military power, and largely cut off from the Mediterranean region by the Mohammedan conquests. The feudal and manorial systems spread throughout the Carolingian Empire and after the Norman conquest of England the military obligations of the feudal system were grafted on to the manorial system already developed by the Saxons. Even in the Carolingian Empire the manorial system varied regionally[1] while Scandinavia and the North Sea coast remained little affected by it, having a trading economy based on stock rearing.

Field shape and utilisation also varied more than was formerly supposed. The open fields, which were not fenced individually and were cultivated in strips,[2] have become identified particularly with the Middle Ages, but in some areas individually-walled fields survived, and in regions of colonisation such as the fens of Holland farmhouses were sited on the individual strips.

Five methods of cultivation have been distinguished:[3]

(1) Temporary cultivation, after which the land was allowed to revert to waste for an indefinite period.

(2) The infield-outfield system of Scotland and Ireland and similar systems in which part of the land was cultivated continuously with heavy manuring, and other parts occasionally.

(3) The two-course rotation, in which the land was tilled and left fallow in alternate years.

(4) A three-year system in which the land was tilled for one year and left fallow for two.

(5) The three-course rotation, in which winter corn (wheat or rye) was followed by spring corn (barley or oats) and then by fallow.

[1] Slicher van Bath (1963).

[2] Beresford and St. Joseph (1958) provide an attractive survey.

[3] Slicher van Bath (1963), 58–59.

Two-course rotations were practised mainly in the Mediterranean area where winter corn utilised the seasonal rainfall, and in northern Europe where the seed bed could not be prepared until spring. In the intermediate zone both winter and spring grains could be grown. The three-course system offered increased production but not sufficient to meet the needs of a rapidly expanding population.

In the late Middle Ages (the second half of the twelfth century and the thirteenth century) rising population and growing circulation of money led to a great increase in cereal prices which stimulated reclamation of marshes and forests and ploughing-up of pastures. As in later periods of population pressure, colonisation extended into marginal lands which, in the absence of adequate manure, soon lost their accrued fertility. Farms on the more fertile lands were subdivided until in many areas they became too small to support the people dependent on them. The economic change of this period and the depression that followed in the fourteenth century led to the gradual abandonment of the manorial system. Villeins were able to buy their freedom and in some cases were compelled to do so. A new class of small tenant farmers and cottars became widespread.

From 1300, wheat prices fell steadily. Plagues, including the Black Death of 1347–57, swept Europe, and the depression deepened in the fifteenth century. Cropping was reduced and livestock increased, sheep being especially favoured to meet the growing demand for wool. Even before the end of the twelfth century many of the Cistercian farms, their superior organisation facilitating improvements,[1] were specialising in sheep rearing, but it was in the fifteenth century that the widespread adaptation of agriculture to commercial farming occurred. Industrial crops, including hops, flax, hemp, dye-plants and oil-seeds, became more important and more vineyards were planted.

In the sixteenth century cereal prices rose again, reflecting new expansion of the population and increased use of horses. A new wave of reclamation took place and the search for higher yields, with intensified manuring, extended to both food and industrial crops. The colonisation of tropical and sub-

[1] Donkin (1963).

tropical areas led to the invention of the plantation system for commercial crop growing.

There were periods of depression in the seventeenth and eighteenth centuries and fluctuations in emphasis on arable and pastoral husbandry according to their relative prosperity, but the general growth of population and the improvement of communications were setting the stage for the new husbandry which began to spread across Europe in the late eighteenth century. The transition to the new methods was slow and often indirect. The replacement of methods involving fallow by continuous rotations, including root crops, took place in stages which varied from place to place and was spread out over several centuries. Slicher van Bath lists eleven distinct tillage systems involving varying periods of fallow or fodder crops found in the seventeenth and eighteenth centuries.[1] Turnips, rapes and clovers were already an important part of the farming systems of the Low Countries.

The Agrarian Revolution

The agrarian revolution was intimately interwoven with and dependent on the industrial revolution. As has often been pointed out, these were no sudden revolutions, but complexes of slowly evolving technological improvements which became gradually more widely disseminated. Thus, although Abraham Darby was smelting iron with coke at Coalbrookdale by 1709, similar methods were not adopted outside the Coalbrookdale and Wrexham districts until after 1750. Many improvements had to be incorporated before coke smelting could be used for all types of iron but as the new methods in iron-working became more widely adopted iron became cheaper and more readily available to other industries, including agriculture. Steam power became generally available, and was put to work in farmyard as well as in factory. The construction of canals, and later railways, linked the factories to their raw materials and provided the transport for agricultural produce to the growing urban markets. The factories and ancillary services grew apace and their demand for labour was insatiable. Labour was drawn away from the land, and although this resulted in some labour shortage, it stimulated attention to more efficient

[1] Slicher van Bath, (1963), 244.

agricultural methods. Above all, it facilitated the re-arrangement and enclosure of fields that were a vital pre-requisite of the agrarian improvements.

Specialisation was an important feature of the new agricultural methods. Limited by primitive transport and commercial services as well as by traditional techniques, most farmers had little notion of producing a surplus for sale before factories, mines and transport networks had created a landless working force which had to be fed by a surplus from the land. Subsistence agriculture satisfied the requirements of the cultivators, more or less, for food, drink and clothing. A particular crop, such as wheat, in regions where it was favoured, was produced on land little suited to it, as well as on suitable land. Yields were low, and recuperation of the soils under fallow was inadequate. The introduction of roots not only enabled fertility to be better maintained, while yielding extra crops, but facilitated a degree of specialisation, as between turnips for stock and potatoes for human consumption.

In the arable fields continuous cultivation to keep down weed-growth was made possible by Jethro Tull's drilling and horse-hoeing husbandry, whereby seed was sown in straight lines by drills so that inter-row cultivation was possible. This was incorporated with the principle of alternating exhaustive and recuperative land uses in the Norfolk rotation. Temporary grass followed spring corn (barley or oats), and was ploughed-in, to be followed by winter corn (wheat), and finally roots, to complete the rotation. It was later found necessary to winter large numbers of stock in order to manure the land. This became the standard system of the light soils in the eastern parts of England.[1]

More important for the wetter districts was the harnessing of the clovers and related plants to improve the nitrogen cycle in the grasslands. The ryegrass-clover sward and its variations provided the basis of improved pasture and also meadows which yielded hay sufficient to keep livestock through the winter in increased numbers and improved health, so permitting an increasing supply of meat and dairy produce from the regions not suited to arable farming.

The regional variations in land use that developed in the

[1] Smith (1949), 23.

eighteenth and nineteenth centuries could exploit more fully the potential of the European climates because of the improved breeding of livestock. In cattle breeding, as horses became more widely preferred to oxen for work in the fields, emphasis was placed increasingly on selection for meat and milking qualities. Further adaptation to local climatic, soil and transport conditions led to refinement of breeding to improve either the milking or the fattening qualities, so producing the specialised dairy breeds such as the Jersey, Friesian, Ayrshire and Dairy Shorthorn and the beef breeds, Hereford, Aberdeen-Angus and Beef or Scotch Shorthorn. Sheep breeds, similarly, were improved by selective breeding, to serve the needs of the manufacturers for different grades of wool, and of butchers for different classes of meat. At the same time, the more specialised breeds were able to exploit more efficiently the varying regional environmental conditions, so encouraging further specialisation on the individual farm.

The improved agricultural systems did not become generally adopted in all districts and by all farmers, even in the British Isles, until not merely decades but a century or more had elapsed but by the beginning of the nineteenth century 'the new order was dominant and the old recessive'.[1] The farming of the lowlands had then been largely brought into line with the new techniques, which were being carried rapidly into the more remote and less productive hill regions.

As the nineteenth century progressed, improving transport of the age of steam made available in Europe the produce of the new lands, particularly the Americas. By adaptation of European methods to exploit the large areas of land available, utilising less labour and more machinery, costs of production were cut to the point where grain could be shipped and marketed in Britain more cheaply than the local produce. With demand continuing to increase rapidly and the industrialists seeking cheap food to keep down wages, and, thereby, manufacturing costs, the Corn Laws in Britain were repealed and British farming had to adjust itself to being part of a world economic system. This was only the first of many such changes which affected not only Britain, but all the European countries in varying measure. By the middle of the nineteenth

[1] Smith (1949), 44.

century all the main groups of factors that influence agricultural distributions today could be discerned, operating on a dynamic pattern. Later aspects of the historical evolution of modern agriculture will be touched on in subsequent chapters, but it is now appropriate to turn to examination of the individual factors and forces that make up the environment which agriculture exploits and with which it has to contend.

CHAPTER 2

Physical Factors Influencing Agriculture

The physical factors will be considered under three main headings; climate, soil and relief.

CLIMATE

Climate is the principal aspect of the physical environment affecting agriculture. The characteristics of the soil, the essential medium for plant growth, are largely the product of present and past climates and the vegetation that has flourished in them, and the effects of relief are to no small degree expressed through resulting climatic variation.

Every form of plant or animal life requires certain conditions from its environment for it to be able to survive, and somewhat more stringent conditions if it is to reproduce naturally. Agricultural systems usually make use of only a small number of the economically valuable plants and animals that are suited to a given environment, the actual selection being in response to economic and social conditions, present or past.

Precipitation and Water Relationships

Agriculture makes use of water derived from the soil and underground water table for most plant cultivation and water collected from rainfall or drawn from rivers and streams for livestock. Wells also provide for livestock as well as for human consumption and any source of free-flowing fresh water may be used for irrigation.

Since plants must derive the bulk of their water requirements through their root systems in order to make use of it, water must be available in the soil in the quantities needed by the plant. Too little water in the soil will result in the withering of the plant, too much will cause waterlogging and disease or death of the plant. Consequently, the relationship between climate and the characteristics and condition of the soil are of maximum importance for plant growth. The efficiency of precipitation is indicated for general purposes by the comparison of evaporation with precipitation, conveniently expressed as P/E. Given only precipitation records and measurements of evaporation this is a simple and convenient indication of the value of a climate for agriculture in terms of water availability. For the productivity of any particular soil, however, what really matters is how much water enters the soil, i.e. the level of infiltration and the extent to which it is retained in the soil. Infiltration varies according to the nature of a soil, especially its texture, its condition (whether compacted, cultivated, etc.), relief, and the amount and type of plant cover. It also varies according to intensity of rainfall and its duration, and temperature conditions. Infiltration levels below 50 per cent. and above 90 per cent. are encountered. Since infiltration approximates to rainfall less run-off, in order to measure infiltration it is necessary to record run-off as well as rainfall for each type of soil and vegetation cover. This presents considerable technical difficulties, which can be overcome for practical purposes by use of a variety of infiltrometers and other instruments.

Infiltration is usually much less beneath arable crops like corn, cotton and potatoes than beneath grass, trees or mulches, and this must influence cropping policy in areas where soil moisture is limited. The beneficial effects of protecting the soil by mulching when intensive tillage is undertaken in dry conditions is a lesson stressed by American soil conservation authorities.

While all plants need water in order to survive, the requirement varies. It depends on the extent to which structure protects the species from transpiration, since nearly all the additional water required by a growing plant is to replace its essential water content as this is lost by transpiration. Per ton of dry matter produced, cereals transpire 400 to 500 tons of water, and grasses more than 800 tons, according to the evaporative power of the atmosphere. A field producing 3 tons of dry matter per acre may transpire from 1200 to 2500 tons of water, equivalent to 12 to 25 inches of rain.[1]

[1] Watson and More (1962), 38.

Plants vary also in their ability to extract water from the soil. In favourable conditions the roots of lettuce and spinach penetrate only 12 to 15 inches, those of potatoes and peas about 2 feet, tomatoes and tobacco 3 feet, field corn and asparagus 4 feet, and alfalfa (lucerne) and grapes down to 8 or 10 feet or more.[1] This indicates one of the reasons why in any given physical conditions the range of cultivable plants is limited. Within this range, the maximum utilisation of any given conditions can be achieved only with suitable crops. A classic example of this is the introduction of alfalfa to the Argentine pampas where the water table is 5 to 15 feet below the surface of the ground. This solved the problem of fodder production, which could not be met by unsuitable native grasses, and so made possible the development of the beef industry.

For animals, apart from the water needed for the growth of their food, direct water requirements are considerable. Dairy cows naturally have the greatest needs. A Friesian cow yielding 80 lbs. of milk per day may require about 190 lbs. (19 galls.) of water for liquid consumption. A Jersey cow producing about 30 lbs. milk might consume about 100 lbs. of water. Beef cattle need about 70 lbs. of water when fattening, and about 35 lbs. for a maintenance ration. Sheep require much less, 5–13 lbs. of water per day on dry range, 0·3–6 lbs. when being fed on rations of hay, roots and grain, and very little when grazing good pasture.[2]

Regular and frequent watering is essential for cattle. When water is rationed severely, milk production falls, and considerable expense in capital equipment to provide high-yielding cows with continuous supplies of water has been found justifiable. Sheep, in certain conditions, will also respond to good supplies of water. At the Desert Range Station in Utah it was found that sheep on the range gained an average of 3·4 lbs. each in a 40 day period when they were watered daily. They lost 6 lbs. each when they were watered only every third day.[3]

Water needs of animals vary, of course, according to their environment. The moisture losses from the body by evaporation

[1] U.S.A. Department of Agriculture (1955), 359.

[2] U.S.A. Department of Agriculture (1955), 17.

[3] U.S.A. Department of Agriculture (1955), 15.

increase with temperature, enabling the animal better to withstand high temperatures by getting rid of heat, but necessitating replacement of the water used up.

It is obvious why livestock industries flourish most easily in humid temperate regions, and in particular why dairying is severely limited in hot, dry regions. The adaptability of sheep is well known, but the difficulties of an environment like the desert margins of Australia will always clearly impose limitations on the productivity even of sheep, and necessitate adherence to a breed like the Merino, which is hardy, and produces a useful product—its fine fleece—in such conditions.

It will be clear that it is difficult to overstress the importance of water needs of plants and livestock, or the need to consider evaporation at the same time as precipitation in examining climate in relation to agriculture. This makes a classification of climate which gives prominence to the water balance of particular value to agriculturalists and agricultural geographers. The classification developed by C. W. Thornthwaite[1] has been widely adopted for such practical purposes as calculation of amount of water to be applied in irrigation schemes , as well as being academically valuable for regional studies.

The essence of the Thornthwaite classification is recognition of the function of storage capacity of the soil as a kind of bank, from which, directly and through the needs of plants, water is removed, and in which the funds are restored by precipitation. Since evaporation is related to temperature it is possible to use records of temperatures to calculate evaporation, and these combined with records of precipitation will yield a budget of water availability which can be maintained from day to day and month to month.

When climatic records are available the calculation of the water balance has practical application in assessing the suitability of regions for plants of known water requirements, and in calculating the amount of water required in irrigation schemes, for estimation of either long term needs or day-by-day applications.

Seasonal distribution of precipitation is hardly less important than the total amount. Plants need water most during their growing season, and hence, except to the extent that they can

[1] Thornthwaite (1948).

draw on water stored in the soil or receive artificial irrigation, it is during the growing period that rainfall is most needed. In countries where rainfall is seasonal, as in tropical monsoon and Mediterranean types of climate, late arrival of the rains may have serious consequences for food supplies. Failure of the season to produce normal rainfall, or early cessation of the rains, may similarly be serious.

Regularity of rainfall is also important for some crops. Thus for rubber trees (*Hevea brasiliensis*) the optimum rainfall is 70–150 inches, distributed so that no month has less than 3 inches. Tapping is hindered, however, on wet days, so that it is preferable that rainfall should be concentrated on not more than about 150 rain-days per year.

Destructive Aspects of Rainfall

So far we have discussed water only in its beneficial and productive aspects, but its destructive roles are also of importance in agricultural geography. In particular, rainfall is an agent of soil erosion. Geological erosion is a natural phenomenon and is beneficial in its exposure and transport of mineral elements and other materials which build up rock and soil when deposited. When we speak of soil erosion, however, we mean accelerated erosion, the removal of soil at a rate faster than it accumulates, so that the product of centuries or even millenia is dispersed in the form of non-productive and even destructive sediments.

Water, as it falls on to the surface of the land and as it runs off, erodes by splash erosion and scour erosion. Rain consists of drops of many different sizes, and heavy rain contains many of the larger drops, 3 to 6 mm. in diameter. Practically all drops are falling at maximum velocity, about 30 feet per second, when they strike the ground, and this may be increased by a driving wind. The amount of soil set in motion by each drop is directly proportional to the square of its velocity. Particles of fine sand are moved readily even by fine rain, while heavy rainfall can lift particles of several millimetres. Rainfall intensity, soil texture, condition of the soil, and slope are the more important factors affecting erosive power. Similarly, erosion by run-off varies with the energy of moving water. The velocity of run-off on slight slopes is small compared with that of falling rain, but increases rapidly as slope becomes more marked, leading to rill, gully and sheet erosion. Protection against erosion calls for maintenance of vegetative cover, contour ploughing and construction of contour ridges, banks, stream control, etc. Erosion is most serious in climatic conditions which allow soil to dry out well between falls of rain, so making individual particles easily detached, and in such conditions it is normal for plants to be slow to colonise bared ground. The risk of erosion should inhibit many farming practices and ought indeed, in some regions, to be a major factor in deciding on the type of farming to be practised, but all too often warning signs are ignored and erosion is allowed to proceed until removal of soil is far advanced.

When water cannot drain sufficiently quickly off the land by percolation and run-off, flooding results. Even in areas of low rainfall and high evaporation, sudden rains of high intensity or prolonged duration cause severe flooding. In the arid regions of Australia, almost continuous drought is occasionally interrupted by catastrophic flooding. Erosion of topsoil and destruction of vegetation intensify flooding, by reducing infiltration of water into the soil and so increasing run-off. Protective works may have to be elaborate and therefore expensive. Long term control usually resides in improvement of management in the watersheds and higher reaches of rivers, but these are precisely the areas to which it is difficult to direct investment, because such lands are in themselves generally of low value.

The characteristics of soils developed in waterlogged conditions and the formation of peat are discussed later, and there is further reference to accelerated erosion at the end of this chapter.

Snow

Where snow falls only for short periods each winter, and snow cover is intermittent, as in the British Isles, its main impact is in the hardship it places on livestock. Hill sheep farming in the Scottish Highlands, the English fells and the Welsh mountains is adapted to snow conditions and the sheep are moved to the safer areas when snow threatens. Even so, shepherds are frequently unprepared for sudden storms. Sheep can live for two weeks or so in snow drifts but rescue operations are arduous and losses in bad winters are heavy. On lowland farms also snowy winters may cause severe losses, and always lead to shortages of fodder. Heavy snow late in the winter is particularly serious as it may cause the death of large numbers of newborn lambs. Further losses occur when large masses of snow melt and floods result.

In countries where snow cover of longer duration is to be expected, adaptation is more complete. In the Alps and the Scandinavian mountains, all livestock are housed, having been brought in from the summer grazings before the autumnal snowfalls make them unusable.

Snow insulates the ground from low air temperatures and so retards deep penetration of frost. In moderately cold conditions in the U.S.A. a depth of 12 to 18 inches of snow has prevented frost penetration and in severe freezing penetration has been avoided with a covering of 24 inches of snow. Soil freezing will often start before the accumulation of snow but if this builds up to a cover of 30 to 40 inches, and remains as deep, thawing will begin from the lower edge of the frozen zone as heat rises from below.[1] This will make the soil available more quickly for cultivation when the snow thaws. This is particularly important where spring-sown crops are grown. Land cannot be prepared for sowing until the snow has cleared and excess moisture dispersed.

Alternatively, advantage may be taken of the protection afforded by snow cover for suitable grains to be sown in autumn. However, although the snow protects the crop from frost and from drying winds, which when the ground is frozen may cause death through evaporation when there is no replacement water available, there are other hazards. Certain parasitic fungi find suitable conditions for breeding under snow cover and attack plant seeds. This is one of the factors discouraging cultivation of winter wheat and rye in northern Sweden.[2]

Temperature

The germination of seeds and the growth of plants require suitable temperature conditions. The optimum temperature is

[1] U.S.A. Department of Agriculture (1955), 183.
[2] Fullerton (1954).

usually between 65 deg. and 75 deg. F. Low temperatures permit only slow growth, the minimum for rye being about 36 deg., for wheat, barley and beet about 40 deg. and for maize about 48 deg.[1]

Since some plants need more warmth than others in order to mature, it seems that the amount by which each day's temperature exceeds the threshold should be significant for the plants grown and the degree of growth that takes place. Day by day throughout the growing season more day-degrees above the threshold will be added, so leading to the concept of accumulated temperature. Wheat, for which the threshold temperature is 40–42 deg. F. (5–6 deg. C.), needs about 1960 day-degrees of accumulated temperature. The marginal character of most of Scotland and Northern Ireland for wheat growing, based on this figure, is shown by maps of accumulated temperatures compiled by Gregory for the British Isles. Rice needs 3000–4000 day-degrees and an average temperature during the growing period of at least 68 degrees.

Opinions differ on the value of the concept. Gregory sums up conflicting evidence, 'it would seem, in fact, that if accumulated temperature has any significance and value, it lies in its definition of the *minimum* temperature conditions of growth of particular plant species, whether the limits of these be altitudinal or latitudinal'.[2] Maps of accumulated temperature should be of value in defining areas suitable for growing particular crops, in conjunction with field experiments. A limitation is the lack of suitable climatic statistics in many areas. However, whereas the tables for the calculation of accumulated temperatures prepared by the Meteorological Office[3] were designed to be used in conjunction with daily maximum and minimum temperatures, Gregory has achieved promising results with monthly means of temperatures, which are more widely available and lend themselves to rapid calculation. Gregory's method was simply to subtract the chosen threshold value from each monthly temperature in turn, the annual value being arrived at by summing the twelve monthly values.

[1] Watson and More (1962), 32.

[2] Gregory (1954).

[3] Meteorological Office M.O. Form 3300 (1928).

Frost

Of less controversial evaluation is the frost-free period, the effects of killing and damaging frosts being all too readily apparent in crop cultivation. The breeding of varieties of cereals which can mature in shorter frost-free periods is a major part of the battle to push cultivation further north in northern Europe, Siberia and Canada. The zone of permafrost, where soils are permanently frozen only a little below the surface, is similarly a zone of challenge in economic utilisation. Through Siberia permafrost extends as far south as Outer Mongolia, limiting the taiga forest to larch and other trees which can survive with a shallow root system developed in the soil zone above the permafrost. This zone which thaws in summer is low in nutrients and drainage is hindered by the frozen subsoil, so that cultivation offers small rewards and is limited to the most favoured pockets of land.

Frost is one of the chief factors in altitudinal limitation of cultivation. Least troubled by frost are locations close to the sea, which benefit from the amelioration of the climate by the proximity of sheets of water, and by the movement of air on the coast. At the other extreme are bottom lands into which cold air drains. Higher slopes may remain free of frost in such circumstances, and hence the preference for sloping sites for orchards, since fruit is particularly vulnerable to frost. Methods of protection against frost include burning of paraffin under the trees or spraying with water throughout frosty periods. Either method, but particularly the former, is expensive and laborious.

Abnormally late frosts are particularly damaging since they catch a high proportion of plants at the seedling or early leafing stages when they are most vulnerable. Recovery, however, may take place if the frost is not too severe or repeated. Otherwise the farmer's only remedy is to re-seed with later maturing varieties, which is not always possible.

Frosts are never met in lowland equatorial and many tropical regions. For example, frosts are unknown in Malaya. The lowest temperature ever recorded in Malaya is 36 deg. F. in the Cameron Highlands.

Light and Sunshine

Light is essential for the growth of plants, the process of

forming carbohydrates which make up a large proportion of their bodies being initiated by the intake (through photosynthesis) of energy contained in light from the sun. Direct sunshine is not essential, but is desirable for rapid growth and the ripening of crops.

Length of day is a factor in plant growth which enables vegetation to grow rapidly in zones of high latitude. During the short summer when the sky is never dark plants can complete the flowering and seed formation essential to reproduction of the species. More rapid photosynthesis to enable useful plants to exploit the long day is one of the aims of plant breeding. Not all plants, however, respond to long days. Most warm temperate and sub-tropical plants require ten or more hours of darkness for their flowering, while for some species the hours of darkness and light are unimportant.

In maritime areas cloud cover often reduces the amount of light theoretically available. This is of greatest importance in cold and cool temperate regions, where ripening of crops and their harvesting in a dry state is frequently in doubt. It is, however, also relevant in tropical regions. Although Malaya grows a considerable amount of rice for internal consumption and has for some years been endeavouring to increase production so as to be able to reduce imports, it has too cloudy a climate for maximum yields of rice. Cloud cover and excessive rainfall also prevent double-cropping which might otherwise be widespread.

Wind

Winds are of importance in agriculture chiefly for the increased rates of evapo-transpiration and consequent increased water needs which they produce, and the physical damage they wreak when excessive. On the other hand the wind may be put to work on the land to drive windmills for pumping water or for the generation of electricity.

In regions subject to strong winds, like the British Isles, cereal crops are frequently blown over or 'lodged' and strength of stalk is an important factor in choice of variety sown. Very strong winds sometimes thresh the crop while it stands leaving only a straw residue to be harvested. 'Killing' winds in many countries are associated with particular directions of origin.

The *mistral* of the south of France, a cold, northerly wind funnelled by the Rhone valley, sometimes brings heavy losses to growers of olives, citrus and other fruits on the Mediterranean lowlands. Large windbreaks are planted to protect the orchards. In contrast, the *sirocco* from the Sahara is a hot drying wind feared on north African coasts.

Hot, dry winds have commonly derived their character from descent after passing over mountains, the best known example being the *föhn* of the Alps. Another is the *chinook* of the Rocky Mountains, the onset of which will speed the melting of snow. No such advantage can be offset against the damage caused by the *bohorok*, which descends from the Karo Mountains in Sumatra and is particularly feared by tobacco growers in the Medan district.

Strong winds, and particularly those that are dry, are also important agents of soil erosion. The most publicised of all cases of soil erosion, the 'dust bowl' of Kansas and Oklahoma, was the work mainly of wind on bared soil. Movement of soil particles is by suspension, surface creep, and saltation—the particles leaping and bounding. Reduction of surface velocity is one of the main principles in control of wind erosion. The force of wind varies with the square of its velocity and so even a small reduction in velocity is valuable. This can be achieved through keeping the land covered, or making the soil up in banks.

Fallowing, as practised in dry farming, when the land may be left without a crop for 20 months or so in order to conserve moisture for the following crop, clearly lays the soil open to erosion. This is the more likely since the practice of dry farming implies that the soil will be so dry as not to clod readily. It is, of course, the finest soil particles that are most vulnerable, while small clods of soil are particularly valuable because they have a high protective surface in proportion to their weight.[1] Such non-erodable clods are larger than a wheat kernel or bean, and, to be resistant to movement, soils need to contain at least two-thirds by weight of non-erodable fractions. These conditions are most likely to be met in soils of medium texture, with clay content of 20 to 30 per cent. and a high silt content.

Unless protection can be seen to be adequate, bare fallow,

[1] U.S.A. Department of Agriculture (1957), 312.

and, if necessary, cropping, should be avoided and the land kept in grass, which gives a good protective cover and is well anchored.

Soils

Since the soil is the essential material on which agriculture is based, any comprehensive survey of the geography of agriculture should include a fairly thorough treatment of soils. This is not practicable within the scope of this book but there are many excellent texts[1] to which the reader may refer, as indeed there are for climate and other factors only briefly discussed. Therefore, in this section as in others, treatment will be confined to discussion of some points which seem to be particularly in need of stressing in any approach to agricultural geography.

Soil is composed of four major constituents: inorganic particles, organic material, water and air. The factors, active and passive, that determine the character of a soil may be grouped as:

(*a*) Parent materials
(*b*) Climate
(*c*) Relief
(*d*) Vegetation
(*e*) Soil fauna and bacteria
(*f*) Man's utilisation.

All of these act through time, which may also be considered a soil-forming factor, though not separately considered here.

Parent Materials

The soil is formed from the rock on which it develops, together with other materials which are deposited on the site in the course of its formation. The latter include organic materials derived mainly from the decay of plants, of which some of the more primitive kinds can obtain a foothold on bare rock as soon as it begins to weather, and so contribute to its erosion and the formation of soil. Partially-decomposed organic matter which is being incorporated in the soil is called 'humus', and it

[1] A standard English text is Robinson, *Soils*. Duchaufour (1960) is strongly recommended but is not available in English. Vilenskii (1957) and other Russian studies have been translated in Israel. Brade-Birks (1944) gives a good introduction. Bunting (1965) concisely presents a geographer's approach.

combines chemically with some of the mineral products of the weathering of the rock. Rock is weathered by mechanical and chemical agents, the resulting partly weathered material being known as the *weathering complex*. The character of the weathering complex and of the soil that develops on it depends partly on the character of the parent rock. The great variety of soils found on differing geological strata in close proximity led to early soil scientists giving rather too great an emphasis to the role played by the underlying rock, to the neglect of the influences of climate and vegetation. Nevertheless, lithology does have great importance, and this is especially so from an agricultural point of view, because the texture and chemical content of a soil are largely dependent on the parent material, and these are obviously of fundamental importance to the farmer.

Texture varies with the proportion of clay, silt and sand particles which make up the mineral basis of the soil. These particles are classified according to the international scale as follows:

	Millimetres
Clay	0–0·002
Silt	0·002–0·02
Fine Sand	0·02–0·2
Coarse Sand	0·2–2·0
Stones and Gravel	Over 2 mm.

Soils are classified according to their different combinations of sand, silt and clay by mechanical analysis, grouping being shown graphically in texture-triangles, (Figure 1).

Accumulations of materials of the extremes in texture—pure sand, silt or clay, cannot be regarded as soils, but they may in the course of time develop into soils with the aid of the various agents, in which case of course the texture changes. Sandy soils are generally infertile because they are incapable of retaining needed chemicals in the soil. Sandy loams, however, with their higher percentages of clay and better structure, may be very valuable soils, especially in areas where soils which are 'heavy' i.e. containing much clay, are liable to waterlogging. They are easily 'worked' and warm up early in the spring. They do not, however, have the potentiality for high fertility

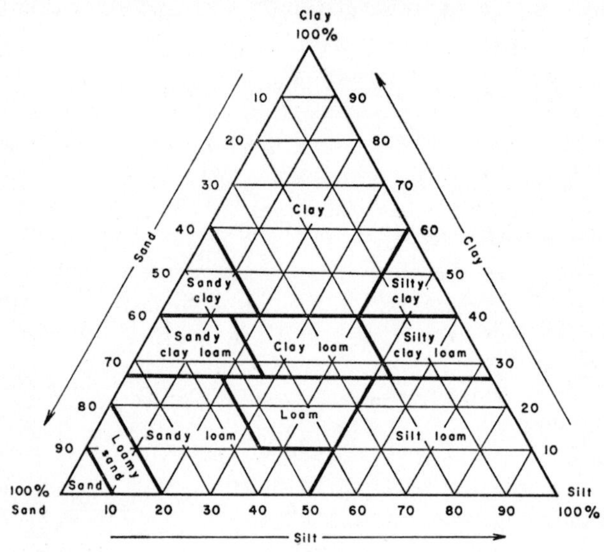

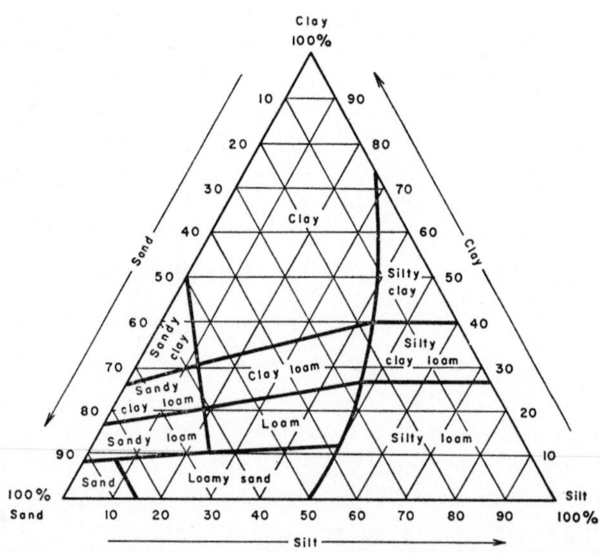

Figure 1. Texture triangles, used for the classification of soil according to mechanical analysis by the U.S.A. Department of Agriculture (above) and as modified by Marshall (Australian C.S.I.R.O.) to fit the international fraction sizes.

Source: N. Comber, revised W. N. Townsend, *An Introduction to the Scientific Study of the Soil.*

that is contained in soils with more clay. Medium loams are often regarded as ideal soils because of their combined qualities of retentiveness of water without tendency to waterlogging, normal richness in plant foods and receptiveness of fertilisers, and general ease of working. They also offer the maximum alternatives in switching from arable cultivation to grassland, and the most even and sustained productivity in a crop and grass rotation.

The greatest inherent fertility and suitability for some crops resides, however, in soils with rather high clay fractions. Provided drainage is adequate, or is made adequate by the insertion of drains, some 'heavy' soils provide not only highly productive and durable pastures, but also excellent land for growing wheat and other crops with a high level of demand for nutrients. This is because of the virtues of the clay particles. Whereas sand particles are chemically inert, clay particles are chemically active. Intricate chemical changes occur between them and the organic materials in the soil to form the *clay-humus complex*.

The clay fraction is made of clay minerals, such as kaolinite and montmorillonite, which are composed of sheets of alumina and silica bonded by oxygen atoms in respectively 1:1 and 2:1 ratios. Through ionic substitution of atoms, the clay crystal receives a negative charge. This results in attraction between the clay particles and other particles with a positive charge, e.g. hydrogen, calcium, magnesium, sodium and potassium ions. The attracted ions are held in the soil solution but in response to changes in this can be released from the soil particle or 'exchanged'. Such exchangeable positively charged mineral ions (cations) account for the *base status* of a soil.[1]

A clay-humus complex which is rich in exchangeable bases is potentially a fertile soil. It is, however, continuously exposed to the *leaching* action of rain water, which is a dilute solution of carbonic acid (H_2CO_3) able to exchange its hydrogen ions for the nutrient ions in the soil. These are then carried away as dilute salts in the drainage, and the clay-humus structure is increasingly left with hydrogen ions which make it acid. The desired nutrient ions must therefore be replaced by further mineral particles from erosion or organic decomposition. To

[1] For a further but brief description, see Eyre (1963).

remedy deficiencies caused by absence of, or slowness of, the natural supply we apply manure and chemical fertilisers.

The proportion of exchangeable bases in a soil is obtained by the process of measuring the concentration of hydrogen ions. It is assumed that the proportion of other ions which can be held by the clay-humus complex depends on the 'space' left by the hydrogen ions. The proportion of free hydrogen ions in the soil solution is measured and stated as the pH value.[1] pH7 is neutral, values below this indicate an acid soil, values above indicate alkalinity. Most agricultural soils are between pH5 and pH8. Some moorland and other extremely acid soils are of pH4 or 4·5.

The pH value gives an indication of the potential value of a soil. A low pH value, indicating an acid soil, will be sufficient to discourage planting on that soil of lime-loving crops unless lime is added, while a high value may indicate unsuitability for a plant that grows best under acid conditions. At the same time it must be realised that pH indicates only relative acidity. A soil with a high clay fraction and a relatively low pH may have more exchangeable bases than one with a low clay fraction and a high pH value. For a full picture of the soil it is therefore necessary to have measurements of each of the main exchangeable bases, or *cation-exchange capacity*.

Cation-exchange capacity of a soil, as already noted, will vary according to the texture of the soil. Sandy soils will have low cation-exchange capacities because the sand particles provide only a skeletal structure and the relatively small amounts of humus and clay present will not be able to offset this inherent weakness. Silt particles, it should be added, are intermediate between sand and clay in this respect, but nearer to the sand fragments in character, with very limited chemical activity. A higher cation-exchange capacity will be found in a clay soil, but this will vary according to the type of clay minerals present. Thus, montmorillonoid materials have large cation-exchange capacities, whereas those of kaolin minerals are small. Soils high in organic content have high base-exchange capacities because the humus particles develop the required large negative charges.

[1] A description of the derivation of pH values may be conveniently found in 'The Chemistry of Soil pH' by N. T. Coleman and A. Mehlich in *Soil* U.S. Yearbook of Agriculture, 1957, 72–79.

The cation-exchange capacity is usually expressed as milli-equivalents of cations required to neutralise the negative charge of 100 grams of soil with the pH held at 7. An example of this kind of analysis appears in Table I.

TABLE 1

CHEMICAL ANALYSES OF TWO NEW ZEALAND SOILS

Soil	Paparua sandy loam		Templeton silt loam	
Locality and grid reference	2 miles W.N.W. of Winchester: S102. 772787		3 miles N.W. of Winchester: S102. 768808	
Depth (in.)	0–6	15–20	0–6	15–18
Horizon	A	B	A	B
pH	6·0	6·5	6·1	6·3
1% citric acid soluble P_2O_5%	0·035	0·037	0·020	0·007
Organic C %	3·4	0·6	2·8	0·55
Total N %	0·29	0·09	0·26	0·08
$\frac{C}{N}$	12	7	11	7
Exchange capacity m.e. %	17·1	13·0	14·8	11·2
Total Bases m.e. %	11·7	11·2	11·2	9·0
Base Satn. %	68	86	76	80
Ca. m.e. %	9·3	10·3	8·7	7·2
Mg. m.e. %	2·3	1·3	2·0	1·7
K m.e. %	1·00	0·30	1·50	0·35

Source: Soils and Agriculture of Part Geraldine County New Zealand, Soil Bureau Bulletin 13, New Zealand Department of Scientific and Industrial Research, 1959, 18.

The exchangeable cations vary from one soil to another, according to natural characteristics and past management. Sodium is found in high proportions in strongly alkaline soils, calcium and magnesium in nearly neutral soils, and hydrogen and aluminium in acid soils.

From the foregoing it will be evident that the parent materials contribute greatly to the character of resulting soils. Since most sedimentary rocks are the product of materials previously sorted by suspension in water or air, it may be expected that the weathering complex derived from a sedimentary rock will be less varied in mineral content than one derived from an igneous or metamorphic rock. Sandstones will yield soils with a high proportion of quartz particles, so that the texture will be sandy, whereas shales tend to break down into clays. Among igneous rocks, granite breaks down into sandy soils which are generally poor in nutrient minerals, whereas basalt, a basic rock, will tend to yield clayey and potentially fertile soils.

Climatic Influences on Soil Development

Although certain characteristics of fundamental importance in the soil depend on the parent material, just how these characteristics will be developed depends on other forces, of which climate is the one which is universally important. The Russian soil scientists recognised the dominant influence of climate through the persistence across the great spaces of Europe and Asia of latitudinally arranged soil belts. The concept became generally accepted with the discovery that similar relationships between soil and climate could be seen in North America and elsewhere on the continental scale. The view has been expressed recently that climate has perhaps been over-emphasized to the negelect of the role played by vegetation,[1] but there is no room to doubt the basic validity of the concept of the great soil belts associated with major climatic types.

Soils that thus correspond with the great climatic belts are called *zonal* soils. Those that depart from the surrounding zonal soils because they are derived from parent materials, such as limestone, which give them special characteristics, are called *intrazonal*, while those in which time has not been sufficient for recently deposited materials to weather in the form appropriate to the climatic zone are called *azonal*. This broad classification has only limited application for agricultural purposes but consideration of any soil should take account of its positioning in this classification and what may be learnt from it.

Of immediate practical value is the preliminary subdivision of zonal soils into *pedalfers* and *pedocals*. Excessive leaching of iron, together with calcium carbonate and other substances, from the upper horizons of the soils characterise the pedalfers. Pedocals, in contrast, are soils in which lime is accumulated in the upper parts of the soils, this being possible where precipitation does not exceed evaporation. Pedalfers thus include the soils of humid climates, fully-developed podsols, other podsolic soils and lateritic soils of warmer climates. Pedocals range from desert soils to the fertile black-earths or chernozems.

[1] See, for example, on the limitations of the zonal concept Eyre (1963), 39–42.

Many works describe the great soil groups of the world in varying detail.[1] Here only a few comments are practicable and for illustrative purposes they will be confined to the pedalfers.

Classification into the great soil groups is carried out mainly by consideration of the characteristics of profile, well illustrated by the podsol (Figure 2) and the variation that occurs in podsolic soils according to the detail of climate, relief, vegetation and usage. Podsols are subjected to persistent leaching, so that the bases are carried down from the eluvial A horizon (topsoil), characteristically ash-grey in colour, to be redeposited in part at greater depth in the B horizon of illuviation (subsoil). Such a soil is not naturally fertile. Furthermore, the parent material of much of the podsol zone is glacially-smoothed rock which has not had time since the retreat of the ice for the weathering that would release fresh nutrients, while the natural vegetation that has contributed to the growth of the soil is usually coniferous forest or scrub with acid leaf-litter. To be agriculturally productive, podsols need the addition of lime, and commonly other nutrients, including phosphate, potash and nitrogen. When a podsol is ploughed and manure or 'artificial' fertilisers have been added so that the soil becomes fertile and the horizons become intermixed, the soil may be described as an 'agricultural brown earth'.

The brown earths, or brown forest soils, which are the product of less intensive leaching and a covering of deciduous forests, are by their nature more promising agricultural material. Brown earths which are also loamy in texture are perhaps the most productive of the world's mature soils under the systems of mixed farming that they are able to support.

On the other hand, whether brown earth or podsol, a soil in a cool and humid climate in natural or cultivated conditions may develop in its illuvial horizon a layer of impermeable material—hard pan or iron pan—which impedes drainage. Unless this is broken up, the soil will eventually become waterlogged, especially if it is not covered by trees, which are efficient at intercepting rain and consume much soil water.

[1] For an excellent brief study see Commonwealth Agricultural Bureau, *Soil, Vegetation and Climate.* Recent Russian work is detailed in *Soil-Geographical Zoning of the U.S.S.R.*, Academy of Sciences of the U.S.S.R., 1962, trans. 1963.

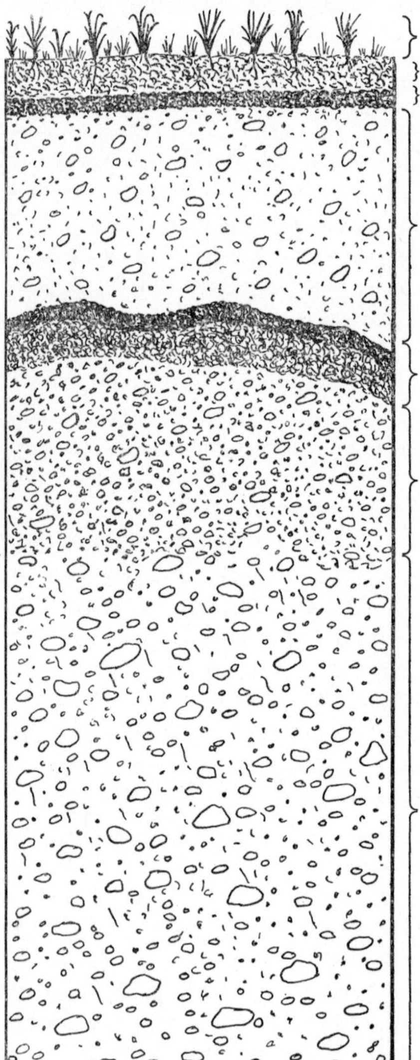

Figure 2. A typical podsol profile.

Source: G. W. Robinson, *Soils, their origin, constitution and classification.*

Land which is saturated for long periods has gleyed soils—characteristic green and blue mottling distinguishing the profile. In cool and humid climates, such as in north-west Europe, gleyed soils are also impoverished soils, leached of mineral bases, and acid—pH value 4·0 to 4·5 compared with the neutral value of 7·0. They are accordingly low in productivity, and permanent pasture, often with rich but unwanted growth of rushes, is the characteristic land use. Improvement can be effected only after provision of adequate drainage.

Where a high P/E ratio allows water to remain long on the surface, drainage improvements must extend from the individual field to the outfall of main watercourses at the sea. Thus, whereas if soil erosion is an acute danger ploughing should always follows the contour, where soils are constantly moist and the main need is to drain off surplus water it is perfectly legitimate to plough up and down slope. Field ditches, minor streams, rivers and canals must be dealt with if increased run-off at one stage is not to result in worsened flooding or saturation at lower levels. Pumping may be necessary to speed the flow.

More or less permanent saturation leads to the growth of vegetation which is anaerobic, i.e. tolerant of the absence of oxygen. Fen, bog and swamp are some of these conditions, the former two being distinguished by the formation of peat from partially decomposed vegetation.

Peat, which is not, strictly speaking, soil, is of two main kinds, acid and basic. Acid peat occurs in regions of cool and humid climates and may cover large tracts of hill and mountain country, being then known as blanket bog. Drainage may not be difficult, owing to the relief of the land, but harsh climatic factors and acidity (pH3·0–4·5) of the peat soils make the land of low agricultural value. Forestry is an alternative use for improved blanket bog in the British Isles. Basic or fen peat may accumulate in depressions into which water drains, if this water contains sufficient lime. This peat has high potential value and when drained may produce some of the highest class arable and horticultural land, as in the fenlands of eastern England. Reclaimed peats also provide valuable soils in very different climates, as in Malaya, where they are used for growing pineapples.

For peat to form under tropical conditions, where evaporation is high, not only must drainage be poor but rainfall must be very heavy and well distributed throughout the year. Under heavy rainfall and with good drainage in tropical conditions, the podsol of the cool regions has its counterpart in tropical red and yellow podsolic soils. The red and yellow colours are believed to be caused by the presence of sesquioxides, left when silica is leached out. In tropical conditions, however, the horizons associated with podsolisation are commonly absent, and there is a great depth of comparatively uniform accumulation of fine clays, rich in aluminium and iron oxides and low in silica. These red earths may have been derived by a different process known as laterisation and the soils are often called lateritic. In extreme conditions true laterite is produced. This is a hard material similar to the iron pan accretions of podsols, which has led to the suggestion that laterites may be the exhumed illuvial horizons of podsols of great age.[1] The depth and colour of the tropical red earths and the luxuriant vegetation which grows rapidly upon them led early investigators into the error of believing that such soils were inherently fertile. In fact the excessive rainfall rapidly leaches out the deposited plant nutrients, resulting in low fertility. The more fertile tropical soils are the young, immature, alluvial soils which are almost devoid of profile changes, and in which renewal of nutrients from river deposition is regular and frequent. Good examples of the periodic flooding of alluvial plains by silt-bearing waters occur in the basins of the Mekong and Menam Chao Phya in south-east Asia.

Relief as a Factor in Soil Development

Mention has already been made of relief as one of the factors influencing the amount of water that infiltrates the soil. This relationship may be seen by comparing a flat and a rolling area. The flat land receives whatever precipitation falls on the area, but water reaching the rolling area varies between the knolls which receive the precipitation less run-off and the hollows which receive precipitation plus run-off. The soils of the knolls are locally arid while those of the depressions are locally humid. (Figure 3).

[1] Carter and Pendleton (1956).

The extent to which moisture is retained in soil on a slope depends of course partly on the texture of the soil. Soils with a very high clay content in a cool, humid region can become waterlogged even on quite steep slopes. In Ireland, on slopes of 10 degrees on drumlins, marked gleying of soils is found. The water table is at greater depth high on the slope than lower down, and between the drumlins it may be at the surface, creating marsh or bog.

Soil on a slope is subject to the forces of gravity like any other mass and consequently even in conditions of great stability there is some movement downslope of soil particles. Movement is initiated mainly by running water, frost action, wind, falling vegetation or the passage of animals. It is greatest where slopes are bare, least where they are well vegetated. When natural conditions of comparative stability are upset, accelerated erosion may become serious, taking the form of sheet, slip, rill and gully erosion of the mineral soil. In severe conditions the whole of the topsoil may be stripped off, with erosion continuing into the subsoil.

Downslope movement will always result in soil at the bottom of a slope being deeper and richer in nutrients than higher up—unless of course it is being scoured away at the foot. Cultivation increases movement and, therefore, the contrasts in depth of soil. This is particularly so if ploughing is carried out up and downslope, as is common in humid regions, where even sloping lands are likely to remain excessively moist for long periods.

Vegetation and Soil Development

As noted above, the role of vegetation in the development of a soil has been underestimated in the past. In fact, in natural conditions soil and vegetation evolve in intimate relationship. Thus, with the same climate and parent materials, a difference in grazing pressure will result ultimately in different vegetation. For example, a fence protecting woodland from grazing may ensure survival of the trees, while on an adjacent area regeneration is prevented by grazing and pasture develops. If the grazing is uncontrolled, this may degenerate into bog. In each case the course of further soil development will be different, according as there is different leaf-fall, infiltration and

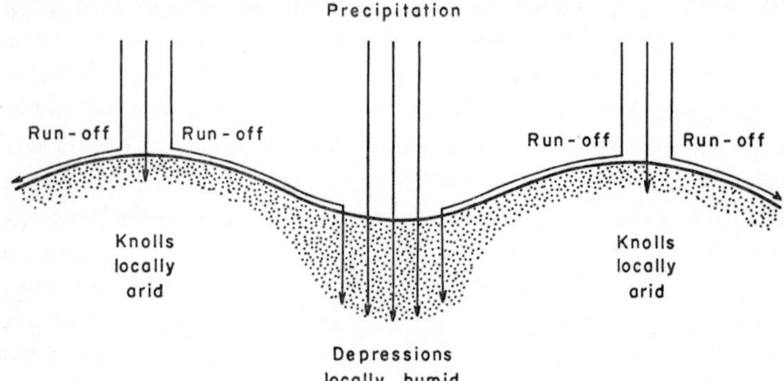

Figure 3. Variation of supply of water to the soil with relief.
Source: J. H. Ellis *The soils of Manitoba*

evaporation of water, root development and other factors. After a long period of time the soils of the three land-use types—woodland, pasture and bog—become respectively podsols, gleys and peats. If agricultural development is then applied to all three the techniques required will vary and the potential productivity will vary, at least for a considerable time.

Soil Fauna and Bacteria

Animals that live on, or in, the soil necessarily affect its development in many ways directly as well as through their effect on vegetation. If they are burrowing animals they open up channels under the surface which in moderation may be beneficial in facilitating rock weathering and soil aeration, but in excess may contribute to accelerated erosion. The work of earthworms is of great importance, their burrows extending often several feet into the ground and the passing of soil through their bodies having an important effect on its structure. The addition of earthworms to areas deficient in them has become recognised as a means of improving fertility.

Bacteria occur in their millions in soils and carry on beneficial work. They contribute to the decay of plants and the 'processing' of the remains of animals and their waste products. They liberate carbon dioxide which promotes rock weathering and some kinds of bacteria fix nitrogen. Although plants are surrounded by nitrogen in the atmosphere they are unable to use it directly. Their essential needs can only be met through the soil and thus bacteria that form suitable compounds (nitrates) are most beneficial. The nitrogen-fixing value of clovers, beans and peas is well known, these plants having nodules on their roots which contain colonies of nitrogen-fixing bacteria.[1]

Different soil bacteria are found in different conditions. For example, in anaerobic conditions there will not be the same bacterial life as in well-aerated soils, but other forms will occur, especially those which live in the humus characteristic of gley and peat soils. One of the functions of adding lime to soil is encouragement of desirable types of bacteria and the work they perform on soil structure and chemical content.

Effects of Man's Utilisation on Soils

Relationships between a soil and the soil-forming factors being as intricate as they are, it will be apparent that the introduction of man on the scene, especially modern man with a great range of crops, livestock, machinery and chemical compounds at his disposal, will produce far-reaching changes. In extreme cases, such as the conversion by prolonged cultivation and fertilisation of comparatively poor, sandy soils into market-gardening land, it may be difficult to ascertain the original nature of the soil. Nevertheless, many such developments are impermanent and if attention is relaxed reversion to lower fertility occurs. Attempts to change the character of a soil are sometimes hazardous and always expensive, and so are limited in practical farming. Although great changes are eventually made in soil even in normal cultivation, the soil on which work is commenced in any season is basically the same as it was the previous season. The relatively permanent characteristics of soils make possible classification which is of practical value to farmers.

For practical purposes the division of soils, whether zonal, intrazonal or azonal is made on the basis of qualities of the individual soil. What the farmer calls 'a soil' in a particular field or part of a field is the *soil type* of the pedologist and soil surveyor. It is only by the mapping of soil types that eventually it may be possible to build up an accurate picture of the great

[1] See, for example, Brade-Birks (1944), 82–85.

soil groups of the world. A soil type is distinguished by a name made up of a place name, perhaps the place where it was first identified, or is typified, and the texture class. For example, the house in which these words are being written is situated on Waimakariri Silt Loam—a soil derived from the alluvium deposited by the Waimakariri River in one of its former courses across the lower part of the Canterbury Plains.

To be included within a particular soil type a soil must approximate closely to the original in parent material, texture, depth and drainage. It will therefore be found only in similar physiographic conditions. It may be subdivided, where one characteristic varies, into *phases*, e.g. stony phase, very stony phase. Soil types which are similar in the most important features but vary in some, notably texture, are put together as *soil series*. The soil series may then be built up into the great soil groups.

As already noted, the great soil group may indicate certain features of agricultural importance, including common nutrient deficiencies, and response to lime, fertilisers and trace elements, but thorough appreciation of the potential of land for agriculture demands investigation of the *soil type*.

In agriculture, man is continuously faced with the problems posed by his physical environment. Whatever the resources of factory and laboratory at his disposal directly or indirectly, he must always apply these resources according to the nature of the land on which he works and the climate in which he works. He will, however, be able to sustain and increase the yield of the land if the social and economic environment permits him to take advantage of the opportunities that are offered by the physical environment as interpreted in the light of technological innovation.

Relief

The relief of a land surface affects agricultural utilisation through (1) altitude, and (2) slope. The effects of altitude are felt mainly indirectly, i.e. through climate, while slope controls are partly indirect through climate and soil, and partly direct, such as limitation of cultivation by steepness.

Climatic Effects of Altitude

The primary consequence of high altitude is lowered air

pressure, because of the reduced amount of the atmospheric 'envelope' above a raised surface. Only in exceptional cases does this have direct agricultural significance, because the effects of decreased pressure are generally evident only above the levels at which climatic controls limit land utilisation. The secondary effects of decreased mean temperatures and increased precipitation and wind forces are the economically important consequences of higher elevations.

Mean temperatures decrease with altitude because, with the lower content of the rarified air in carbon dioxide, moisture and other particles, the sun's rays pass through it with less warming effect. Consequently, a high proportion of solar radiation reaches the ground surface which heats up rapidly in the sun. This in turn may cause extreme desiccation. Conversely, the ground loses heat rapidly in the free radiation of night. The effects of increased altitude are thus not directly similar to those of high latitudes, where the sun's rays, because of their low angle to the surface of the ground, have always to penetrate a thicker 'blanket' of atmosphere and be more diffused over the surface. On the other hand, high latitudes derive some compensation from long days in their summers. The net result is that there is some similarity in the life forms of natural vegetation in their zoning respectively through latitudinal and altitudinal belts. At both sea-level in cold temperate regions and 15,000 to 20,000 feet in some equatorial regions, for example, needle-leaved coniferous trees are dominant forms of vegetation if other environmental conditions permit. Similarly, within these latitudinal and altitudinal zones the hardiest cereals find their limits and livestock herding forms an important source of food and raw materials.

At intermediate latitudes the altitudinal variation is correspondingly adjusted. In the Himalayan ranges—outside the tropics—wheat and barley are cultivated above 10,000 feet while summer pasturage is found at 12,000 to 15,000 feet. In the French and Swiss Alps the summer grazings are usually between 6000 and 10,000 feet. 6000 feet is roughly the limit of tussock grasslands in New Zealand at a latitude of about 44 deg. S. In the British Isles, mountain sheep find grazing to about 3500 feet, and coniferous forests find their limits at about 2000 feet in the east and much lower in the west where wind is an important factor inhibiting growth. Hay, oats and potatoes are grown up to about 1000 feet in favourable circumstances. In the south of Scotland the growing season decreases from about 8 months at sea level to 6 months or less at 1000 feet and $4\frac{1}{2}$ months at 2000 feet.[1]

The handicap imposed on crop growing by higher altitudes, and high latitudes, is not simply one of restricted vegetative growth but of difficulties with ripening. In the Alps, retarding of the harvest has been recognised as a day for every 100–130 feet of altitude.[2] This emphasizes the value of crops which are useful for stockfeeding even when not fully ripened, such as oats and barley.

The decrease in temperature with altitude is not regular but depends on many complex factors. The actual lapse rates vary widely, and temperatures on the ground surface will vary still more widely according to conditions of slope, aspect and exposure. In the British Isles the figure of 3 degrees F. per 1000 feet or one degree per 300 feet is accepted as a reasonable average, but three times this figure has been recorded on British mountains between sheltered valleys and exposed sites. The lack of high level stations recording temperature data has hindered investigations into correlations between the altitude limits of different crops, dates of sowing and harvesting and other aspects of altitude. Some tentative conclusions for Northern Ireland are reproduced in Figure 4. In this diagram the values of accumulated temperatures for selected lowland stations have been plotted (Graph A). Similar values were computed and plotted for a series of heights above the meteorological station at Aldergrove (217 feet) based on a lapse rate of 1 degree F. per 300 feet. The diagram suggests that the upper limit for cereal production (in terms of day-degrees of accumulated tempeatures) is here reached at about 1000 feet. In fact, only isolated fields of improved land are found as high as this and the normal limit of cultivation is about 700 feet. When famine conditions prevailed in the nineteenth century, crops were grown at higher levels than is regarded as economic today, but the present low altitudinal limits suggest that conditions are more severe than the graphs indicate,

[1] Halstead (1958).
[2] Peattie (1936), 25.

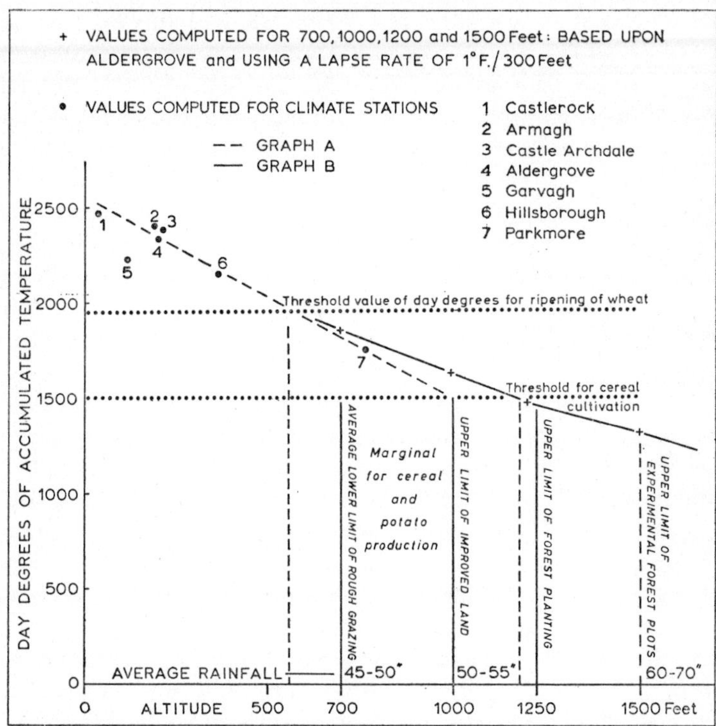

Figure 4. Upland climates and land use in Northern Ireland.
Source: N. Stephens *Land use in Northern Ireland,* (ed. L. Symons,)

contributing factors being high rainfall, humidity and wind speeds.[1]

The increases in rainfall and wind with altitude may be no less important for agriculture than are decreased temperatures. Since the capacity of air to hold moisture varies directly with its temperature, and this decreases adiabatically in ascending air, high land is commonly subjected to heavy precipitation. This is particularly so, of course, where prevailing winds carry a great deal of moisture and are very persistent, as in the westerlies in the temperate zones. This is well illustrated in the South Island of New Zealand. Annual rainfall on the westerly slopes of the main divide (8000 to 12,000 feet) varies between about 100 and 400 inches. On the foothills of the

[1] Stephens (1963).

eastern slopes it is only about 70 inches and this falls to 25 inches or so on the Canterbury Plains. On the wet, western slopes, temperate rainforest is dense, and when this is cleared agriculture is hampered by the rainfall, while former forest on the eastern side has given way entirely to arable and grassland farming.

The combination of sufficient altitude and moisture results in snow, which severely impedes agriculture in most mountain areas in temperate regions. Mention has already been made of measures adopted in the European mountains to meet this problem.

Precise information on windiness at high altitudes is limited partly because of the high cost of the instruments necessary for recording. Further, anemometers are usually located to serve the needs of meteorological research, engineering or other occupations which do not reflect conditions on agricultural and pastoral land. One survey which did, however, produce information which throws light on the conditions of the hill grazings in the British Isles was that related to the generation of electricity by wind power.[1] Many of the sites on which anemometers were placed were the summits which rose comparatively little above surrounding hill and moorland grazings and were, in fact, also grazed. The recording anemometers were mounted on masts, generally 10 to 30 feet high, and records obtained for periods of from 8 months to 5 years in the areas quoted. The results for a number of sites, coastal and inland, in south-west Scotland and Northern Ireland are tabulated below:

TABLE 2

AVERAGE ANNUAL WIND SPEEDS AT SELECTED SUMMITS

Height range of summits feet	*No. of summits in group*	*Mean of average annual wind speeds m.p.h.*
300—1000	4	20
1000—1199	5	21
1200—1499	5	23
1500—2200	6	24

[1] Tagg (1957).

The official isovent maps based on lowland stations show average wind speeds of about half these levels—for example, a large part of the north of Ireland is shown as having wind speeds of less than 12·5 m.p.h.

High winds not only act as a further deterrent to the growing of crops on high land but lower sensible temperatures, as experienced by grazing livestock, are of primary importance in necessitating reliance on hardy and often slow-maturing breeds. Moreover, the danger from snow is much increased by drifting.

To reduce the effects of high winds, shelter belts are desirable in exposed areas, but it is in just such areas and partly because of the wind that trees are difficult to establish, and liable to be destroyed by exceptional gales just when becoming useful.

Mountain Soils and Vegetation

As in other conditions, the soil profile summarises the various environmental conditions acting over time. The soils of mountain and hill regions in the temperate and cold zones are poorer in nutrients than those of lower areas. In a region where forest brown-earths are the soils of the lowlands, hills of height sufficient for the climatic deterioration to be marked will carry podsolised or skeletal soils. In regions where the lowland soils are podsols, as in the north of the British Isles, profiles on the hills commonly degenerate into peaty podsols and are ultimately replaced by blanket bog. Acidity characterises both mineral soil and peat, a condition reflected in the calcifuge vegetation, dominated by species such as heath (*Calluna vulgaris* and *Erica spp.*), rushes and sedges (*Juncus, Carex and Scirpus spp.*), coarse grasses, such as the moor mat grass (*Nardus stricta*), and mosses, notably the bog moss (*Sphagnum spp.*). Few of the species are agriculturally of much value, though heather plays an important part in the feed of hill sheep, especially when more nutritious grass is lacking or covered by snow.

The extreme acidity and the rapidity with which lime is washed out of the soil militates against the conversion of moorlands of this type into improved grassland. British hill pastures normally require the addition of two tons of ground limestone per acre before any substantial improvement can be effected, and this is rendered difficult and costly by the remoteness of the grazings and the difficulty of access caused by steep slopes and bogs. In other conditions, as in New Zealand, where the addition of two cwt. of superphosphate per acre, together with seed, is normally a satisfactory top-dressing for the improvement of low-tussock grassland, the use of aircraft can overcome some of the problems created by relief. So far aerial topdressing has proved of little value in overcoming the problems of the British acidic moorlands but may be useful in certain circumstances.[1]

Increased altitude does not always mean poorer conditions for agriculture. In tropical conditions the reverse is commonly true, the temperatures and humidity of low lying and coastal regions being unfavourable to many crops and most kinds of livestock as well as human beings. Here it becomes a question of the needs of individual crops. Thus, in Java, where there is sufficient relief of land there are vertical zones of crops corresponding to the altitudinal zones of vegetation. Further differentiation takes place according to the variation of rainfall and other factors, but sugar cane is confined to low ground (below 650 feet generally), rubber is found from sea-level to about 2000 feet, while the highest yields and best qualities of tea are obtained from between 4000 and 6000 feet. But higher yet, on mountain ranges, the deterioration associated with montane and alpine zones occurs as in temperate countries.

Exceptions also occur in the details of soil pattern, associated with local variations in relief and parent materials. Well-drained, basic volcanic soils, for example, are more fertile than the soils of other parent materials which may lie below them at more promising altitudes.

Slope

As already noted, the effects of slope on agriculture may be considered as acting either directly or indirectly. With regard first to the indirect effects, some pedological and climatic effects of slope have already been considered, including the position of the water table, downslope movement of soil, air drainage and relative freedom of slopes from frost.

At any altitude the climates of different slopes vary according to their aspect. In the European Alps many studies have

[1] Symons (1959). See also pp. 130-1.

been made of the contrast between the sunny slope (French *adret*) and the shady slope (*ubac*). In such regions of high relief the contrast resulting from the angles at which the sun's rays strike the ground surface is heightened by the difference between the number of hours of possible sunshine that can be received by different slopes. Where cloud cover is usually of comparatively short duration, so that free radiation prevails during much of the time when the sun is not warming the land, the contrast is heightened. For plant growth it is the difference in soil temperatures rather than air temperatures between the *adret* and *ubac* and at different altitudes which appears to be significant.

Methods have been devised[1] to present cartographically the contrasts between the local climates of sunny and shady slopes and other features of insolation in mountainous terrain. Cartographic analysis is necessary to correct unsatisfactory generalisations which are too easily made regarding the value of the contrasting slopes. In the Defereggental (Hohe Tauern massif), for example, shady slopes of gullies and embayments were found to be entirely used for forest and meadow while south-facing slopes, however small the area, were used for cereals. Calculations for intensity values in other localities in this region, however, generally show that cereals *can* be ripened when intensities fall below these gully values.

> This illustrates, therefore, what might be described as the *selective* rather than the *prohibitive* influences of insolation, for the economy of the valley demands a high meadow acreage, and as there is often a better crop on a shady rather than a sunny slope, the concentration of cereals on slopes of one aspect and of meadow on another merely reflects the selection of slopes to which each is best—but not exclusively—adjusted, in terms of both insolation and the local economic requirements of the commune.[2]

In the siting of settlements and the cultivation of crops, long duration of sunshine was seen often to be more important than its intensity. Plants achieve a relatively high rate of assimilation of weak light, and a site cut off from early morning or late

[1] Garnett (1937).
[2] Garnett (1937), 52. See also Peattie (1936).

afternoon sun is not fully compensated by the strength of midday sun.

Slope and Cultivation

The most obvious of the direct effects of slope on agriculture is in the limitation of cultivation. In spite of the importance of slope controls there has been surprisingly little written concerning them. Drawing attention to the absence of precision in reporting on slope, Macgregor[1] suggests correlations between slope and land use in Britain, given below with some further suggestions.

6 DEG.: GRADIENT 1/10

Slopes of up to 6 degrees present no serious obstacle to cultivation unless there are irregularities in the surface. Since water will flow briskly on a slope of ½ degree, even this slight slope can ensure adequate drainage if ditches are kept clean. Macgregor suggests the term *gently sloping* for a slope of 3 deg. and a *moderate slope* for one of 6 deg.

11 DEG.: GRADIENT 1/5

This, Macgregor states, is about the limit for ground that is to be ploughed and cut annually.

18 DEG.: GRADIENT 1/3

Macgregor says that this is about the maximum slope that may be found under cultivation in Britain and it is then generally under permanent grass. While agreeing with this conclusion as applying to the great majority of cases I think it should be noted that there are slopes of 20 deg. and even more that are ploughed regularly in the British Isles.

Macgregor suggests that this and the following should be called *steep* slopes. If this term be accepted for the 25 deg. slope, and perhaps a slope of 20 deg., it would seem that *moderately steep* would be a suitable term for the present category.

25 DEG.: GRADIENT 1/2

This is undoubtedly a *steep* slope, too steep for cultivation, but suitable for afforestation if soil is present.

[1] Macgregor (1957).

Cultivation can be carried on without detriment to the soil cover on slopes in Britain that would, if cultivated in drier conditions, be likely to suffer from serious erosion. It is, however, technically possible to cultivate slopes steeper than are commonly attempted in Britain if discs rather than ploughs are used to break up the ground. In New Zealand slopes of 25–30 degrees have been cultivated with discs, though they are generally maintained subsequently in pasture.

It is highly desirable that some general and international nomenclature should be adopted for the description of slopes. A study by the British Geomorphological Research Group[1] suggests the following as the most satisfactory categories for landform analysis, Macgregor's classes having been added for comparative purposes:

TABLE 3

CLASSIFICATION OF SLOPES

B.G.R.G. (1962) Degrees		Macgregor (1957) Degrees	
0 – ½	Flat		
1 – 2½	Gently sloping	3	Gently sloping
3 – 6	Moderately sloping	6	Moderate slope
6½ – 13	Strongly sloping	11	Fairly steep
13½ – 19	Moderately steep	18	Steep
19½ – 31	Steep	25	Steep
31½ and over	Very steep		
	Cliffs		

With the substitution of 'strongly sloping' and 'moderately steep' for Macgregor's corresponding terms, there is no clash between the two classifications. A further advantage of the categories proposed by the British Geomorphological Research Group is that they correspond closely with those used by the United States soil scientists[2] and already adopted, with slight modification by other soil scientists, for example, in New Zealand.

Another problem arises out of confusion between the single slope, to which the above classifications are directed, and the

[1] The British Geomorphological Research Group, Report No. 5, December, 1962.

[2] U.S.A. Department of Agriculture (1951), 162–164.

compound slope. Table 4 illustrates both the difference in concepts of steepness, and the complications that arise when compound slopes are considered.

TABLE 4

CLASSES OF LAND FORMS ACCORDING TO COMPOUND SLOPES[1]

Symbol	*Name*	*Slopes*
0/	Flat	
1/	Flat to gently undulating	
2/	Easy rolling	Most slopes under 5 deg.
3/	Rolling	Most slopes under 12 deg.
4/	Moderately steep	Most slopes under 23 deg. many between 12 and 23 deg.
5/	Moderately steep to steep	Most slopes under 30 deg. many between 18 and 30 deg.
6/	Steep	Many slopes between 30 deg. and 38 deg.
7/	Very steep	Many slopes of 40 deg. and over

Run-off and erosion vary according to steepness of slope, and experiments have shown that, by and large, the erosion per unit area increases 2·5 times as the degree of slope is doubled.[2] During run-off, water accumulates as it flows down a slope. Consequently, more water flows over the lower part of the slope, and it flows faster than it does over the upper part of the slope. As a broad average, soil loss increases 1·5 times per unit area when the slope length is doubled.[3]

Although liability to erosion is always greater on steeper slopes than on gentle ones, this liability does not increase at the same rate for all soils. Thus, on a slight slope sand may erode less than clay, but on a steep slope the clay may erode more than the sand. Table 5 shows that ease of detachment of sand particles becomes more important on a steep slope than the ease of transport of clay particles.

[1] New Zealand D.S.I.R. (1962), 30.

[2] Kohnke and Bertrand (1959), 103.

[3] Kohnke and Bertrand (1959), 104.

TABLE 5

EFFECT OF SLOPE ON DETACHMENT AND TRANSPORTATION[1]

Soil type	lb. of water required to move 1 lb. of soil — *Slope* *8 per cent.* (*$4\frac{1}{2}$ deg.*)	*16 per cent.* (*9 deg.*)	Soil characteristics — *Infiltration capacity*	*Detachment hazard*	*Transportation hazard*
Sandy loam	179	7	High	High	Low
Silty clay loam	65	24	Low	Low	High

To control erosion and facilitate cropping on slopes various forms of terracing are used. Found in many countries are bench terraces, formed by building walls across a slope so that the soil can be accumulated upslope at a lower angle of rest than the natural slope. Stone-faced terraces in Peru date back probably four thousand years, while some in China, Japan and the Philippine Islands are over two thousand years old. Other old examples are found in Mediterranean countries, and more recent ones in the United States of America. In the U.S.A., however, they are no longer built because run-off water is difficult to control and erosion may continue to be serious.

Irrigation terraces are constructed by levelling sections of the slope and building retaining walls. Water is conducted from terrace to terrace by a system of flumes and weirs. Such are the well known terraces of south-east Asia, permitting wet rice and other crops to be grown on quite steep slopes, with almost no erosion. The Philippines provide the most spectacular examples. In northern Luzon terraces have been built to altitudes of over 5000 feet. In some cases they are only 10 feet wide, separated by almost vertical banks of up to 50 feet in height. Irrigation water is carried in bamboo conduits for two or three miles in some cases.

Terraces such as these are not suitable for mechanised agriculture. If large machines are to be used terraces must be broad-based with drainage channels. These are widely used in the U.S.A., but are difficult to build and utilise with heavy machinery on slopes of more than about 8 degrees. With mechanised farming, terracing is mostly on land of less than 5 degrees slope, and, where slopes are long and climatic and soil conditions facilitate rapid erosion, terracing is undertaken on slopes of less than 1 degree.

[1] Kohnke and Bertrand (1959), 110, quoting Duley and Hays (1932).

CHAPTER 3

Social and Economic Factors Influencing Agriculture

In the complex of social arrangements and organisations that underlie and influence the types and patterns of farming throughout the world, a recurring theme is the identification of agriculture with the peasant way of life. The word 'peasant' comes readily to mind when we think of those who work the soil in such diverse regions and with such differing economic organisations as are to be found in Greece, Chile, Japan and Russia. On the other hand we do not think of the smallholder in England, the U.S.A. or New Zealand as a peasant. The differences that are recognised almost instinctively are not easy to define, but we must have a little more certainty as to what we mean when we use the term.

'The word has always carried an implication of rustic inferiority, and we tend to apply it to countries other than our own', writes E. Estyn Evans,[1] who has specialised in the study of peasant communities and folklife. 'Yet the word implies a permanent link with the soil—the *paysan* with his *pays*—so that we hesitate to apply it to the shifting cultivators of tropical Africa.' Evans, considering peasant life in western Europe, continues, 'For our purpose I take the peasant to be the self-employed farmer (as distinct from the non-operating land-owner) who is largely dependent on the labour of his family; and we may expect the contribution of this labour to be more important than the contribution of capital.'

Acceptance of this definition would not prevent us from using the term, as is common, for the agricultural peoples of southern Asia or South America. It would apply to the Russia of the Tsars, but puts us in difficulty if we try to apply it to the

[1] Evans (1956), 220.

same people now organised in the collective and state farms of the U.S.S.R. Similarly, the word 'peasant' seems to belong with 'Chinese', but does it fit the worker now serving in the communes? Perhaps the difficulty that has been experienced in the U.S.S.R., eastern European countries and China in trying to organise agricultural production like a factory industry confirms that all these people are really peasants, to whom the permanent link with the soil, *their* soil, is fundamental. The partial modification of the idea of the collective in Russia, with the allocation of private plots to the individuals who are employed in the collective farms, certainly recognises this demand for a personal piece of land inherent in people whose way of life is rooted in the soil more permanently than are the crops they grow.

Ownership of the land is not essential to peasant status, for as Evans points out, in many European countries ownership came to the peasant only in the nineteenth century, and 'land ownership is no part of the immemorial peasant tradition'. Serfdom was a common state for peasantries as far apart in time and space as ancient Rome and nineteenth century Russia, but even when nominally free most peasant families were by tradition and force of circumstances tied to one estate.

The differences between the peasant and the farmer seem to centre on the amount of land controlled. The terminological boundaries are nebulous but some cases are clear, as already mentioned. Evans says 'it is doubtful if the name (peasant) can be applied, for example, to the family farmers of England with their 100–300 acre holdings'.[1] A possible criterion might be the ability to employ labour. It could only be ability to employ, not actual employment, because so much depends on the size and inclinations of the individual family, and varying economic circumstances. Evans's point about the relative importance of land and labour is helpful, for the man who has a holding large enough to be capable of yielding sufficient income to employ a labourer full-time has normally a significant amount of capital invested in his farm, if not in the land. The farmer then becomes an entrepreneur in a small way, which is very different from the status of the peasant. All this means that the farmer, even though the size of his holding

[1] Evans (1956), 220.

suggests the qualification 'small', has a degree of independence not normally associated with the peasant.

The yeoman farmers of England, a class recognised as standing between the lesser tenants and the landowners in the England of the agrarian revolution, represent a status well removed from that of the peasant by the attributes already mentioned. A further quality attributed to the yeoman farmers was the readiness to adopt the improved kinds of crops and livestock and the new machinery introduced by the improver-landlords. A peasant would still be wielding his spade when the yeoman farmer harnessed his own team of horses to the new steel plough.

It would probably be reasonable to argue that the peasantry of England disappeared in the changeover to modern mixed farming, with enclosure and redivision of land, and the movement of large numbers of the poorer people from the land to the factory towns. This was a change unparalleled on the continent of Europe or in Ireland. On the continent, the peasantry has been transformed in some countries, such as Denmark, where modern mechanised agriculture has been grafted on to an old society, and little changed in others, as in the south of Italy and Greece. In Ireland the change has been considerable, with ownership of land replacing the landlord-tenant system that was at the root of much of the strife in Ireland right up to the present century, but again this has not fundamentally altered the attachment of the Irishman to a small and often uneconomic plot of land. Much of the difference in the agricultural landscapes of England and Ireland, especially the west and south of Ireland, where peasant ways and values are least changed, stems from this difference in the contrasting disappearance and survival of peasant societies.

It is widely accepted that the crux of the problem posed by the growth of world population and the failure of many countries to upgrade their living standards is to be found in their agricultural systems and particularly in the low productivity of their peasants. The 'agriculturalisation' of the peasantry has been quoted by Franklin as one of the factors producing crisis in peasant societies.[1] He cites in particular Italy and India, where population increase has not been

[1] Franklin (1962).

accompanied by a proportionate increase in non-agricultural opportunities but rather by a decline in rural industries. Rediversification, he concludes, is important to the improvement of local conditions. It may be added that diversification must not be used as an excuse for lack of action in redistribution of land or educating the peasantry to utilise it better. Traditional methods of cultivating and dealing with livestock are deeply rooted in peasant societies and improvements will be slow, unless intensive education can be coupled with redistribution of land and provision of capital, as in Denmark in the nineteenth century.

Development of Peasant Societies

Today, Franklin notes, the majority of peasant societies stand in need of programmes of development and organisation. He proposes a simple classification of peasant societies based on the types of development or reforms they need.[1] In the first group he sees the peasants of western Europe who, though disrupted by the process of industrialisation, have shared the benefits arising from it. They are now subordinate to richer industrial sectors which can provide subventions for their reorganisation and improvement. The collectivised peasants of eastern Europe and the U.S.S.R. are on the fringe of this position, after having themselves borne much of the cost of industrialisation.

The second group is of peasant societies which are in a much worse position owing to agriculturalisation, the growth of population and lack of a strong industrial sector which could provide them with subventions. The large groups of peasants in Asia and the Middle East and, provisionally, the mass of those in Latin America would come in this category.

The third group comprises those who are not sedentary cultivators, or who lack many of the elementary features of peasant life, but who may acquire the features of a modernised peasantry. Franklin sees the plans of western experts as providing the conditions for this change, but it may be inferred from the discussion of subsistence agriculture later in this book that this change is likely to take place more and more widely whether or not consciously planned. Land shortages, population

[1] Franklin (1962), 11.

growth and negligible industrial sectors are features of some of these societies.

This third category are folk culturally on the edge of the peasantry, opposite to that already discussed, where the dividing line between peasant and farmer was examined. At this other extreme, many authorities would not refer to the non-sedentary folk as peasants at all, but rather as tribesmen. Evans, we have noted, says 'we would hesitate to apply it [the term "peasant"] to the shifting cultivators of Africa'.

Three features have been suggested[1] as differentiating peasantry from tribes and these at the same time summarise important aspects of peasant life and outlook. In the peasant,

(1) Landownership and inheritance become very important. Property, savings and investment enter into all calculations.

(2) Domestic animals, where they are part of the system, make man a slave to time as well as to property.

(3) Individual motivation and competition begin. In tribal society individual competition is generally not prominent.

The fact that ownership of land is not essential to peasant status, as noted by Evans, does not invalidate the first point above, because if he does not own land it is usually a prime concern of the peasant that he should be able to do so, or at least to obtain more to cultivate, and the idea of personal and inheritable property is usually well developed.

Major changes in peasant societies come from above, i.e. from estate owners or governments, usually the latter, because it is often in the interests of the landowners to preserve the status quo. In the case of the English enclosures this was not so since economic conditions favoured change being imposed by the landowners. In Soviet Russia (dealt with in a later chapter) government intervention was made to implement the tenets of the Communist party as well as to increase agricultural efficiency. In Ireland, land reform was imposed by the British government when long-continued agitation from the exploited peasants could no longer be denied.

Ireland affords an example of land redistribution in the

[1] Tax (1956), 421.

spatial arrangement of holdings as well as in the ownership of land. This was achieved without compulsory removal of people from the land—a feature associated with adjustment to sheep farming in the Scottish Highlands. The form of occupation of the land in Ireland was the same as that prevalent in Scotland, though in Ireland it persisted later. Known as 'runrig' in Scotland and 'rundale' in Ireland, it was basically an openfield system, but quite different from the manorial openfield systems of England and Europe. An 'infield' comprised all the easily cultivated land and received almost all the manure. The 'outfield' was used mainly for grazing but patches were dug over for crops from time to time in some sort of rough rotation. Hill and bog land was grazed in the summer months. This was a system suited to a country where rough land and local changes in soil types abounded. The infield was divided into strips, and any one man would have several strips in different parts of the field, so that he shared in all qualities of land. He would hold shares on the mountain in proportion to his plots in the infield, these shares enabling him to pasture a certain number of sheep or their equivalent in other livestock. The system had many disadvantages, notably the fragmented nature of a holding. To make matters worse, the strips in some cases were changed annually to make doubly certain that no man then had an undue share of poor land, but in practice this meant that no one had much incentive to improve his own land. On the common or jointly-owned hill land all the livestock intermingled so that attention to improved breeding or ridding animals of disease was doomed to failure.

This system persisted in Scotland well into the eighteenth century, and in Ireland until at least a hundred years later. Investigation into land tenure in Ireland revealed the hopeless muddle that reigned.[1] The replacement of this system by one of consolidated farms was accompanied by colonisation of hill land, usually enclosed in long narrow stripes or 'ladders' running from the cultivable valley to the rough grazing. Some of the jointly-owned grazings were similarly divided. Many of these, however, remain to indicate something of the complexity that was associated with the rundale system. Thus, one mountain slope in Northern Ireland, comprising little more

[1] Devon Commission: Digest (1847).

than 1400 acres, is shared by 23 lowland farms, the souming or grazing rights being allocated in fractions of 400. Two holdings have only 7/400ths each; the largest is 32/400ths.[1] This latter share would provide grazing for about 60 sheep. Even in cultivated land some traces of the former confusion can still be found in fragmented holdings. (Figure 5).

As the rundale system was eliminated, so it became possible for constructive action to be taken to transfer ownership of land from the landlords, many of them absentees in England, to the farmers themselves. Legislation to achieve this end was introduced in 1870, some twenty-five years after the Great Famine had stressed the urgency for reform. It was not, however, until after the Ashbourne Act of 1885 that much progress

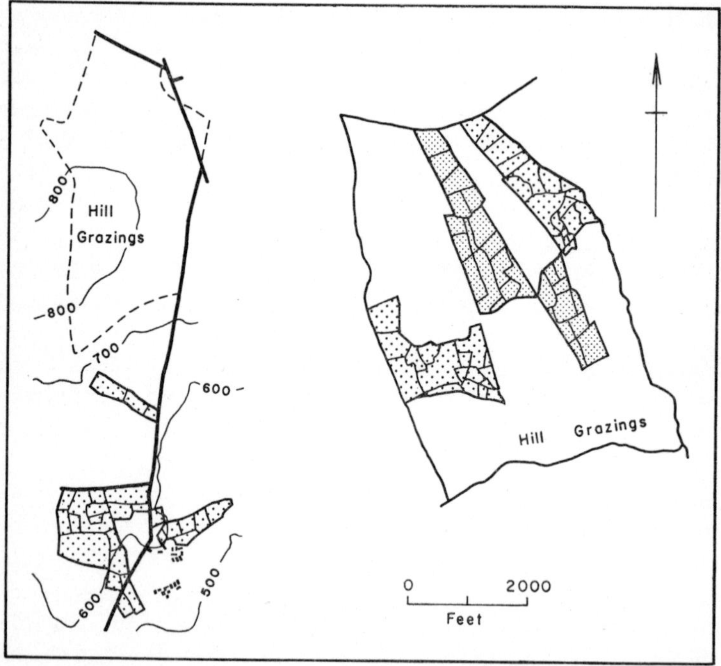

Figure 5. Examples of fragmented farms in Northern Ireland. On the left are shown the cultivated fields (stippled) and hill grazings comprising an upland farm in County Antrim. On the right two farms are distinguished in a County Londonderry townland. This diagram has not previously been published.

[1] Symons (1955–6), 72.

was made. This authorised the advance to tenants of the entire purchase money for their farms. From then until after the partition of Ireland in 1920 the process of breaking up the estates continued. Nearly all farms now are owned by their occupiers, subject to annuity payments. The small size of farm, shortage of capital, and lack of education of rural folk, both generally and in agricultural extension work, reduced the beneficial effects that might have been expected from such a comprehensive movement. The force of economic circumstances and emigration has, however, facilitated the amalgamation of farm units so that the position is slowly improving, especially in the eastern regions, where the changes took place earliest and the land is generally fairly fertile. In the west a peasant society is still widespread, though even here it may be said to be decaying or evolving, according to one's point of view.

Land Tenure

It has already been noted that ownership is no criterion for defining peasant status. When considering the condition of a peasant society we must, however, have regard to the tenure by which it occupies its land. Similarly, in consideration of any agricultural society or region, the forms of land tenure of the past and the present must be examined.

The concept of land tenure must itself be defined. It is taken here to mean the system, or individual agreement, whether written or not, under which land is held or occupied. It is not restricted to the meaning which may be placed on the term of law. It includes all forms of tenancy and also ownership in any form.

Form of tenure will affect farm operations in many ways. Among the most important are:

(1) Length of time available for planning the development of the farm and profiting by the results.

(2) Extent to which investments in the holding could be realised if need arose.

(3) Whether the occupier is dependent solely on his own resources in exploiting the farm.

(4) How much income must be set aside to meet obligations in respect of rent, mortgage, etc.

(5) Preference for investment in the land as compared with investment in livestock or other movables, investment off the farm, or consumption—obviously linked with (2) above.

(6) Possibility of extending or contracting operations by purchase or sale of land or adjustment through letting.

There is a widespread assumption that owner-occupation is necessarily to be preferred to tenancy systems because of the incentive to improve a holding that is owned compared with one that is merely rented. It cannot be denied that there is a special and powerful incentive to preserve and develop an asset which is under the complete control of the occupier and may thus be devoted to the welfare of his family and heirs. Qualifications, however, need to be made.

If a man is to farm well he must also have sufficient free capital to invest in fixed and movable equipment for the farm, good seeds, fertilisers, livestock and other necessities for the full exploitation of the land. He must also have the knowledge required to exploit these assets, and be able to call upon technical and economic advisers to supplement and keep up to date his own knowledge. To develop his enterprise he will probably also need credit. A legal system or tradition that discourages subdivision may also be necessary for the best use of the land in the long term.

These are the advantages that a well-regulated tenancy system operating in favourable circumstances can offer. In many tenancy systems it is the custom for the landlord to provide buildings and some other items of 'fixed' capital while the tenant provides his own livestock, machinery and other movable capital. This means that a tenant who starts off with limited capital can concentrate on adequate supply and quality in these assets without the problem of financing either the outright purchase of the land and buildings, or the purchase of the one and the construction of the other. It may be easier financially to go on paying rent indefinitely than to raise a large capital sum. Obviously the balancing of these two alternatives depends on the level and control of rents, the availability of capital or credit, and the terms on which the latter can be obtained. In some societies it is virtually impossible to borrow substantial sums at a moderate rate of interest even with reasonable security. Farming is not a business distinguished for security based on earnings, nor is the person who seeks credit to set up in farming likely to have much else to offer as security, other than the farm assets themselves. Where occupation of the land is almost entirely by ownership, good potential farmers may be kept out of the industry entirely through lack of capital.

For a tenanted farm to offer a prospect attractive to maximum care in husbandry and improvement of land and fixed capital, however, there must be a sufficiently long lease. It is here that tenancy systems usually fail to meet the needs of good husbandry. A tenant who has a lease of 20 years or more has considerable incentive to make his own improvements to buildings, drainage and fencing, if the landlord is unwilling or financially unable to invest in these. Such leases are, however, rare. Shorter leases may have similar effects if there is full and reliable provision for a tenant on outgoing to derive adequate benefit for improvements carried out. This, however, can impose a burden on a landlord who may be called upon to make payments for his tenant's labour and investment which he would not have initiated himself, and might not be able to recoup from an incoming tenant. Raising a rent to meet compensation of this kind may be difficult, especially if government control is exercised over rents to prevent exploitation by landlords.

Very short leases and consequent insecurity for tenants are common. In Ireland the fear of landlords regaining control of farms has led to restrictions on long-term letting but these have allowed a pernicious system of short-term letting to flourish. This is 'conacre', or eleven months' letting, whereby an individual field or a whole farm is let for a period of less than one year. The practice pre-dates owner-occupation but appears to have increased rather than diminished. Very high rents are obtainable—£25 per acre for a single year is not uncommon—owing to the demand for land to supplement small farms. It has been suggested that the system enables a farmer to adapt his holding to his immediate needs but there is strong temptation for a man who is working the land only for one year to extract as much as he can from the land and put back the minimum, and systematic rotation of crops is lost. Many farms are let piecemeal year after year by owners who do not want to work their land but will not part with it because they can get bigger profits through conacre letting. The system also makes for high prices for the few farms that are offered for sale, and makes it extremely difficult for a young man with limited capital to enter farming as either an owner or a tenant.

A central problem in the economic development of many countries today is the rearrangement of farm boundaries to provide more efficient units, and in many cases to encourage the consolidation of holdings into larger and more economic farms. This may necessitate the reversal of previous trends. Inheritance laws and customs have led to subdivision of farms and over the centuries units have become extremely small in many countries. In some, however, the opportunities of work in the towns have led to some degree of consolidation by those remaining on the land.

The situation in some western European countries within the last decade or so is shown in Table 6, where the proportion of farms of less than 5 hectares, and in some instances less than 2 hectares, is detailed. Italy stands out with over 90 per cent.

TABLE 6

PERCENTAGES OF FARMS UNDER 5 AND UNDER 2 HECTARES IN SOME WEST EUROPEAN COUNTRIES

		0—5 hectares		0—2 hectares	
COUNTRY	*Date of Source*	*Per cent. of all holdings*	*Per cent. of surface area*	*Per cent. of all holdings*	*Per cent. of surface area*
Austria	1951	48·0	6·0[1]	24·3	1·6[1]
Belgium	1950	87·7	26·5	—	—
Denmark	1956	20·9[2]	3·8[2]	—	—
France	1957	37·0	5·4	—	—
Ireland	1956	—	—	24·0	—
Italy	1957	93·3	31·0	83·3	17·4
Norway	1949	81·9	38·6	59·0	9·7
Spain	1952	77·4	28·3	—	—

[1]Total agricultural and forestry area.
[2]Minimum size enumerated 0·55 hectares.

Source: Land consolidation in Europe, International Institute for Land Reclamation and Improvement, 1959.

of holdings under 5 hectares (11 acres) and over 80 per cent. under 2 hectares (5 acres), but Belgium, Norway and Spain all reported over three-quarters of their holdings as being less than 5 hectares. The criteria by which the economic viability of a farm may be judged are mentioned later in this chapter. For the moment it may merely be noted that nearly all these small farms, and many considerably larger ones, cannot be economic units. The size of holding judged suitable for a family farm varies according to the region and the type of farming practicable. Given average conditions, farms of 10–20 hectares are considered appropriate in the Netherlands, Sweden, Denmark and West Germany. In southern Europe, where intensive crop cultivation with irrigation is possible, smaller farms are practicable.

The value of many of the small holdings is reduced by fragmentation. When fields are separated by land belonging to or farmed by other people, working efficiency is much affected, and there is increased scope for disputes. Modernisation, such as enlargement of fields and conversion to electric fencing or improvement of access to fields, is hindered or made impossible.

Recognition of the need for action to remedy both excessive subdivision and fragmentation of holdings has led to the adoption in many countries of schemes of agrarian reconstruction. The magnitude of the task in western Europe was indicated in a study prepared by the Food and Agriculture Organisation of the United Nations: 'It can safely be said that about 50 million hectares in Europe still wait for land consolidation, 5·7 million of which are located in the Federal Republic of Germany, 14 million in France, 10 million in Italy and a very considerable area in Norway'.[1]

In other continents similar trends have been apparent and subdivision has been carried to extreme lengths in some countries, notably Muslim societies in Asia. But, writing of paddy land, B. H. Farmer has argued that given the circumstances of the present time, especially the lack of alternative employment, subdivision is better not discouraged.[2] Since paddy rice is a crop which responds well to intensive methods, and demands very careful water control which produces 'self-contained' units of land, 'there is no inefficiency in the

[1] International Institute for Land Reclamation and Improvement (1959), 22–23.

[2] Farmer (1960).

sort of subdivision of paddy lands which goes on'. In any case, it is argued, legislation to control subdivision would attack only a symptom, not the disease, which is an economic system geared to a static population, but faced with a rapidly expanding one. Similar arguments are not applicable to tea and rubber lands, where economies of scale are relevant, and would cease to appy if massive development of the economy took place.

Marketing

Apart from the purely subsistence economy, now of limited occurrence in the world and becoming rapidly more so, farmers will give priority in production to commodities for which there is an effective demand. This demand may be exercised by people in the locality, necessitating only the simplest forms of market, in which producer and buyers deal directly. At the other extreme, the consumers may be 12,000 miles distant from the farmers, as is the British market for New Zealand produce, with a complicated machinery connecting the two groups.

Unless farmers develop some form of group control they are usually in a weak position in relation to their markets. In the simple market place buyers have the opportunity of dealing with many sellers and conditions approximate to perfect competition. If one seller is offering a standard commodity at a lower price than elsewhere, the others will not be able to sell their goods—unless there are non-economic considerations—until the cheaper stocks have been sold. This tends to lead to price-cutting and inadequate returns. Only by agreeing among themselves the prices at which they will offer their goods can the sellers hope constantly to obtain remunerative prices in conditions of balanced supply and demand.

Where an intermediary or merchant buys from farmers in order to resell in the markets, the farmer is again in a weak position. There are many more farmers than merchants and it is relatively easy for the merchants to dictate the terms on which they will buy. They know the market position better than do the farmers, and can insist on their own assessment of a reasonable margin to cover their risks. The sum of the margins of each intermediary may result in a very low price to the farmer (who has little alternative in selling) and a high price to the consumer or shopkeeper (who has few suppliers).

While individual merchants may adhere scrupulously to fair principles in their dealings and aim only at moderate profits, farmers in many countries have found it necessary to form co-operatives for disposing of their cash crops and livestock. The existence of a producers' co-operative inevitably has a salutary effect on the conduct of private dealers, who may still retain the allegiance of many farmers, but only so long as they maintain reasonable standards in their transactions. Some commodities lend themselves particularly to co-operative marketing schemes, dairy products being an example. Liquid milk must be collected from the individual farm and sold almost at once, while butter cannot long be stored except under deep-freeze conditions. Co-operative dairies solved the problem of the small producer in Britain and Ireland, not only by providing a ready market for milk, but also in being able to produce a standardised butter, which overcame the objections of variability in the product of the individual farm. Danish co-operatives pressed standardisation and grading of produce to remarkably high levels in the building-up of their national export trade.

Where controlling agencies are needed for marketing farm produce, but the producers have not themselves the necessary finance or skill to set up and administer co-operatives, government action is called for. Pre-war price falls and war-time problems led to such action in British West Africa and after the war Marketing Boards were formed to deal with all of the major export crops of this area. Government agencies buy from farmers and dispose of the crop at world market prices, retaining any surplus over the agreed price to build up funds from which local prices can be subsidised when world prices are low.[1]

The existence of co-operative agencies, producer-boards, and government bodies which carry out similar functions, has profound geographical significance. Without such organisation the production of a crop may be inhibited, even if the region concerned is well suited to it. Fluctuating market prices and exploitation by commercial operators interested

[1] See Pedler (1955) esp. ch. 17.

only in short-term gain mean insecurity for the producer. This may result in the decline of even a well-established farming system. If specialisation on cash crops produces disastrous results in several years the farmers will be forced back on subsistence or near-subsistence economies to the detriment of themselves, their would-be buyers and the whole economy. In contrast, a good marketing organisation can do much to ensure the economic stability of a region, the maintenance of a pattern of production suited to the geographical environment and steady development of the economy.

Transport

In addition to the organisation required to obtain fair remuneration for the farmer and orderly placing of the produce on the market, it is, of course, essential to have transport systems able to convey the goods from producer to buyer. Further reference may be made to West Africa to illustrate the point. In the northern region of Nigeria great piles of groundnuts were once to be seen along the railway tracks awaiting movement to the coast for overseas shipment. Shortage of rolling stock aggravated by poor maintenance resulted in the railways being unable to move the season's crops. 'The history of Nigeria has been a continuous tale of export crops or minerals that could not be moved'.[1] A few years later, after extensive modernisation works, the crops were being cleared effectively even with a record harvest.[2]

Many forms of produce require of their transport agencies more than mere capacity. Perishable produce demands speed and frequency of movement, or special measures for preservation, or both. The dairying and meat exporting industries of Australia and New Zealand could never have entered world markets without the advent of refrigeration. Banana plantations, with their immense output, also must have high-capacity refrigerated freight vessels for their economic operation. This, however, does not mean that special consignments of high-grade produce may not be able to withstand the high costs of air transport if this enables them to be placed fresh on suitable markets. At the time of writing

[1] *The Times*, London, 15th November 1951.

[2] *Glasgow Herald*, 15th November 1956.

(1964–5) selected lamb carcases are being flown from New Zealand to the London market by normal air-freight services, and trial consignments of strawberries have been flown from New Zealand orchards to Britain and Italy and peaches to Hong Kong.

Such developments suggest possibilities of long-range marketing by air. Short-range air freighting is already well developed and includes, for example, the marketing of beef in northern Australia, and of fruit and flowers for Britain from the Channel Islands, Scilly Islands, France and other warmer regions. Again one sees the use of aircraft for perishable commodities. The Australian 'air beef' is exported frozen, the advantage of air freight being that the cattle can be saved the exhausting and time-consuming trek from inland stations to the ports, killing being carried out on the stations.

Air transport can cope only with the exceptional and rather sensational cases.[1] Even in local transport, however, speed is a factor where produce is perishable. Market gardening normally uses road transport in which lorries are owned by the farmers themselves or are closely geared by local transport agencies to their needs. As in other geographical patterns, road transport has made possible the diffusion of market gardening over a wider area than was formerly possible, though it is still noticeable that big cities retain near them areas of horticulture. In general the nearer the vegetable grower is to market the better are his chances of profitable operation, and the intensity of working makes possible the paying of rents which cannot be met by other types of farming (see Chapter 9). The producers of the slightly less perishable and more easily bulked commodity of milk have been able to supply the cities from greater distances through the media of special trains and tanker vehicles.

With less perishable goods, frequency of transport may be as important as speed. The less the time spent by consignments on the wharf, in loaded wagons or in transit sheds, the less the need for speed in actual movement, as well as the lower the costs. The farmer, or the market organisation supplying markets overland, has here a great advantage over those who must

[1] The appearance (1965) of the Russian Antonov AN22, capable of carrying 80 tons on hauls of over 3000 miles heralds a more important role for air transport.

send by sea, with all the transhipping involved, as well as waiting for less frequent services. Thus the Irish producer of cattle or potatoes for the English market is at a disadvantage compared with his counterpart in England. The crossing of the Irish Sea means a longer time for calling forward supplies and greater risk of missing the best prices in markets with short supplies. Most services between Ireland and Britain are operated on six nights per week, but goods have to be alongside early enough for handling between rail or road vehicle and ship. The total time taken by a consignment of butter from an Irish factory to London is not much less than a Danish consignment takes. The disabilities in transport that have to be overcome in marketing New Zealand produce in the British Isles are referred to later (Chapter 5).

Transport must always be evaluated not only in terms of capacity, but also of cost. If transport charges are higher than production can bear there will be no incentive to produce for the market. Transport affects the farmer, of course, not only in the outward shipment of his produce, but also in the supply to the farm of seeds, fodder, fertilisers, store livestock and all other goods required for the farm and household. Transport charges almost always loom large in costs of agricultural production, and minimizing these costs will extend the area of production for given markets.

Tariffs and Import Restrictions

While transport serves to extend the area within which produce may be sold, other forces operate to impose restrictions. These are the tariffs, quota restrictions and other import controls that are employed in one form or another by most countries.

Import controls are employed mainly to protect high-cost home produce from low-cost imports. Tariffs may be *ad valorem* or at varying rates according to the specific items of produce. Among the great trading countries which have recourse to tariffs to protect their own farmers are the United States of America and the countries of the European Economic Community. The E.E.C. countries have accepted the principle of eliminating tariffs between the member states and maintaining a common external tariff for produce from all other countries. The level of this tariff varies from low rates or zero for products which the E.E.C. countries cannot produce at all, such as tropical foodstuffs, to high rates for products of temperate regions which would compete directly with their own. Even with a high tariff to pay, low-cost producers such as New Zealand can market produce at prices which enable them to compete with the high-cost home product, so quota restrictions are used in addition. Quotas limit the amount of any one commodity which may be imported from any one country. They may be legally imposed, or accepted voluntarily by exporters who might otherwise face complete exclusion from the market.

At the time of expansion of world markets early in the nineteenth century Britain restricted the import of agricultural produce, but from the repeal of the restrictive Corn Laws in 1846 Britain followed a policy of free trade for nearly a century.[1] This enabled the country to draw supplies of food cheaply from the low-cost new lands of the Americas, Australia and New Zealand as well as from tropical areas. Home farmers suffered because they could not produce as cheaply on farms which were relatively small and inefficient, and therefore high-cost. With no other major international markets open freely to them, the overseas producers concentrated on exports to Britain and when world prices declined sharply after the World War of 1914–18, prices in Britain for agricultural produce fell drastically. The British government, therefore, was forced to abandon free trade and at the Ottawa conference of 1932 restrictions were accepted by exporting countries.

Restriction of imports, however, whether by tariffs or by quantitative measures, has not appeared to successive British governments to meet the circumstances of an economy based on world trade and importing approximately half its food requirements. Since 1938, when the increases in food production needed to enable the country to face a major war were sought, subsidies and grants have been used to enable the home producer to obtain sufficient income to be able to sell his produce in competition with low-cost imports. With few exceptions, such as temporary control of butter imports, when supplies

[1] For a recent study of this period and subsequent agricultural policies in Western Europe see Tracy (1964).

offered from abroad have been unduly high and prices consequently low, the subsidy system has coped with the problem of enabling the British producer to command a good share of the market without shutting out foreign produce. The subsidy bill, however, rose so high that in 1963 government policy turned towards some restriction of imports and to control of import prices. By allowing prices for home produce to rise it was hoped that the subsidy bill would be reduced. Success has varied according to commodity supply situations and more radical changes are undoubtedly needed.[1]

At the same time there is considerable interest in many countries in reducing tariffs so as to stimulate world trade. The General Agreement on Tariffs and Trade (GATT) has been in operation since 1947 and there are complicated bilateral and multilateral agreements between countries both inside and outside GATT. Unfortunately, tariff reductions usually threaten the income of home farmers, and the strong force exerted by these farmers through their voting power makes reduction of tariffs hazardous for governments whose political future is not assured. Hence low-cost producers continue to be largely shut out from markets like the U.S.A. and Europe, even though this in turn severely restricts the amount the exporting countries can spend on purchases of manufactured goods and other needed imports. New Zealand is the classic case of a country which produces farm produce at extremely low prices in spite of a high standard of living, yet which, because this produce is denied more than very limited access to American and European markets, has to tolerate rigid limitation of imports. Uneconomic development of small scale industries follows in order to supply needs which could be met much better by the manufacturing countries, which in turn have to tolerate high food prices because of their own tariffs.

New Zealand is fortunate in being able to maintain a generally high standard of living in spite of these limitations. Such is not the case for India and other underdeveloped countries whose trade is limited by the tariffs and restrictions imposed by the wealthy manufacturing countries.

It is impossible to evaluate fully the effects of these financial controls on the geographical distribution of agriculture. It is,

[1] Peters (1964).

however, fairly obvious that if free trade in agricultural products were general, adjustment in the high-cost food producing countries would have to be widespread and would undoubtedly be painful to the agriculturalists. Most of the small farms of Europe might become amalgamated rapidly into much larger and more efficient units with a high degree of mechanisation to correspond more closely with conditions in the low-cost producing countries. As long as the small farms persist, sheltered by tariffs and supported by subsidies, a variety of crops and livestock may be maintained, some of which would disappear if truly competitive conditions prevailed. In the low-cost producing countries, access to wider markets at remunerative prices would encourage greater intensification of agriculture, though it is less easy to visualise the landscape changes which would follow there.

Political influences apply at the local as well as at the national level. The effects of state legislation and municipal land zoning ordinances on dairying in southern California provide an interesting example.[1] The northern milkshed, in the San Joaquin valley, has the lower production costs, but its advantage compared with the southern area, near Los Angeles, is neutralized by the prices set by the state agency. The state is divided into marketing areas and the prices established in each area are based on local production and marketing costs. The additional costs in the southern area are incorporated in higher prices. Restrictive zoning of land use to protect dairying has been achieved by landholders taking advantage of the state laws that permit any area with more than five hundred persons, with the consent of the majority of landholders, to incorporate into city status and establish its own zoning ordinances and local property taxes.

Farm Income and Type of Enterprise

Subject to special restrictions relating to plant or animal health and personal preferences, a farm will normally be devoted to the type of production which pays best—or which the farmer anticipates will pay best—over a number of years. To the practical farmer, except in conditions of national emergency or to maintain fertility, there is no point in increasing

[1] Fielding (1964).

costs unless income is likely to be increased by a greater amount. A decrease in income can be tolerated if costs can be decreased equally or more. The latter case was illustrated throughout Britain in the depression of the nineteen-thirties, when good arable farms were turned over to 'stick-and-dog farming' on land 'tumbled down to grass'. Sheep were carried on many farms at a density more applicable to a hill farm.

Small farms must be worked more intensively than large farms if their owners or tenants are to obtain reasonable incomes. There is a limit to which costs can be cut, and it should be worth a farmer's while to intensify his farming at least until he has eliminated under-employment of himself and any members of his family who are readily available to give him assistance. In Britain, for example, the most intensive forms of farming practised, apart from horticultural production, are pig and poultry keeping. Hence these are favoured for the small farm, and cannot easily be dispensed with on farms of less than 40 acres. Both pigs and poultry can be reared profitably on a mixture of home-produced and purchased foods, the former including wastes, so minimizing demand on land and freeing it for other enterprises.

Dairying is the next most intensive enterprise, but at least two acres are needed for the year-round maintenance of a dairy cow, and it is generally judged economical and advantageous to maintain some younger stock for herd replacements on even a small dairy farm, so the size of dairy herd that can be maintained is severely limited. Some farms of as little as 20 acres, with only four or five cows in milk, sell to the Milk Marketing Board, but it is only a generous national pricing policy that enables such small units to remain in business.

Cattle rearing and fattening are less intensive enterprises, best suited to the relatively large farm, where cost of labour or indifferent soils militate against more intensive enterprises. Labour demands are low, except during calving periods, so area is usually the factor limiting the size of herd. Up to three acres of grass per head of cattle is needed for fattening purposes. Low rate of turnover makes it difficult to obtain an income on which to raise a family by this means with less than 100 acres, able to fatten about 70–100 cattle per year in two drafts. Nevertheless, there are many much smaller farms subsisting mainly on cattle fattening at a low standard of living.

Cattle rearing, i.e. raising store cattle to $1\frac{1}{2}$ to 2 years old to be fattened on other farms, is less intensive than the finishing process in income per acre, even though more beasts may be maintained per acre. Fattening needs feed of high protein level, which cannot be attained by farms on hill and rough land, which forces them to be satisfied with the rearing stage. Farms devoted to rearing probably ought to exceed 200 acres in order to make satisfactory incomes, but there are many of a tenth of this size in the poorer districts, especially in Ireland.

Arable cropping is also a form of farming of fairly low intensity and hence most suited to large farms. This was, of course, one reason why grain imported from the large farms of newly-opened America and Australia could easily undersell British grain in the nineteenth century. Potatoes, a labour-intensive crop, are more suited to the smaller farm, but the unbalanced demand for a great deal of labour for a short harvesting period discourages farms from devoting high proportions of their area to the crop, and the risk of disease from successive similar crops is another factor limiting their applicability on the small farm.

On a small farm (30–50 acres) profit per acre from pigs and poultry may easily exceed £20 per acre, which may well be twice that from dairying, or mixed livestock and cropping enterprises, and four times that of cattle feeding.[1] It is to be expected, therefore, that a farming landscape will reflect in its farm enterprises the size of farm unit prevalent in the district.

Most intensive of all is market gardening, which in Britain may return a net income well in excess of £500 per acre. But vegetable crops, although having a degree of natural protection from imports by loss of quality in transit, do not receive the protection of guaranteed prices accorded to most farm products, and prices fluctuate sharply according to availability of supplies and the state of demand. This is a case where, given large enough holdings, less intensive production may be more attractive financially in the long run than the

[1] This is the pattern of results shown in the official survey of farms in Northern Ireland, see Thomas (1963). For a practical discussion of farm economics in Britain see Dexter (1961).

more intensive forms, and changes in this direction have been seen even in the south of England where land values have risen and demand for produce has grown rapidly during the past half-century. Other factors of production and marketing have changed, and with them there has been a tendency in Britain for intensive cultivation on small holdings with rapid successions of crops, heavy manuring and hand labour, to give way to a divergence of types of enterprise in vegetable cultivation. Highly intensive cultivation in glasshouses now contrasts with more extensive market gardening on a large scale using farm methods, as in the Fens and, more recently, in Bedfordshire. Conditions which brought about this change in Bedfordshire can be summarised[1] as:

(1) The end of supplies of cheap stable manure provided by London.

(2) The economic security obtained by growing large acreages of farm crops with guaranteed minimum prices as well as vegetables in which prices fluctuate.

(3) The development of fragmentation on the holdings as some growers bought up plots from others.

(4) The introduction of Brussels sprouts, a hardy crop with a wide market as a winter vegetable, aided by motor transport.

(5) A labour shortage encouraging cultivation of easily-harvested crops such as Brussels sprouts, cabbage and lettuce.

(6) Economies of specialisation, including special low haulage rates for large consignments by both road and rail.

Different vegetable crops vary in the intensity of cultivation which is profitable and in their pattern of production, discussed in Chapter 9.

Marginal Analysis and Marginal Production

For reasons such as those outlined above, the individual farmer has little control over the prices at which his produce will be sold. As we have already inferred, in order to obtain a

[1] Beavington (1963).

surplus, or personal income, to cover domestic expenses, he will concentrate on production which will be marketable at prices which adequately cover his costs. If necessary, he must adjust his farming to keep costs at an appropriate level. It is worth while to increase production by intensifying farming or increasing the amount of productive land only so long as the increase in revenue exceeds the increase in costs, i.e. marginal revenue exceeds marginal costs. The most profitable point in production is achieved when marginal costs and marginal revenue are equal, provided that total revenue is higher than total costs.[1] If producton is increased beyond this point, using less favourable factors of production or involving loss of efficiency through the increase in size of the enterprise, gross income may continue to rise but net income (total revenue less costs) will fall.

Although the farmer may not think in these terms, as expressed by the economist, his notion of profit will be based on these inescapable facts. He may never attempt to calculate marginal costs or even average cost per unit of output[2] but if he is aiming to increase profits he will consider whether the employment of extra factors of production, e.g. labour, fertilisers, machinery, 'will pay' through yielding more than their cost. Although he has never heard of marginal analysis he may use the word 'marginal' to describe an expenditure which he thinks will barely 'pay for itself'.

The balancing of costs and anticipated revenue to achieve farm profitability is inevitably reflected in the landscape. The division of the land into farms of particular size and shape reflects past assumptions as to what comprises an economic unit; similarly with size and shape of fields, and the actual use of the land in terms of crops and livestock. This is not, of course, to say that the units will necessarily, in practice, be

[1] For an explanation of marginal analysis and economic theory in general, see Samuelson (1964) or other modern texts in economics. Thomsen and Foote (1952) deal with the application of economic theory to agriculture. Chisholm (1966) relates geography and economics.

[2] Average cost is lowest when marginal cost is still rising and may rise further before the most profitable point of output is reached, i.e. average costs do not directly indicate the most profitable level of production. However, the difference between average cost and average revenue per unit of production does indicate the level of profitability of operation and is more easily calculated than marginal cost.

economic. They may not even have been economic when first laid out, because there has been a tendency throughout the ages and in all parts of the world for farms to be too small for satisfactory rewards to be earned. Furthermore, field arrangements which were efficient before the machine age may now be hopelessly outdated.

Farming regions where successful adjustments have been made to changing cost-price relationships and changing income requirements are distinguished by an appearance of prosperity in the landscape. Where fields are well cared for, free of noxious weeds, soundly walled and fenced, with healthy crops and livestock and good buildings further characterising the farms, it is evident that the farm units are of economic size.[1] When costs are cut to preserve financial margins, maintenance of buildings is reduced, new outlays are avoided, and cheaper seeds mixtures, less labour, drainage work, etc. may be revealed in poorer land use.

For any particular crop or animal product certain places are particularly favourable for production, i.e. because of climatic, labour and other production factors, and convenient markets, income comfortably exceeds outlay. Away from these favourable areas, costs rise and returns are lower, until eventually the zone is reached where the particular type of production does not pay. Unless this is at the edge of a desert which has literally no use, some other product will be more profitable. Here then is the margin of profitability for two types of production—where it may be said that production of either commodity is 'marginal'. There may, or may not, be a clear physical margin coincident with the economic margin, but physical factors will enter into the position of the economic margin, even if only in the matter of physical distance from markets.

The margin of profitability for any particular product will shift areally according to the gap between prices and costs. Thus, given a rise in the price of sugar, and other prices not moving similarly, at the edges of a sugar-beet producing area where transport cost or less favourable soils have inhibited

[1] Subject to the proviso that where the amount of labour on a farm is excessive in relation to production, i.e. over-employment exists, great care may be taken to preserve land and buildings, so giving an appearance of prosperity which belies the facts. Even in this case, the lack of new investment should be apparent.

production, there will be an incentive for some land to be turned over to beet production. In many areas there is constant fluctuation of land use, reflecting a situation which faces farmers more or less permanently with marginal conditions.

It will be apparent that any land will be marginal in relation to some form of use, so care must be taken with the overused term 'marginal land'. This term is often used when what is meant is simply land of low productivity, i.e. where yields are low in absolute terms or in relation to input. Such land is genuinely marginal if its use fluctuates, or if it is likely to be abandoned from all use because it is so poor. If it is in established use, as on an extensive basis for rearing range cattle or sheep, and there is no prospect of this use changing, it is not marginal land.

In the British Isles, for example, hill farming land is often incorrectly described as 'marginal land'. Some hill farming land is marginal in that afforestation presents an attractive alternative to its use for hill sheep and cattle, and at the lower edges of the hill farms there will be land on which the growing of crops, or the sowing out of improved pastures will be economically as well as physically marginal. Above the practical limits for afforestation, however, the hills are marginal only in so far as there may be competition between sheep farming and hunting interests. Possible fluctuations in use between deer, grouse and hill sheep, at perhaps one sheep to ten acres, does not seem to call for description of the land as marginal. It may be relevant that all these are extensive uses, whereas a more intensive use is represented by forestry or cultivation. It is where there is fluctuation or likely change as between such uses, and therefore between more intensive and less intensive categories of use, that the term 'marginal land' and its implications seem justified and desirable.

It is somewhat easier to be specific about what constitutes a marginal farm. Here the emphasis is firmly on the financial aspects of the farm unit. A farm should be regarded as marginal when it is unable to yield regularly a satisfactory profit, e.g. at least a worker's wage for the farmer plus interest on the capital, after making allowance for housing and other perquisites.[1]

[1] This definition was employed in a survey of marginal farms by the Department of Agriculture for Scotland (1947) and accepted by Ellison (1953).

Confusion, however, may arise because a farm which is inherently marginal by this definition may not include any marginal land, in the sense discussed above, while a farm comprising wholly marginal land may not be a marginal unit. The crux of the problem of the marginal farm is generally size. However poor the land, as long as it is capable of raising some crop or animal for which there is a demand, sufficiently large units will be profitable. Thus, there is nothing marginal about Australian stations supporting one steer per square mile because the stations comprise thousands of square miles. The only marginal feature on a typical Scottish hill farm of 7000 acres, supporting 2000 sheep and cattle, is probably the lowest and best land on which it is barely economic to raise fodder crops. Such a use might not be economic if the farm could rely on purchased supplies of winter fodder. The whole farm would, however, become a marginal farm if prices for lambs and wool fell seriously, because the land would not permit of any other adequately remunerative use in farming.

Although, as noted above, marginal land and marginal farms are not always coincident, much marginal land is grouped in marginal farms, and many marginal farms are in their precarious financial state because their land is marginal and they have too little of it. This can be seen most readily in terrain which is difficult for farming and which has been colonised by people whose resources have been slender and whose efforts to make viable farm units have been frustrated by the lack of sufficient acres to offset the poor quality. There must be few countries which cannot provide examples, and all too often one may see adjacent areas of poor and better land with the farms on the poorer land smaller than those on the better. Many examples occur in Scotland[1] and Ireland.[2]

Labour

The labour available is a further important factor in farming. Labour requirements of different crops and different classes of livestock vary immensely. In typical British conditions, for example, about 3½ man-days work are required annually per acre of wheat, about 17 man-days per acre of sugar beet and

[1] Darling (1955), 202.
[2] McHugh (1963).

about 100 man-days per acre of hops. Further examples are given in Table 11 (pp. 222–3). Here we may merely note the great range in requirements, and consequent limitations on types of farming where labour is short. Scarcity of labour in newly-settled regions such as Australia and New Zealand and the western territories of America in the nineteenth century restricted agriculture to forms and methods which demanded little labour in relation to the land area available, such as wheat growing—making maximum use of machinery—and stock ranching. As population built up, more intensive farming became possible and desirable, permitting the closer division of the land into smaller holdings.

At the other extreme, where there is a dense population living on the land, intensive forms of agriculture, capable of providing maximum subsistence, are necessary. The best-known crop of this kind is paddy or wet rice which can absorb over 4000 man-hours per hectare per year, or, say, the work of two people for 313 days per year for roughly 6½ hours per day, and feed a dozen people. No crop can progressively absorb labour input without encountering diminishing returns, however; even paddy has an optimum labour input in terms of yield per worker well below that at which it is cultivated in many densely populated countries. As long as the labour can not be better employed elsewhere, because of lack of alternative employment as in typical non-industrialised countries, and some additional food is being produced by the extra hands, there is justification for such disguised under employment until the developing economy can take up the slack. If labour input continues to be increased, however, diminishing returns will eventually extend to the point where the marginal return of labour is zero. Clark and Haswell quote[1] some interesting examples of this situation. They note that the Japanese Ministry of Agriculture publish rice yields and labour inputs for the 46 prefectures of Japan, and there is no discernible statistical relation between these two. Labour inputs range from 1400 to 2500 man-hours (including female labour) per hectare per year, all apparently above the economic limit. This result suggests the conclusion that above this limit additional labour inputs yield, in general, no return. Clark and Haswell further quote

[1] Clark and Haswell (1964), 89–90.

the analysis by Maruta[1] showing that output of oranges and tea on 30 small farms in the province with the lowest agricultural income per head in Japan can be almost entirely explained in terms of the inputs of land and capital. With average labour input as high as 2700 man-hours per hectare per year, the marginal product of labour appeared to be only 50 yen per day, or 0·075 kg. wheat equivalent per man-hour, the farm price of partially-milled rice being 67 yen per kg. For 2700 man-hours this gives a total wage equivalent of 202·5 kg. compared with an estimated general subsistence requirement of 250–300 kg. of grain equivalents per person per year.[2]

Such very low marginal productivity of labour can be tolerated only where labour is not hired, unless wage rates are to be correspondingly low, and below subsistence level. Clark and Haswell find an appreciable amount of evidence in support of de Farcy's contention[3] that three kilogrammes of cereals is a normal reward for a day's work in a subsistence economy, examples being quoted from eighteenth century France, nineteenth century Belgium and Ireland, and surveys of conditions in Africa, Guatemala, India and elsewhere in the 1930s and more recently. In commercial agriculture, wages of farm labourers must be reasonably close to those available in other unskilled occupations if hired labour is to be obtained, and an appropriate marginal productivity of labour must be achieved if the employing farmer is also to receive due rewards. Difficulty in achieving this is an additional reason for specialisation in agricultural systems with low labour content in countries where labour is scarce.

Mechanisation

The effects of mechanisation of agricultural operations may be grouped as (1) displacement of labour and (2) extending the range of practicable operations.

In economic terms, replacement of labour by machinery occurs at the margin of profitability, i.e. when a farmer

[1] Maruta (1956).

[2] Clark and Haswell (1964), 51.

[3] H. de Farcy, *Revue de l'Action Populaire*, April 1962, quoted by Clark and Haswell (1964), 91.

considers that investment in machinery, taking into account capital charges and depreciation, will increase profits through reduction in labour costs. Mechanisation may, of course, be stimulated by acute shortage of labour, as in the 'new' countries to which reference has just been made, but the economic rule holds good because the immediate result of shortage of labour is high wages for such men as are available. Mechanisation does not invariably reduce the demand for labour, since more intensive operations may become necessary, and absorb manpower on extra tasks, but the required skills change, with emphasis on mechanical knowledge replacing experience with simple implements and draught animals.

The history of agriculture has been a succession of examples of the extension of cultivation with improved tools, from the introduction of the first light plough, referred to in Chapter 1, and its successors in heavier and more efficient ploughs, to horse-drawn implements and eventually, mechanically-powered machines. It has been calculated that in England in the seventeenth century one acre could be ploughed in a day with oxen or 1½ acres with horses, but the steam plough of the nineteenth century made it possible to plough 12 acres in one day.[1]

> Perhaps the best way to illustrate progress during the last century is to calculate the minimum number of man-hours needed to produce a certain quantity of cereals from a given area. In 1830 the production of 1800 litres of wheat on one hectare, using the ordinary plough, harrow, sickles and flails, took 144 man-hours. In the United States in 1896, with the aid of the machines in use at that time, this had been reduced to 22 man-hours; in 1930, when using tractors and combine-harvesters, the time was brought down to 8¼ man-hours. Thus between 1830 and 1896 a saving of 85·6 per cent. in time and 81·4 per cent. in cost was effected.[2]

Many soils which were difficult to work, or on which cultivation was practicable only during limited periods of the year so that speed was essential, could only be brought under the

[1] Slicher van Bath (1963) ,299.
[2] Slicher van Bath (1963) ,300.

plough when suitable machinery became available. Examples may be quoted from fertile but intractable areas within the world-famed arable region of East Anglia to the arid regions of Kazakhstan.

The increase in output available for human consumption may be noted from considering the economies of working land with tractors compared with, say, a team of six or eight horses which had to be cared for throughout the year and which would consume the produce of a large proportion of the land they cultivated. For this reason alone, cultivation of many lands of moderate fertility became practicable only when the tractor became cheap and reliable.

Areas which could not previously be cultivated for technical reasons have also become more productive with improved and specialised machinery. The example of steeper slopes becoming cultivable as discs have supplemented or replaced the mould-board plough was quoted in Chapter 1. Other examples are numerous, such as the stump-jump plough which enabled land in Australia not completely cleared of tree stumps to be brought under cultivation,[1] and the mole-plough which makes possible cheap drainage of clay and peaty soils.[2] Finally, brief mention must also be made in this section of the use of aircraft for top-dressing, sowing and application of insecticides, a topic which will be developed in Chapter 5.

Specialisation of Area

It has been indicated through references to income and marginal analysis that it is the balance of costs and prices that decides ultimately what commodities, out of the physically practicable range, will be produced on a given farm at a given time. Money can be viewed as a common denominator through which comparison can be made of unlike commodities, and similarly, if one can get the data, of the operation of unlike factors in the physical and economic environment. This is not to say that one can, or should wish to put a monetary value to every influence in life, but, used intelligently, the financial yardstick is a valuable, and, indeed an indispensable tool of the geographer as well as of the economist.

[1] Wadham, Wilson and Wood (1957), plates 3 and 5.

[2] Watson and More (1962), 64.

Because what is economically advantageous for one farmer will be attractive to his neighbours, with appropriate modifications for size of farm and other variations in detailed circumstances, there is usually a similarity in the operations of neighbouring farms. A degree of uniformity is found throughout what we may call a region (leaving consideration of this term and the delimitation of such an area until later), so that we may speak, for example, of a wheat-growing region, or, to refine this, a spring-wheat region. A hundred miles away we may be in quite different country which we may recognise as a cattle-ranching region. Between the two there is likely to be a zone where the two grade into one another—where the marginal revenue to be derived from devoting an acre to cattle rearing is much the same as that to be derived from spring wheat and its associates.

The localisation of industry, which became significant with the industrial revolution, involved the separation of manufacturing, henceforth increasingly concentrated in factories, and agriculture, which itself became more specialised. This specialisation extended not only to concentration on farming to the neglect of domestic industry and crafts ('agriculturalisation'), but also specialisation within farming. By specialising, costs involved in a particular form of production could be spread out over a greater turnover, and economies of scale realised.

Specialisation of area makes easier the recognising of economic or agricultural regions, like the spring-wheat region and cattle-ranching region cited above, but regions may be distinctive without specialising. Thus, two regions may both answer to the description of mixed-farming regions, but production of a distinctive crop as a minor but recurrent feature of the farms in one of the regions may be the justification for distinguishing it from the other.

On the other hand, specialisation is not to be confused with monoculture. Areas of monoculture necessarily specialise but the reverse is not true. R. O. Buchanan makes this point clear[1] by reference to Denmark where 'we find a most beautifully designed pattern of an intensive long-rotation arable agriculture focused primarily on the support of dairy cows for

[1] Buchanan (1959).

milk, and through them on the production of bacon and eggs. There is no more highly specialised commercial agriculture area on earth, though it is by the system rather than by the product that it is characterized'.

The extreme specialisation of newly-won lands in the nineteenth century reflected the cost of the relevant factors of production. Land was normally plentiful and cheap, but labour very scarce and consequently costly. Extensive farming systems, with the emphasis on getting maximum return from labour, were the logical development. If sheep would survive and yield a marketable product with minimum attention, then sheep were likely to become the mainstay of the region. But as the population increased there would come both the economic incentive to subdivide large properties, and the labour to work the land more intensively and so yield a family's livelihood at probably improving standards on smaller areas of land.

Here we note that specialisation of area is a changing phenomenon. Not only do the internal circumstances of a region change, as in labour supply and rising land values, but also the external factors, including demand, transport, tariffs and the volume of produce from competing regions. It is all these things that are reflected in world commodity prices, and it is on these prices, as modified by local tariffs and subsidies, that the profitability of individual specialisation must be judged.

Even so, there is in any agricultural region a resistance to change, and it may well be that the more specialised it is, the greater will be the inertia—or the momentum—of the existing system. There is invested capital such as machinery, buildings and vehicles for specialised handling of particular crops or livestock, which is by no means limited to the farms, but includes the transport systems, commercial institutions and perhaps processing plants. Equally important is the accumulated knowledge of all the people involved, and the natural reluctance of most of them to make fundamental changes in their work before they have to. This is particularly so with the farmers themselves since (as often as it has been said, the truth of the statement bears repetition) farming is not simply an occupation but a way of life. For the sheep farmer, that way of life may well seem limited to sheep and a change to cattle or cropping harder to envisage than moving to a new country. This was exemplified in the mobility of the men who settled the new lands of North America and Australia.

At the margins of economic regions, change may be common and frequently rapid. Elsewhere it is more gradual, and though it will take place eventually in response to changing local and world circumstances, stability is a characteristic of most agricultural regions. Over the earth as a whole, the major agricultural regions, though changing all the time in detail, are stable enough for a map drawn thirty years ago still to have some value in depicting them. To this world pattern we shall now turn briefly.

PART II
SYSTEMS OF EXPLOITATION

CHAPTER 4

Agricultural Enterprises and Systems

The study of the effect of climate, soils, land tenure and other factors or forces on agriculture is analytical. The analysis is of complicated economic systems, the understanding of which is furthered by the analytical procedures. But these procedures are only tools for the dismantling of the mechanism. When it has been dismantled and its component parts examined it can be reassembled and its total form visualised more satisfactorily. Reassembly into a functioning whole, or synthesis, leads us to the recognition of the many different types of agriculture that exist in the world.

A farmer, influenced by these various factors, but making the final decisions himself according to his understanding of the forces with which he has to contend, adopts certain forms of work and production, or enterprises. Several enterprises are usually combined on a farm, the combination being called a type of farming. The dominant and associated enterprises of farms found in a territorial area enables recognition to be made of the area's agricultural types. The word 'type' stresses the combination of similar attributes, but several types may be integrated to form the whole complex or system of agriculture of the wider region, e.g. store cattle and sheep grazing (one type of farming) in hill country, and stock fattening with cropping (another type) on lower ground, the two being integrated in an agricultural system.

The areal extent of types or systems may or may not correspond with physical regions or political units. Hence, the identification and description not only of farming types and systems but also the areas, or regions, which they occupy, has long been a major concern of geographers. The methods of delimiting regions will be deferred until Chapter 9. For the moment we may concentrate on the identification of types and systems of agriculture and accept as a hypothesis to be tested later that these may be grouped spatially as regions.

Heavily committed as Great Britain was to the pursuit of international commerce, it is not surprising that early in the existence of geography as a separate subject in British universities, its exponents gave more attention than had been given in other schools of geography to the classification and elaboration of the world's agricultural resources and products. The *Handbook of Commercial Geography* by George Chisholm of the University of Edinburgh appeared in 1889 and has seen editions up to the present time. Work by German geographers correlated the distribution of forms of agriculture and climatic regions, but a systematic approach to the classification of agricultural systems and regions based on the qualities of the agricultural enterprises themselves had to wait until much later.

From 1925 onwards a series of studies of agricultural regions, continent by continent, appeared in the American journal, *Economic Geography*. These added very substantially to the readily available knowledge of both world agricultural systems and the regions within which they prevailed. In 1936 Derwent Whittlesey's classic study of major agricultural regions appeared,[1] employing a classification developed by the author and W. D. Jones at the time the articles in *Economic Geography* were first appearing.

Whittesley identified thirteen types of agricultural occupance[2], with a further category for land totally unused for agriculture:

(1) Nomadic herding
(2) Livestock ranching
(3) Shifting cultivation
(4) Rudimentary sedentary tillage
(5) Intensive subsistence tillage with rice dominant
(6) Intensive subsistence tillage without paddy rice

[1] Whittlesey (1936).

[2] Whittlesey used the terms 'type' and 'system' interchangeably, but it should be noted that a system is a functioning unit, which may be a single farm, or a group of interrelated farms. Farms of similar attributes which are not interrelated do not together form a system but are of the same type.

(7) Commercial plantation crop tillage
(8) Mediterranean agriculture
(9) Commercial grain farming
(10) Commercial livestock and crop farming
(11) Subsistence crop and stock farming
(12) Commercial dairy farming
(13) Specialised horticulture

Much criticism of this classification could be offered, and subsequent writers have modified the classes and the map which accompanied the original article (Figure 6). Some suggestions concerning the use of the terms 'commercial' and 'subsistence' appear in Chapter 8. It may be generally agreed that the classification needs more thorough alteration, but this constitutes a major task. Meanwhile the original classification still provides a basis for discussion of all systems of agriculture within an easily comprehended outline. It therefore seems desirable to reproduce here the original classification, which has the advantage of stressing to the reader the origins of the work, which, though thirty years old, still provides the basis of text book treatments of world types of agriculture and current atlas maps.[1]

With this framework available, attention will then be given to several systems of agriculture which appear to the author to provide sufficient material to illustrate the approach to synthesis of the factors previously reviewed. It is necessary, however, to stress the interrelationship of the various factors and the dynamic character of any system. In a small book this can be done better by dealing rather more fully (though still only in outline) with a few systems with which the author is reasonably familiar than by attempting to cover in attenuated form even the main ones found throughout the world. These fuller descriptions (Chapters 5, 6 and 7) will not be dealt with under Whittlesey's headings, but the way in which they may be fitted into Whittlesey's classes, or overlap his classes, will become apparent by comparing them with the following summaries of Whittlesey's descriptions, given with very brief additional comments.

[1] For example, in *Goode's World Atlas*, 1964 edition.

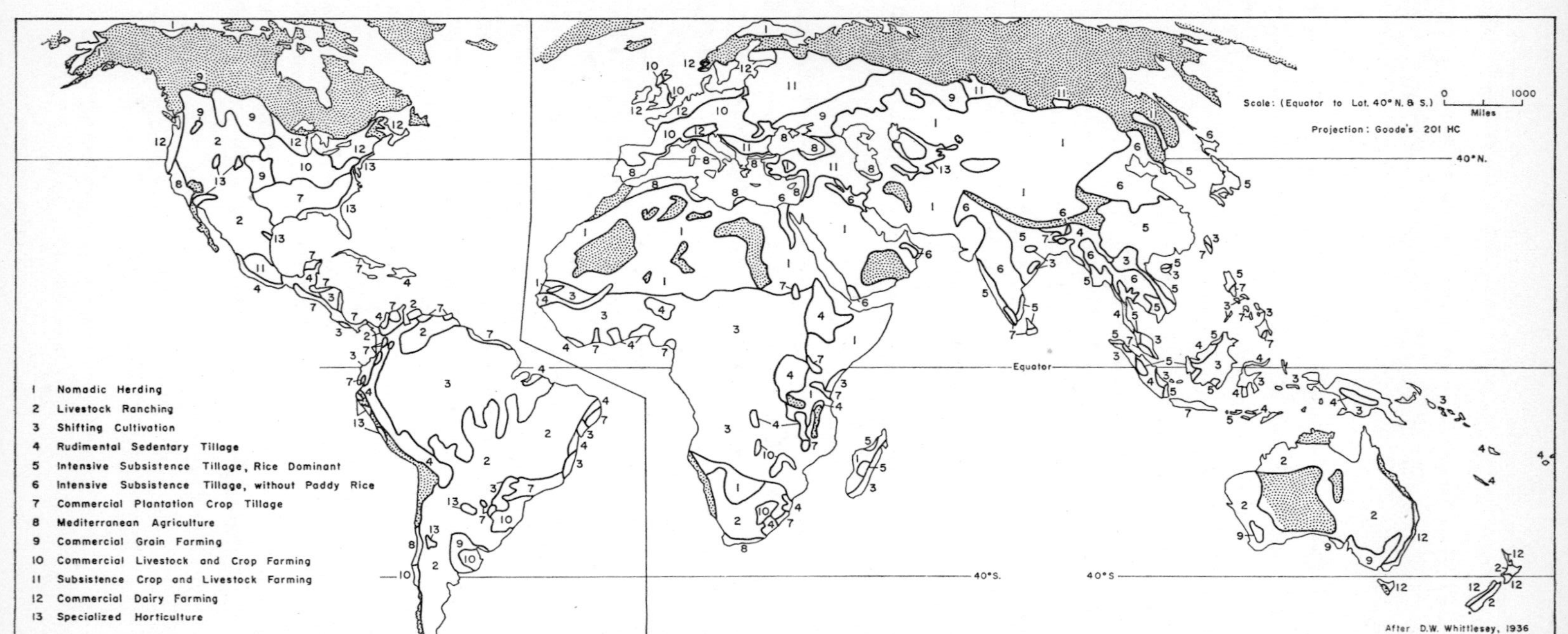

Figure 6. Major agricultural regions of the earth.
Source: D. Whittlesey, *Annals of the Association of American Geographers*, Vol. 26, 1936.
Compare recent detailed analysis of areas shown in Figures 7, 16 and 17

Nomadic herding is the simplest form of pastoralism. Based on sheep, cattle, goats, camels or reindeer, it is primarily a subsistence form of exploitation of dry regions. The length of stay of the nomads in one place and the direction of movement are governed by the availability of water and natural forage. The habitation is a tent, a cave or snow hut, easily transported or replaced. Nomads have suffered reduction of their grazing areas as livestock ranching has moved into drier regions, and pressure has been put on many communities to adopt sedentary ways of life, notably in communist collectivisation of agriculture.

Livestock ranching represents commercial use of physical regions similar to those of nomadic herding. Such regions in the Americas, Australia and New Zealand could be used only when herd animals and horses were introduced from the Old World. The movements of stock are normally confined to the ranch although there may be seasonal movement or *transhumance* to distant pastures. The ranch is a permanent base. Ranching methods are the outcome of European adaptation to environments demanding very extensive forms of agriculture. Cropping is limited to provision of fodder for periods when natural grazing is unobtainable or inadequate. The provision of better supplies of fodder, together with water control and improved care of stock are the principal ways of increasing the yield of these farms.

Shifting cultivation is a primitive form of utilisation of the poor soils of tropical rain forest and bush areas. Farmed plots are moved every few years in search of accrued fertility, and dwellings are moved as necessary. Fire and hand tools are used for clearing the ground and for simple cultivation. This and the following types of subsistence cultivation are further described in a later section.

Rudimentary sedentary tillage employs methods often not much more advanced than are found in shifting cultivation, and may arise from the settling down in favourable places of nomadic or shifting communities. Lack of fertiliser may necessitate fallowing of plots, and so the type is not sharply separated from shifting cultivation, but, as the community develops its settled life, contact with commerce is likely to lead to cultivation of crops, especially tree crops such as cacao, oil palm and rubber, with which can be bought a few manufactured goods and food for the lean period before the harvest.

Intensive subsistence tillage with rice dominant is, along with its companion type which excludes wet rice, the basis of life in south and east Asia. Deltas, floodplains, coastal plains and terraces to which water can be directed are utilised mainly for rice, which with its high yields per acre offers the best available subsistence to the dense populations. Land which cannot be so used is planted with other crops including tree crops. Fish supplement the agricultural produce. Work in the fields is arduous and unending and little assistance is available from machinery for tillage or irrigation, though ploughs may be hauled by water buffaloes. Whittlesey's emphasis on the subsistence aspect of the type does not reflect the growing influence of trade on intensive rice cultivation communities to which reference is made in Chapter 8.

Intensive subsistence tillage without paddy rice.[1] Many regions of dense population which lack the conditions suitable for rice have types of agriculture differing from the foregoing mainly in the absence of wet rice. Some land is irrigated but more emphasis is placed on dry grains, and tree crops are also commonly important. South and east Asia and oases of inner Asia and north Africa, especially Egypt, are cited as the main areas of this type. Similar, but less intensive, methods are practised in the Kano district of the Western Sudan and the Mexican highland.

Commercial plantation crop tillage. This alien system, introduced into regions suitable for production of tropical commodities needed by the industrial countries, occupies in the aggregate a very small area compared with the other types outlined. It is, however, important commercially and has resulted in the introduction into regions of subsistence agriculture of staff, methods, crops, machinery, fertilisers and finance from abroad. The principal crops are sugar, tea, coffee, cacao, rubber, oil palms, sisal and bananas. Most of these crops are also grown by smallholders. An example of this form of production is given in Chapter 6.

Mediterranean agriculture. The climate and its association with mountains has created a distinctive stock and crop association

[1] Whittlesey uses the term 'paddy' to mean only wet rice but this term is also employed for upland rice, or 'hill paddy'.

of related functioning forms; all-year or winter crops grown with rain, all-year or summer crops grown with irrigation, and livestock—mainly small animals—grazed on lowlands in winter and on highlands in summer. Tradition, market and government policies influence attention to particular crops, e.g. vines, citrus fruits, wheat. In the regions of Mediterranean-type climate in the other continents there are many similarities in type of farming, though in California wealth has made for many differences in irrigation and mechanisation, visible also in the corresponding regions of Australia.

Commercial grain farming arose with the availability of the steel plough, harvesting machinery and transport systems capable of cheaply handling export crops in bulk. Sub-humid continental climates with short summers, which could otherwise be commercially exploited only by livestock ranching, produce grain, mainly wheat, by extensive methods. Crop failures are common. The best known areas are in North America and Argentina, but mention is made in Chapter 7 of the Russian lands of this type, which have been transformed by collective farms and state land development schemes.

Commercial livestock and crop farming is also commonly known as 'mixed farming'. It is found in Europe, where it originated, and in the humid middle latitudes of all the other continents except Asia. Its development, however, is governed closely by marketing possibilities, with tariffs, subsidies, etc. influencing choice of crop or livestock. In the light of these and of climatic influences, varying emphasis is given to the different grains, root crops, cattle, sheep and pigs. Mechanisation, crop rotation and use of fertilisers are normal. The British Isles and New Zealand are chosen to illustrate variations in this type of farming in Chapter 5.

Subsistence crop and stock farming originated in northern Europe and resembles the foregoing type in some of the crops and animals found on the farms, but little or nothing is sold off the farm. At the time when Whittlesey wrote, this type was in decline with the beginnings of reform in Russia and, to a lesser extent, in other countries. These changes have now progressed so far that as originally described it is relatively unimportant, though there are still many regions where sales off farms account for only a somewhat small part of the gross output.

Commercial dairy farming also evolved in Europe but has spread to other regions which can take advantage of large demand from urban populations. It remains true, as Whittlesey wrote, that the radius for shipping fresh milk is, roughly, overnight; for cream twice as far; while refrigerated butter and many kinds of cheese can be supplied across the world. For marketing of milk in the stringent conditions imposed in the modern cities and for economic participation in the sale of graded dairy produce, high grade farming is required. Some further discussion of this type of farming appears in the sections on agriculture in the British Isles and New Zealand.

Specialised horticulture has also developed in response to the large demand in urban centres for foodstuffs, but the most ancient districts of specialised horticulture are the vineyards of Europe outside the Mediterranean climate, some of which were established in Roman times. Burgundy, Champagne, the Moselle, Rhine and Loire valleys, the Swiss lakes, the plain of northern Hungary and the quasi-Mediterranean area near Bordeaux are the most important.

Urban demand for vegetables and soft fruit is satisfied partly from market gardens within a few hours' transport of the cities, partly by more distant 'truck farming' holdings. Market gardens near cities, where high land values obtain, are worked with special intensity, with high inputs of labour, fertiliser and other factors of production. Cultivation under glass increases intensity of work coupled with higher investment.

The more outlying truck farming regions exploit particularly favourable soil and climate, which enable production to be earlier in the season or at lower cost than in the suburban market gardens. Regions of this type of production are the Channel coastlands of France and the Low Countries, the Rhone valley, the north African coastlands, the south-east coastal plains of the United States and regions of drier climates further west, notably in Colorado and California. In some of these districts commercial fruit farming is important, with irrigation commonly employed, as in much of the vegetable growing. Specialised orchards occur also in areas of favourable climate in other regions.

In some districts of this type there is also attention to specialised cash crops such as sugar beet, tobacco and cotton.

The irrigated cash cropping of some of the dry regions is similar to the vegetable and fruit growing of nearby oases. Specialised poultry production also resembles market gardening and truck farming in its organisation near large cities and in California.

In conclusion, Whittlesey comments on the cash basis of the farming types of the occidental middle latitudes and their dependence on the urbanised world created by the industrial revolution. This relationship is elaborated in the first of the following more detailed studies.

CHAPTER 5

Mixed Agriculture — The British Isles and New Zealand

In the intermediate latitudes—those of the temperate climates—the science of agriculture has found its highest stage of development. Not only the technological but the commercial organisation of the industry is at a high level. This is not to deny that there are farms, plantations, even regions in the humid tropics and in other latitudes that individually rival in achievement the most advanced farms of the temperate regions, but such examples are at present abnormal in their environments. In contrast, the high level of development in the temperate regions is general, and farms or areas which are not well organised are rightly regarded as backward and having a retarding effect on the local or regional economy.

Three features characterise the type of farming discussed in this chapter:

(1) The enterprises on the individual farm are mixed to a greater or lesser extent, complete specialisation being exceptional.

(2) The objectives of the farming are commercial, i.e. the bulk of the produce is sold off the farm.

(3) The normal form of organisation is the family farm, and whether occupation is by ownership or tenancy the individual farmer is free to choose his system of farming.

The last feature is an important one to which insufficient attention has been given in geographical literature. The fact that a very large number of farmers operating in a commercial economy should organise their farming to conform to a basically similar pattern without any form of direction is highly significant. Hence the division here of mixed farming of temperate latitudes into agriculture of this type, considered in this chapter, and agriculture of a somewhat similar kind, producing similar products but with state-directed organisation. The latter is discussed under the heading of state and collective farming, and affinities are seen between such forms and plantation agriculture. On plantations, the workers are organised by interests which are predominantly non-rural and not native to the regions concerned, usually limited liability companies which exist for the benefit of their directors and shareholders. The organisation of collective farms is intermediate in its representation of the interests of the workers on the land itself and the degree of non-rural control, though, of course, there are gradations between the different forms.

In reaching the high state of development noted above, the mixed farms of temperate regions have enjoyed two main advantages, both of great importance during the last two or three centuries. Firstly, it has been possible to grow a wide range of products with, in general, a fair degree of reliability. Improving technology has steadily widened this range of products and their yields in given conditions of climate and soil. Secondly, it is these products which have been most consistently in large scale demand. This demand has come from countries where rapid growth in wealth has accompanied industrialisation and expansion in population. Industrialisation results in an increasing proportion of people divorced from food production. Thus, there have been large markets in Europe for temperate foodstuffs produced in the 'new' lands of the Americas, the British Commonwealth and Soviet Asia as well as those grown in the European countries themselves.

The British Isles

So great was the growth of the urban population of Great Britain during the eighteenth century that, in spite of new techniques and reorganisation of farms, production in Britain could not be expanded rapidly enough to provide the necessary food at prices that could be afforded by the factory workers. Hence the reversion in 1846 to free trade—the opening of the great British market to cheap foodstuffs from abroad. The opening of the market to foreign produce resulted in prolonged depression in British farming, but before this occurred the improvements that had been initiated by the pioneers of modern farming had begun to be adopted widely. Although the depression in agricultural prices persisted and worsened as the nineteenth century progressed, the spread of the new techniques continued. Indeed, the more enlightened farmers realised that they could restore their own prosperity only by adopting new methods which would enable them to compete with imported foods.

In the British Isles and western Europe, great extremes of heat and cold are rare, but extremes of water supply do occur. The British Isles and the adjacent coastal areas of western Europe fall within the Cool Temperate, humid or oceanic type of climate, and here husbandry of the land must have regard to the following outstanding conditions:

(1) The climate is particularly suited to the growth of grass. Grass will grow nearly all the year round, and, with appropriate harvesting of some of the grass for fodder, livestock farming may be carried out wholly on grass, and without irrigation. This is the feature that especially distinguishes these regions from others. Two major limitations, however, occur:

 (*a*) On the oceanic margins the high ratio of precipitation to evaporation (P/E) threatens grass through the development of weeds, and, ultimately, forest or bog.

 (*b*) On the continental margins, lower precipitation and high evaporation, associated with clear skies and long periods of sunshine, result in water shortage and scorching of the grass. As these conditions become predominant, cereals become more suitable crops than grass.

Pastoral activity must be regulated accordingly.

(2) Climatic conditions on the oceanic as well as on the continental margins permit certain alternative forms of agricultural land use, based on arable cultivation. Cereals, short ley pasture grasses, clovers, lucernes and roots such as potatoes and turnips are among the crops employed.

The response to these conditions is seen in the patterns of farming that emerge. At the one extreme is pastoral farming, based wholly on grassland. Livestock are used to convert the grass into foods favoured by human beings, and into by-products such as wool, hides and horn. Sometimes these latter are the main products with foodstuffs subsidiary. At the other extreme is arable farming, producing cereal or root crops for direct human consumption or industrial use. More common, however, is some combination of these two forms, such as production of grass, cereals and roots to feed to livestock, any surplus being sold as cash crops. The result is commonly a mixed land cover—grass on some parts of the farm, and arable crops on other parts.

To which of the extremes any particular region will show a tendency, or what manner of compromise may be distinguished, will reflect the varying force of a number of factors which have already been discussed in general terms (Part I), namely:

(i) The local pattern of climate and weather.

(ii) The pressure of other physical factors—landforms, soil, etc.

(iii) The stage of technological development.

(iv) Historical and social factors which affect the response to environment and knowledge.

(v) The economic conditions.

Economic conditions are listed last, because they are at once the outcome of all the other conditions, and at the same time they sum up all the others. In other words, the objective of production is the product which in all the circumstances provides the greatest return for the input.

There are, of course, certain exceptions, where some other conditions override economic decisions. Thus, particular animals may be kept—or avoided—for reasons of personal taste, or because of religious dictates, but these are of limited, very limited, effect in the British Isles. Where commercial sentiments are strong, the economics of practical farming dictate that the farming shall be well within the climatic limits. Within these limits, the variations are in response to economic conditions which reflect the above forces acting in detail. As we examine the refinements in variations of agriculture within the broad climatic possibilities, so we become more and more aware of the operation of other factors. To sum up this argument, climate lays down the broad possibilities of the region; other forces decide how these possibilities will be exploited.

Europe shows admirably the transition from pastoral and semi-pastoral husbandry to concentration on grain between the oceanic west and the dry interior lands and, to a lesser extent, between the cold northern margins and the moderate mid-European latitudes. The transition can clearly be seen in its initial stages in the varying emphasis between pastoralism and arable farming in the British Isles. Because they have been occupied continuously during the evolution of modern mixed farming techniques, and were the scene of many of the innovations that created the system, the British Isles offer particularly rewarding subjects for study. The adaptation of the environment to suit more intensive methods of production may likewise be studied.

Technological Development

British pastures, even of unimproved strains, will support large numbers of livestock in the summer but not in the winter when temperatures fall below the threshold temperatures for growth of about 42 degrees F. (5 deg. C.). Pastoralism alone, therefore, will not provide a healthy agricultural system. Harvesting hay provides a crude means of keeping stock alive but alone is not sufficient for progressive agriculture. The growing of grain is marginal in the cooler, wetter west and north; yields of wheat are poor, oats and barley fare better, but neither from them nor from a combination of grains and hay could winter feed be obtained for all the stock pastured in the summer. Grain was grown in mediaeval England mainly for bread and beer, and there was little food value in the straw that could be spared for the animals. Hence the autumnal slaughtering of mediaeval times, which must surely have been considerable, even though not as drastic as has sometimes been supposed.[1]

[1] Trow-Smith (1957).

As noted in Chapter 1 the introduction of root crops revolutionised British agriculture, but only slowly. Throughout the eighteenth century there was gradual improvement. Potatoes proved a bulky but fairly efficient food for both people and livestock. They tempted the Irish into too much reliance on them, so that famine followed the failure of the potato crops.[1] Turnips were the basis of the agrarian revolution in East Anglia and spread throughout the British Isles as a basis for wintering stock, replacing fallow. The Norfolk system, a four course rotation,[2] was less suitable for the cooler and wetter regions, but was readily modified by the extension of the period in grass and replacement of wheat by oats or barley. In the north of Ireland, Atlantic outpost of arable farming, a sound rotation was found in oats, potatoes, oats and several years in grass.

Meanwhile grassland husbandry was put on to a scientific basis with the sowing out of pastures with the more nutritious grasses and clovers, the nitrogen-fixing qualities of which were fundamental to the maintenance of improvement. Hand-in-hand with the improvements in the feed basis went the development of the livestock breeds. Breeds of cattle, sheep and horses became increasingly differentiated and specialised, adapted to the differing needs of different regions and different types of farming. Thus, while general purpose breeds, such as the Shorthorn cow, were found to be extremely valuable throughout the British Isles, and have remained so to this day, this has not prevented their being developed into more specialised types like the Dairy Shorthorn and Beef (Scotch) Shorthorn. Regional breeds developed, particularly adapted to their local environments, such as the Ayrshire cow, capable of giving good quality milk in rather discouraging conditions of climate and relief, and the Aberdeen-Angus beef cattle. Interchange of breeds has facilitated adaptation to environment and market conditions. In cows, the Jersey and Friesian are good examples. The former supplies milk of high butter-fat content, suitable for high class dairying in areas of high

[1] Salaman (1949).

[2] A root crop, spring-sown grain or peas, a grass crop grazed or cut for hay followed by autumn grain, usually wheat. Sheep were folded on the arable land and consumed the roots, providing dung, and cattle fattened over the winter for the period of high prices.

purchasing power, the latter gives good milk in great quantities and is a most valuable animal on which to base normal town supply.

Social and Economic Conditions

The new farming systems were possible only on land that was enclosed, and the pressure of growing population and food demands stimulated enclosure and redivision of the land. Land use is never static but there are periods when change is stimulated by sharply changing social or market conditions and technological development. In the eighteenth century the influences demanding change were mainly internal—the growth of population and industrialisation—but this was nonetheless the impact of a widening as well as a more specialised economy. In the nineteenth century, the continuation of the growth in the economy was not paralleled by adequate growth in the ability of British agriculture to supply the quantities of cheap food needed in the cities. The supplies offered by newly developed lands abroad led to the freeing of imports. Competition from cheap overseas grain after the repeal of the Corn Laws in 1846 forced a reorientation of British farming.

Less than forty years later another major adjustment was compelled by technological development—the introduction of refrigeration, making possible the shipping of meat from the southern hemisphere. Refrigeration also made possible import of dairy products, so narrowing the field in which the British farmer enjoyed the natural protection conferred by the distance of his competitors. Fortunately for the British farmer there was a continually expanding market for fresh milk and vegetables. There was also a continued high level of demand for home produced meat, with its distinctive qualities. On these products farming could continue profitably as long as there was a generally high and steady level of employment, and consequently of effective demand.

The economic catastrophe of the nineteen-thirties showed the vulnerability of farming, like other sectors of the economy. Agricultural prices in all parts of the country plunged to half the levels obtaining in 1930, and for some commodities to as low as a quarter of the 1921 prices. The depression had not reached its lowest depths in 1932–3 when the land use pattern was being mapped by the Land Utilisation Survey of Great Britain[1] but the survey stressed the declining percentage of land under the plough. An increase in the proportion of grassland might not, in itself, have indicated declining fertility, but it did in the circumstances of the time, the land being commonly allowed to 'tumble down' to grass, with consequent low standard of resulting pastures. Former arable farms were turned over to low-intensity grazing and buildings, fences and equipment deteriorated from lack of maintenance.

Many factors contributed to the crisis, some of them demonstrating the extent to which the geographic pattern of the industry depended on economic and external conditions. The crisis in the economy in the United States of America and the loss of confidence throughout the world of commerce initiated the collapse. In 1926 the gold standard had been readopted by the British government and the pound sterling had been stabilised at a high level. This had enabled other countries to sell their produce on the unprotected British market at prices which were low in relation to the costs of production. The gold standard was abandoned in 1931 and this measure was expected to restore competitiveness in home agriculture, but depreciation of the pound was countered in many of the countries trading with Britain by depreciation of their own currencies. At the end of that year the World Economic Conference failed to achieve an international monetary policy and the depression worsened.

In the face of this crisis, the United Kingdom government resorted to a measure of protection. In 1932 an *ad valorem* tariff of 10 per cent. was applied to some commodities. Under the Ottawa Agreements, exporting countries agreed to limit shipments of beef, mutton and lamb, and by 1934 quotas had been accepted by several foreign countries in respect of chilled beef, frozen mutton and lamb, processed milk and cream, potatoes, fat cattle, oats and eggs.

Whilst imports were being restricted, steps were taken to improve the marketing of home produce and so make for greater efficiency in home agriculture. Pigs and milk were the subjects of two marketing schemes which were much more

[1] Stamp (1948, 1962).

thorough than anything that had gone before in Britain. The government also departed from its policies of merely providing assistance in matters of research, limited credit schemes and help in marketing by reintroducing subsidies, which had been paid during the first World War and then withdrawn. The first of the new subsidies was for wheat. Legislation of 1932 guaranteed a standard price and a secure market for producers of wheat. About 5 per cent. of the area of crops and pasture was under wheat in 1932 in England and Wales and this rose by over one-third to 7 per cent. by 1934 while all other grain crops declined in area. The stimulation this subsidy gave in marginal areas is well seen in the wheat figure for Northern Ireland which rose from 1 per cent. to 3 per cent. of the cultivated area in the three years that followed the introduction of the scheme. More important, however, for farmers in the north and west was the direct subsidy for fat cattle, other than cows, authorised in 1934. This was introduced because, owing to its agreements with Argentina and the Dominions, the United Kingdom government had found it impracticable to employ quantitative restrictions sufficient to raise the price of fat cattle at home. This subsidy resulted in modification of the practice of sending store cattle from hill and marginal areas to be fattened in the richer regions. It was more profitable to fatten locally wherever possible. Thus, the 1933 exports of fat cattle from Northern Ireland to Great Britain were more than doubled in 1935 and remained at about this level until 1939.

Subsidies and grants were greatly extended in the years immediately prior to and during the war in order to stimulate home agriculture. We are not concerned with the temporary distortion of the pattern of land use that followed, though this is of interest in showing the extent of the change that can be wrought by financial measures, backed by administrative orders and controls, in an emergency. Let it suffice to note that the area under the plough in England and Wales expanded from less than 9 million acres in 1939 to 14,588,000 acres in 1944.

Since the war, assured markets and guaranteed prices under national marketing schemes have provided market conditions such as the farmer could hardly have dreamed of in the early 'thirties. The Agriculture Act of 1947 was not for nothing called 'The Farmers' Charter'. Assured markets, guaranteed prices, or deficiency payments related to standard prices, have been maintained for fat cattle, fat sheep and fat pigs, liquid milk, wool, eggs, potatoes and cereals. Other important products, such as store cattle and store sheep, have received good prices because the end product has had an assured market.

Capital Investment

An important objective of financial aid for the agricultural industry has been the preparation of farms for efficiency in the long term, and ultimately economic operation with little or no subsidisation. To this end, prominence has been given to measures encouraging investment in the land. Thus, ever since preparation to meet anticipated war conditions began, government policy has encouraged land improvement by subsidies for liming, fertilising and bringing old grassland under the plough. As early as 1937 purchases of lime and basic slag were subsidised. Monetary grants were offered for ploughing land which had been in grass for seven years in 1939, and later the grants were raised and the qualifying period in grass was shortened.

Schemes for comprehensive improvement of farm units have provided remarkable opportunities for farmers to have their properties overhauled with substantial help from public funds. One of the first such schemes was directed to the improvement of hill farms. The plight of many farmers of hill and marginal land, following decades of low prices, and less favourable conditions even during the war than applied to many other types of farming, resulted in legislation in 1946[1] which provided for grants of up to 50 per cent. of the cost for improvements to land, buildings and equipment of hill farms. An essential condition of the scheme was that the farmer should be prepared to undertake all the improvements government inspectors thought necessary for the operation of the farm as an economic unit.

A decade later the principle of assisting comprehensive improvement was extended to all types of farm. The Farm

[1] Hill Farming Act, 1946, extended by the Livestock Rearing Act, 1951.

Improvement Scheme of 1957 makes grants for improvements to land and buildings, work on farm roads, fencing and installation of electric light and power, and towards the amalgamation of uneconomic units, provided certain conditions are satisfied and the total cost exceeds £100.

Yet another scheme was introduced in 1959 to deal with the special problems of small farms. To be eligible for assistance under the Small Farmer Scheme, a farmer must have not less than 20 acres and not more than 100 acres of crops and pasture, excluding rough grazing, and to require, when improvements are completed, between 275 and 450 man-days of labour, calculated on a standard basis (see Chapter 9).

The increased capital investment in British farming in recent years has permitted many changes in type of farming and land use pattern. Thus, dairying, with the high standards of hygiene demanded by government regulations, has been practicable only on farms which could be equipped with buildings, water supply and cattle of approved quality. Farms which have been able to invest in modern machinery have been able to adjust their farming more readily to suit other changing conditions, such as favourable cereal prices, especially for barley, minimizing hindrance from lack of labour. Mechanisation has, indeed, been a factor in attracting good quality labour to large, well-capitalised farms. Investment in new houses for farm workers has produced similar results on farms which could sustain such investment.

In addition to development schemes which apply throughout the United Kingdom, special help has been made available for farmers in areas of special difficulty. Of these the most important in the extent of the region involved is the aid given to crofters in the west of Scotland. A crofter enjoys a special form of tenure, giving him security in respect both of his enclosed land and of his share of the township grazings. This situation derives from the Crofters Act, 1886, which reversed the previous utterly insecure position of the crofter. Since crofts are defined by special legislation, it is possible to give special forms of aid to the occupiers. Somewhat similar financial help was also given to farmers in Co. Fermanagh and the west of Tyrone in Northern Ireland. Grants of up to 80 per cent. of the cost of specified improvements were given to improve the productivity of marginal land, but these special schemes in Northern Ireland were largely replaced by the Small Farmer Scheme.

Farming in Britain today must therefore be seen as a response to an extremely complicated set of factors. The range of crops which could be grown in the physical conditions obtaining is narrowed by the availability of low-cost imports from abroad, but the pattern of financial assistance given by the government restores to the farmer the ability to produce some of the commodities which, under free trade, he would be unable to place on the market in competition with foreign produce.

Regional Patterns of Land Use

The complexity of explanations of the land use pattern is evident. Nevertheless, the broad trends follow the indications given at the beginning of this chapter. Thus, in western counties of Ireland, where grass grows freely and arable crops suffer from the damp and windy climate, 90–95 per cent. of the improved land is in grass (Co. Leitrim, 96 per cent., Co. Limerick and Co. Clare, 95 per cent.). More easterly counties in Ireland also have a high proportion in grass except where conditions of soil coupled with reasonable demand for arable crops and the somewhat more favourable climate combine to produce locally more attention to crops. Thus, whereas Co. Meath has 89 per cent. of its improved land in grass, and Co. Down has 75 per cent., the percentage falls to 68·5 per cent. in the northern county of Londonderry and the southern county of Wexford. In these counties soil types are suitable for potatoes, oats and grain and though demand fluctuates, two at least of these crops are usually economically as attractive as grass.

In Great Britain there is a similar broad change of land use from west to east. Not only are much higher proportions of improved land used for arable farming in the east but it is here that the arable acreage is most constant. These features are brought out well in recent work by Best and Coppock.[1] Thus, of the improved land of Norfolk, between 70 and 82 per cent. has been under arable in each year since 1870, whereas Oxford shows fluctuation between 68 per cent. and 35 per cent.

[1] Best and Coppock (1962) esp. 78–82.

and Carmarthenshire between 45 per cent. and 10 per cent. In mountainous areas, however, where improved land is severely restricted, a high proportion of cultivable land may be under the plough. Thus, in 1962, Ross and Cromarty, with only 7 per cent. of the total area classed as crops and grass (93 per cent. rough grazings and deer forests) had 38 per cent. of this improved land in tillage, a percentage which compares interestingly with Fife, where 90 per cent. of the agricultural land was in crops and grass and 49 per cent. of this was tilled. In Argyll (95 per cent. rough grazings), on the other hand, only 19·7 per cent. of the crops and grass was tilled.

The balance between pastoral and arable use of the land is only one aspect of land use. Arable rotations usually involve periods in temporary grass as well as crops. When tilled, the arable land may be used to produce cash crops for sale or for feeding to livestock on the farm. If the former, the crops may be for human consumption, for industrial use or for feeding to animals. For some crops, such as wheat, the outlets are well defined. Others, such as potatoes, may be used for any of the above outlets, but the objective is normally to sell most of the crop for human consumption, keeping some for the family on the farm. Chats (undersized potatoes) and others which are unmarketable are, however, fed to livestock. Industrial outlets, such as potato crisp factories, exercise an important demand locally, and in some seasons, over large areas. Farms near areas of large consumption, such as the south of England, find less difficulty in disposing of their produce than do areas further away, even with a marketing scheme applicable to all areas of the country. Again, transport costs lower the actual returns to farmers in the peripheral areas although a guaranteed marketing scheme ensures that the farmer will not be left with produce on his hands, as in the case of fat cattle.

Geographical advantages are, then, still important, even under guaranteed marketing schemes and subsidised agriculture. Returns to the farmer will still be highest in general where the alternatives are greatest, because the farmer can there best adapt to changing conditions. Although it may take a few years to change over from say, wheat to beef, or mutton to barley and pigs, it is an advantage to be able to make this change if circumstances in marketing and wider economic conditions make this desirable. This is probably as important an advantage of farmers in the south and east of England as its favourable climate, when the region is compared with the north and west.

In the fertile parts of East Anglia almost all of the farming practices of the British lowlands are possible. Wheat may be grown in rotation with roots and sugar beet, providing cash crops and some stock-feed. This, with some imported feed-stuffs, is used for fattening livestock, especially in order to put meat on the market while less favoured regions are waiting for the spring grass. In general, arable crops pay better than grass, so grass is reduced to one year, say, in the rotation. In the midlands of England, where rainfall is heavier, sunshine and warmth less, grass grows better than in East Anglia, but the alternatives in land use are fewer, because cereals and root crops fare less well. These deficiencies become more marked further west and north until one reaches the areas of markedly limited possibilities. The east of Scotland is marginal for wheat, but good grain crops are possible and the cool climate confers a degree of freedom from pests. Livestock are fattened to a considerable extent on the produce of the arable land, feeding in enclosed courts which protect the animals from the rigours of the climate. Among cash crops potatoes are important, especially seed potatoes, again because of freedom from pests and disease.

In the west of Britain including Wales and most of Ireland, as already noted, the high P/E ratio makes cereals definitely risky. There exist some advantages compared with the south-east, such as lower land values, but these do not offset substantially the inferiority of these regions of few alternatives.

These are the broad regional trends, established in the economic conditions of a long period during which British agriculture has faced competition from specialised agricultural regions overseas. In general, agriculture in the British Isles has adapted itself to supply the British market with high quality meat and other products for which there is a degree of natural protection accorded by distance and seasonal variations in supply, such as vegetables. The growth of the large urban communities has facilitated specialisation in the supply of milk and vegetables even where physical conditions are not especially favourable. Thus, milk production is protected by difficulties of transport over long distances. London may draw milk from almost any part of England, and Kintyre may help supply the Scottish lowlands, but Ireland lies outside the area of supply to Great Britain with present slowness and costs of sea transport. Even in war conditions it was considered impracticable to ship milk from Belfast to Britain except on a few occasions of extreme emergency, which accounts for the surplus of milk and milk products in Ireland throughout the war. In Northern Ireland for decades only about 30 per cent. of the milk produced has been consumed as liquid milk and 70 per cent. used for manufacture, whereas in Great Britain the figures are the reverse, 70 and 30 respectively. In the inter-war years, this led to Northern Ireland having a different system for payment to milk producers. It was not until after the war that Northern Ireland adopted the British practice of paying farmers a flat rate irrespective of whether their milk was actually used on the high-price liquid market, or for low-price manufacture. Thus, British farmers have had almost a complete monopoly of the home liquid milk market.

In vegetable production, the natural protection of the market is less, but transport of fresh vegetables must be rapid if they are to be marketable as fresh produce. Rarely can imported vegetables command the same price as locally grown ones, so there is economic justification for the devotion of land close to cities to the growing of vegetables. Since horticulture is an intensive form of husbandry, growers are able to resist urban expansion more effectively than can farmers with less intensive systems. Even so, the disappearance of the best market-gardening lands of the London region under the sprawl of the suburbs is well known as a classic problem in town and country planning.

Although improvements in transport have reduced the dependence of urban areas on the vegetables and milk of neighbouring areas, the zoning of farming land around cities is still to be found, demonstrating the over-riding of physical conditions by the economic advantages of intensive forms of agriculture. We may not be able to distinguish the concentric circles of von Thünen or the idealised regions of Jonasson (discussed in Chapter 9), but the overlay of local economic power on the broader regional patterns dictated by climate and soil is undeniable.

Such specialisations as may be seen in the regions surrounding cities and elsewhere can usually be found to have an explanation in particular circumstances. They do not invalidate the general argument that mixed farming is the agricultural-type of Great Britain, and that in this type most farms combine grass and arable land cover, with sales of both crop and livestock products. Examples of such regions, with the varying emphasis that has been stressed above, will form the concluding section of this review of British agriculture.

A Sheep, Dairying and Forestry Region—Kintyre

The peninsula of Kintyre is part of the major region of the Highlands of Scotland, but is distinctive in that the terrain is less mountainous, the climate milder and the economy different from that of most parts of the Highlands. The individual farm is generally large enough to support a family comfortably. Kintyre is not a crofting region like the western seaboard further north,[1] there being only a handful of small holdings in part-time cultivation. Some of the farms are part of large estates, but there has been a gradual transfer of ownership through sales of farms to the former tenants. Ownership of improved land by the farmers rose from 13·8 per cent. in 1913 to 26 per cent. in 1956.

The height of much of the land is over 1000 feet, and the rugged and exposed nature of most of it necessitates hill farming practices. Here are farms of up to 7000 acres, carrying as many as 3000 sheep of the hardy Scottish Blackface breed. Some cattle are carried also on most of these farms, including the long-horned West Highland breed and the equally hardy Galloway. The number of cattle carried must be limited to those that can be supported on the winter fodder available, and there is little land suitable for hay or silage on these farms. A typical farm of 6900 acres has only 55 acres classed as arable with a further 15–20 acres reseeded to give fairly productive grassland. A herd of 20–30 breeding cows is maintained. The main income of the farm, however, is derived

[1] Darling (ed.) (1955).

from the 2000 ewes that find their food on the hills, winter as well as summer.

Hill farming represents one of the more specialised types of farming encountered in the British Isles, and, where fodder cannot be provided economically for cattle farms, carry sheep alone. But farms dependent on the sale of virtually only wool and stock—mostly lambs—are economically vulnerable and need to be large to be sound. Wherever possible, some other enterprise should be practised. It has been recommended by the Department of Agriculture for Scotland that a single-family hill farm should carry at least 500 sheep, 20 breeding cattle, plus pigs and poultry. On most hill farms the only practicable cattle are hardy beef breeds, because of limitations of fodder, the lack of fairly level fields suitable for dairy cattle and the cost of transport of milk. Kintyre, however, is more favoured in this respect, and many of the farms that include low ground as well as hill land combine dairying with hill sheep farming. This rare combination comprises a type of farming found elsewhere in Scotland only in the Southern Uplands. A medium-sized Kintyre example of this type of farming has 103 acres of arable land, supporting about 36 dairy cows, and 421 acres of hill land on which about 130 ewes are kept.

Near the southern end of the peninsula is the Laggan of Kintyre, an area of almost flat alluvial land recently emerged from the sea. Here, fine pastures have been created and dairying is the principal enterprise with supplementary fattening of sheep and raising of arable crops.

A Region of Small, Mixed Farms—the Lough Neagh Lowlands

Ireland is a country of small farms, owner-occupied (as explained in Chapter 3) and engaged mainly in livestock enterprises, with crops locally important. One of the most mixed regions agriculturally is the basin of Lough Neagh. The Tertiary basalts which were here warped downward, leading ultimately to the formation of the largest inland lake in the British Isles, are covered by glacial and post-glacial drifts. These range from clays to sands and peats. Areas of bog, partly reclaimed, lie between drumlins and kames. Within the basin, many minor land use regions have been discerned[1] and may be seen to be related to differences of relief, soil and the history of human occupation, but the larger region provides a convenient unit for the illustration of the mixed farming found here. The farms are organised in small units and devoted principally to livestock, but many variations occur in which enterprises tend to be numerous. Thus, a farm may have five or six cows in milk, twice that number of dry cattle, 30 sheep, some pigs and poultry, a few acres in potatoes for a cash crop as well as domestic use, and oats or barley, some of which may also form a cash crop. Most of the farm is usually in grass, some of which may be harvested for seed as another cash crop. Such a farm is typically of 30 or 40 acres and some land may be added temporarily by conacre lease (described in Chapter 3).

At the southern end of Lough Neagh most farms have some land devoted to fruit growing. Small fruits are commonly found on the drier ridges among the fen peatlands close to the lake, while on the drumlins stretching away deep into County Armagh, apples are the main crop.

Also close to the lake, especially on the County Tyrone shores, are areas of very small and poor holdings which hardly merit the term 'farm'. Many are of only 5 to 10 acres, and much of the work in the fields is still done with the spade. Donkeys are commonly seen here—the only region of Northern Ireland, apart from some areas in Fermanagh, of which this is still true.

The Lough Neagh basin is in the centre of Northern Ireland, with easy access to the Belfast market, and good communications facilitating export to Great Britain of surplus produce. Although not first class, the land is generally of reasonable fertility and, when well managed and particularly when drainage is adequate, can yield good returns in the uses to which it is generally put, as described above. Where poverty exists, it is generally because the holding of land is excessively small for the conditions obtaining. Amalgamation of holdings is gradually reducing the number of such very small units, but many of the resulting farms are still not large enough to be satisfactory economic units. This, indeed, is true of large areas in Ireland.

[1] Symons (ed.) (1963), Part IV.

An Arable Region, Predominantly Grain Growing—Cambridgeshire

Cambridgeshire is selected to illustrate one of the regional variations in types of farming which occurs within the mainly arable area of eastern England. The county is generally recognised as lying within a grain growing belt associated with the occurrence of fairly large farms in Cambridgeshire, Suffolk and adjacent counties. Rarely is grain growing so dominant as to exclude all other enterprises, but in this central belt there is a higher proportion of farms on which it is clearly predominant than in the adjacent counties where roots, both for stock-feed and cash (particularly sugar beet) rival or exceed grain in importance. The emphasis on grain is found on a variety of soils, including loamy, chalky and clay types, with wheat favoured on clays and barley on chalk.

Recent investigations have provided precise information on farm types in this area,[1] not previously published. Grain farms, such as occur in all parts of the eastern counties except the Fens, have an average acreage in cereals equivalent to 70 per cent. of the *arable* acreage and average 185 acres in total size. Nearly half of these farms have a minor livestock enterprise, usually beef cattle, and pigs and poultry are also important subsidiaries.

The combination of an important area of roots with grain is found on farms of similar size (average total size 179 acres, but with a high proportion in the medium-size category of 100–299¾ acres.) In this category also, nearly half of the farms have a livestock enterprise, usually beef cattle, with pigs and poultry important. Output of cash roots becomes more important than grain on smaller farms, of which there are examples in north Cambridgeshire, on the fringe of the Fen country where they are much more numerous. Sugar beet is the typical cash root crop in both types of this combination, with potatoes also favoured, mainly on the medium and large farms.

This region fits the general assumptions that arable farming is associated in Britain with the areas of lowest rainfall, avoiding the low-lying areas of medium and heavy soils on which dairying is favoured. Grain growing occupies a predominant place on larger farms, which can obtain a satisfactory income

[1] Jackson, Barnard and Sturrock (1963).

from it, in spite of its comparatively extensive nature. Even on these comparatively specialised farms, however, it is not usually the only enterprise and the maintenance of livestock qualifies the farms for inclusion in the broad category of mixed farms characteristic of the British Isles.

New Zealand

The islands of New Zealand lie in temperate latitudes and the observed means for temperature and rainfall place most of New Zealand in the same category as Great Britain in the Köppen classification—Cfb. Averages here tend to mislead, for New Zealand enjoys sensibly higher daytime temperatures than Britain, hours of sunshine are longer and snow is rarely seen in the lowlands of New Zealand. The north of New Zealand is warm temperate rather then cool temperate, as may be seen in the successful culture of the vine and citrus fruits. Throughout the islands, however, the climate is humid, except for some of the interior montane basins of the South Island, notably Central Otago. Thornthwaite's classification brings out well these variations in climate.

The combination of moderate temperatures and fairly high humidity gives nearly ideal conditions for growth of grass, and it is on the high-yielding pastures of sown grasses and clovers, maintained with scientific management and heavy fertiliser applications, that New Zealand's prosperity has been based. Only on a narrow belt of the west coast are lowland pastures endangered by excessive rain, but drought can be a serious threat in most other regions. Where grasslands existed at the time of European colonisation, they were composed of native species, mainly of tussock habit, of low grazing value. These had to be replaced by English grasses, and the nitrogen cycle based on clovers had to be harnessed before potential fertility of the lowlands could be developed.[1]

Hence, British settlers who came to New Zealand via Australia found conditions more like the homeland than they

[1] A basic reference for New Zealand geography is *A Descriptive Atlas of New Zealand*, Government Printer, Wellington, 1960. Many publications describing agriculture and other aspects of the New Zealand scene are available from the same source. For a brief description of the grassland of New Zealand, see Sears (1962).

had found in Australia, but those who had come direct would have noticed the differences more sharply.

The European colonisation of New Zealand virtually began only in 1840. The Southern Alps had been sighted in 1642 by Abel Tasman, and Cook had made landings and surveyed the coasts between 1769 and 1777 but the only shore stations successfully maintained before 1840 were for sealing and whaling. Consequently, by the time permanent settlement was undertaken the colonists could draw on the knowledge of the improvers of agriculture in Britain, and the experience gained in developing agricultural land in America and Australia.

Initially, cultivation was on primarily a subsistence basis, there being no markets accessible on which crops could be sold. Sheep, however, brought in the first instance from Australia, provided an exportable product, wool, and during the 'sixties, there developed a substantial trade in wool. Meanwhile, the four main centres and a number of lesser towns had grown sufficiently to provide an urban population large enough to offer outlets for a variety of crops. But it was only with the introduction of refrigeration in 1882 that it became possible to begin to realise the potential productivity inherent in the land and climate of New Zealand. Refrigeration made it feasible to expand the pastoral industries to supply the great market in Britain with meat and dairy products. Whereas compared with Australia, New Zealand had played only a small part in the wool trade, the climate was far more suitable than Australia's for dairy produce. For meat production also, conditions were favourable and New Zealand farmers began the changeover from the Merino, which produced fine wool but a poor carcase, to types of sheep which were more suitable for meat production. As the English market reflected the growing preference for small joints of meat, so New Zealand production settled into concentration on fat lamb production.

Great Britain alone in all the world offered open and remunerative markets for the agricultural products of temperate lands. Nowhere else was there the great imbalance between food requirements and production, backed by the purchasing power conferred by massive exports of manufactured goods and services. New Zealand had the advantage of being a British colony, which was important for trade contacts, but, even had it not been, it could have competed on the British market as did the United States, Argentina and Denmark.

New Zealand suffered from one major drawback—distance from Britain. At 14,000 miles, via Australia, it was about as far as it could be from its market. The opening of the Panama canal in 1914 reduced the distance to 12,000 miles. Although transport has been speeded up, cargo liners on the New Zealand run still normally take four to five weeks on a direct voyage, and about six weeks with calls at Pacific Islands. Furthermore, before the voyage commences, loading of cargo involves a laborious and time-consuming tour of small ports around the New Zealand coast. Thus, many months elapse between the produce leaving the farm and its arrival at the distant market. A round trip from London back to London takes up to twenty weeks. The consequence of this long haul is not only that transport costs are high but that the producer must be prepared for considerable fluctuations in prices before his produce is finally marketed. The normal difficulty of any farmer in trying to anticipate conditions of surplus and shortage is made considerably more difficult. The New Zealand farmer has also to face the fact that his produce is frozen and will never command the highest prices, which are reserved for the fresh commodities marketed by those nearer at hand.

To meet these disadvantages it has been essential to organise production to exploit all the conditions that favour the New Zealander. Climate alone is not a sufficiently favourable factor. It is true that grass growth is at a standstill for only short periods—longest, of course, in the south of South Island, where supplementary fodder is needed—and little housing of stock is required. But these factors would not reduce costs sufficiently for the New Zealander to compete if his farm were small and diversified like the typical British farm. The New Zealander has had to learn to specialise and to accept the risks inherent in specialisation—risks which are all the greater when the specialisation is directed at an overseas market. Specialisation in search of low costs results in there rarely being more than two enterprises on a farm, of which one is usually pre-eminent. The majority of farms can be classed as dairying or fat lamb producing, or a combination of these two. Sheep are combined with cattle for maximum pasture utilisation and control of weeds.

Provision of winter fodder is organised so as to minimize labour requirements and cost. Hay-making has long been mechanised, though silage is widely preferred to hay. In the south, turnips, rape, kale and oats are important fodder, so arable land is seen in conjunction with livestock. Turnips illustrate the economy of man-power. They are not lifted for feeding to stock, the sheep being merely turned into them to eat their way steadily through the crop, controlled for thorough utilisation by temporary fences.

The number of acres and of animals managed per worker is large by European standards. This is another necessity to keep down costs, and, because a family farm may maintain 70 or 80 cows in milk, mechanisation of the milking came at an early date and over nine-tenths of dairy cows are now machine milked. Similarly, with several thousand sheep to be shorn on a farm, commonly in a few days by itinerant shearers, the wool-shed also attracted mechanisation and over four-fifths of the sheep are machine-shorn. Employment on New Zealand farms is limited not only because wages are high but because labour is perennially scarce. Shortage of labour has always been a handicap in New Zealand, following inevitably from a policy of restricted immigration and the distance of the home country, the main source of settlers.

The typical New Zealand farmer assesses his livelihood in pounds of butterfat available for the factory, number of lambs for the freezing works, and weight of fleeces for the wool-broker. His aim is to carry as many livestock as he can feed. Number of livestock per man is the yardstick of profitability, but good quality land is limited in supply, so number of stock is also high per acre in the good quality lands, and often higher than it ought to be on poor, mountainous land. The farms of New Zealand are large by European standards; 38 per cent. of all farm holdings exceed 200 acres in size, and 8 per cent. exceed 1000 acres. The latter group includes the high country sheep stations, which range up to 100,000 acres, of which more will be said later. At the other extreme, there are a good many rather small farms, 12,000 (14 per cent.) being of between 50 and 100 acres. Also, there are more fragmented holdings than is commonly realised.[1]

[1] Johnston (1962).

The need for large farms, permitting large numbers of stock to be carried without detriment to land or animal health is seen when prices for produce are compared. The prices received by the New Zealand farmer are generally not more than half to two-thirds those received by his counterpart in the British Isles for similar products. (Table 7). Clearly, in a country as dependent as New Zealand is on its agricultural produce—which is responsible for over 90 per cent. of its overseas earnings—farmers cannot be subsidised as they have been since 1939 in Britain. The most that can be done is to even out fluctuations in prices from funds accumulated when trading prices are high, and to make government grants available for certain purposes judged to be important to the nation as a whole, such as soil conservation measures.

TABLE 7

REPRESENTATIVE AVERAGE FAT STOCK PRICES NEW ZEALAND AND IRELAND

Category	*1957*	*1958*	*1959*	*Source*
CATTLE:				
New Zealand Ox—schedule price quotation (per cwt. dressed carcase weight)	94s. 7d.	133s. 5d.	144s. 9d.	a
do.—(per cwt. live-weight)	51s. 0d.	72s. 0d.	78s. 1½d.	b
Dublin, fat cattle:				
per cwt. dead-weight	212s. 3d.	223s. 6d.	232s. 0d.	c
per cwt. live-weight	121s. 3d.	127s. 9d.	132s. 6d.	a
N. Ireland, fat cattle:				
per cwt. live-weight	142s. 1d.	144s. 5d.	139s. 2d.	d
do. excl. guarantee payments	112s. 8d.	134s. 2d.	136s. 0d.	d
FAT LAMB:				
New Zealand—schedule price per 1 lb. carcase weight	26d.	20¼d.	18¼d.	a
Dublin, per 1 lb. dead weight	31½d.	30d.	26d.	c
N. Ireland fat sheep and lambs per 1 lb. estimated dressed carcase weight	35¾d.	35¼d.	35½d.	d
do. excl. guarantee payments	29¼d.	29d.	22½d.	d

Sources: a. Commonwealth Economic Committee, *Meat* 1960 H.M.S.O. (1961).
b. do. assuming killing-out percentage of 54.
c. *Statistical Abstract of Ireland*, 1960.
d. Supplied by Livestock Marketing Division, Ministry of Agriculture for Northern Ireland.

(Reproduced from *Journal of the Statistical and Social Inquiry Society of Ireland*, 21, 1960–61.)

At these factory prices, which would be quite uneconomic for the British farmer, with his higher costs in fodder, housing, etc., and smaller turnover, the New Zealand marketing agencies can sell their products on the British market a little cheaper than the home-produced, unfrozen product. They could also easily undersell the home producers in other European countries, North America, and, in dairy produce, Australia. Quota restrictions, or complete prohibition, however, reinforce tariffs in keeping out the genuinely low-cost produce from New Zealand, or in admitting only as much as is needed to balance supply with demand at the prices acceptable to the home farmer. To reduce its excessive dependence on the British market, New Zealand has been trying to develop new markets, particularly in Asia. There, of course, the demand for food is immense, but the effective demand for New Zealand produce is limited to some extent by the lack of familiarity with temperate foodstuffs and, ultimately more seriously, by the lack of purchasing power.

Land Development in New Zealand

In spite of the restricted markets open to New Zealand and the relatively small, though growing, internal market (total population 2·6 million) production has been increased markedly in recent years. A decade ago the annual output of lamb was under 200,000 tons, now it is about 300,000 tons. Increases in livestock numbers are achieved partly by more intensive use of land, but land development continues to be, as it has always been, a feature of the New Zealand scene. Problems of allocation and tenure of land have always loomed large in New Zealand's internal politics. As the population has grown and export earnings have had to be increased, Crown land held in reserve by the government has been released for settlement, and large farms and sheep runs have had to be subdivided and worked more intensively.[1] High valuation and taxation of large estates were among measures used to achieve this end. Many estates were converted into small farms for the re-settlement of returned soldiers after the first World War, and of these a high proportion were too small to support a family. Learning from this experience, present-day practices produce fewer but larger farms.

The state is the main agent of land development in New Zealand. Many of the properties taken over by the Lands and

[1] Duncan (1962).

Survey Department after it became the responsible authority in 1929 were already in grass, and simply required subdivision, and provision of roads, buildings and services. Increasingly, however, development work has been concerned with land previously considered to be uncultivable. Experiments beyond the means of the private individual, and the economies of scale in machinery, materials and labour, have enabled the government to achieve striking results.

Development of quite small blocks of a few thousand acres may be undertaken, but blocks of 50,000 acres or more offer disproportionately greater scope, especially if the terrain is difficult and demands a long-term approach. Initial tasks include destruction of scrub and other existing vegetation by crushing, raking and burning and the construction of roads and drains. The land is then ploughed or cultivated with giant discs. Discs have the advantage over ploughs on steep and stony ground. If discs cannot cope with the terrain it may still be improved by oversowing without cultivation. Lime is applied and pasture established. Cattle and sheep can then be brought in, the aim being to stock the land as densely as possible to improve the pastures through balanced grazing and natural nitrogen enrichment. During this period houses and fences are built and roads improved.[1]

By this approach about 1½ million acres have already been made available for settlement in nearly 4000 farms and over one million acres are currently under development. A typical year's work includes laying down to grass an area of about 40,000 acres. Areas are turned over to private farmers ready to support ten or twenty times the grazing pressure which they received when they were being used for extensive grazing before development began. Selection of the farmers to take over the completed property is by ballot with various qualifications required of candidates.

Areas reclaimed in this way are found in all parts of New Zealand. The biggest blocks have been in the central volcanic plateau of the North Island, including the pumice lands, which could be agriculturally developed only after the discovery of the importance of trace elements, the lack of which had prevented livestock from thriving. There are other large

[1] Ward (1958).

blocks, however, from the harsh 'gumlands' (former Kauri forest country, where natural soils are acid and infertile) of North Auckland to cool and humid Southland. After having been rather neglected in the earlier phases of development, when large reserves of Crown land were available in the North Island, Southland has become a region of major importance in land development. It is now by far the most important area for this work in the South Island, having over 250,000 acres under development. Areas under development include extensive areas of coastal peat land.[1]

In this venture the state aims to work without subsidy from the exchequer and therefore aims for a working profit. Land development costs, however, range from £30 to more than £60 per acre, and the land most expensive to improve is not necessarily the most valuable. Disposal prices of farms reflect their real worth and hence the state subsidises its less profitable ventures from profitable ones.

The Department of Maori Affairs is also involved in land improvement in the North Island, and private interests have undertaken some large scale development work as well as normal farm improvement schemes.

A feature of agricultural improvement in New Zealand which has attracted much attention abroad is the large scale use of aircraft. Although aviation had become an accepted ally of agriculture in many countries, mainly for spraying crops with insecticides, it was New Zealand that developed the application of the light aeroplane to top-dressing and oversowing as a normal aspect of farm operations. It has made possible the improvement of steep and rolling country, particularly the tussock grasslands that have become depleted with fifty to a hundred years of grazing, for which ordinary methods of top-dressing were too expensive. It is also used on all other major types of terrain.[2] The usual dressing is 2 cwt. of superphosphate per acre at a cost of about £2 per acre. The total quantities of fertiliser and lime applied from the air have risen year by year and exceeded 600,000 tons in 1962, treating 5,600,000 acres. This is about the same area as was top-dressed by conventional methods.

[1] Symons (1961).
[2] Brockie (1958).

Aircraft are also used for sowing seed, spreading poison to combat rabbits and weeds, distributing trace elements, spotting stock on large runs and many other tasks. Agricultural aviation is a firmly established business with investment in aircraft and ancillary equipment estimated at £1½ million.

Irrigation is another aid to more intensive use of land which has received increasing attention in recent years in New Zealand. In a number of districts production is retarded by long dry periods, notably South Canterbury and Central Otago. Irrigation has been developed for stock fattening and fruit growing in particular and, because of the high cost of labour, attention has been given to automatic operation of sluices. Much more land could benefit from irrigation, given the market incentives.

The Regional Pattern[1]

The principal types of farming and their regional distribution appear in Figure 7. Relief is the fundamental factor influencing the distribution of the main types. (Compare Figure 8). In his pioneer study which developed many principles of agricultural geography as well as elucidating the farming pattern of New Zealand, Buchanan[2] showed how it was relief rather than climate that limited the distribution of dairy cows as compared with beef cattle or sheep. Dairy cows cannot give high production if they have to cope with steep terrain, even if the altitude is low. A second factor is the availability of good transport facilities for collecting milk from the farms, and transferring the output of the dairy factories to the ports. Hence, the North Island, having the combination of flat and undulating valley, terrace and down country with a humid climate, has the greatest development of dairying, and some 90 per cent. of all dairy cows in New Zealand. Higher rainfall in the North Island is found on terrain which is generally higher and steeper, and here less intensive forms of production —sheep and cattle rearing—are found. Similarly, in the South Island, the highest rainfall areas are found on the west coast but here dairying is limited by the shortage of flat land, acid, gley soils and poor communications. Dairying

[1] For regional descriptions in more detail, see Cumberland and Fox (1962).

[2] Buchanan (1935).

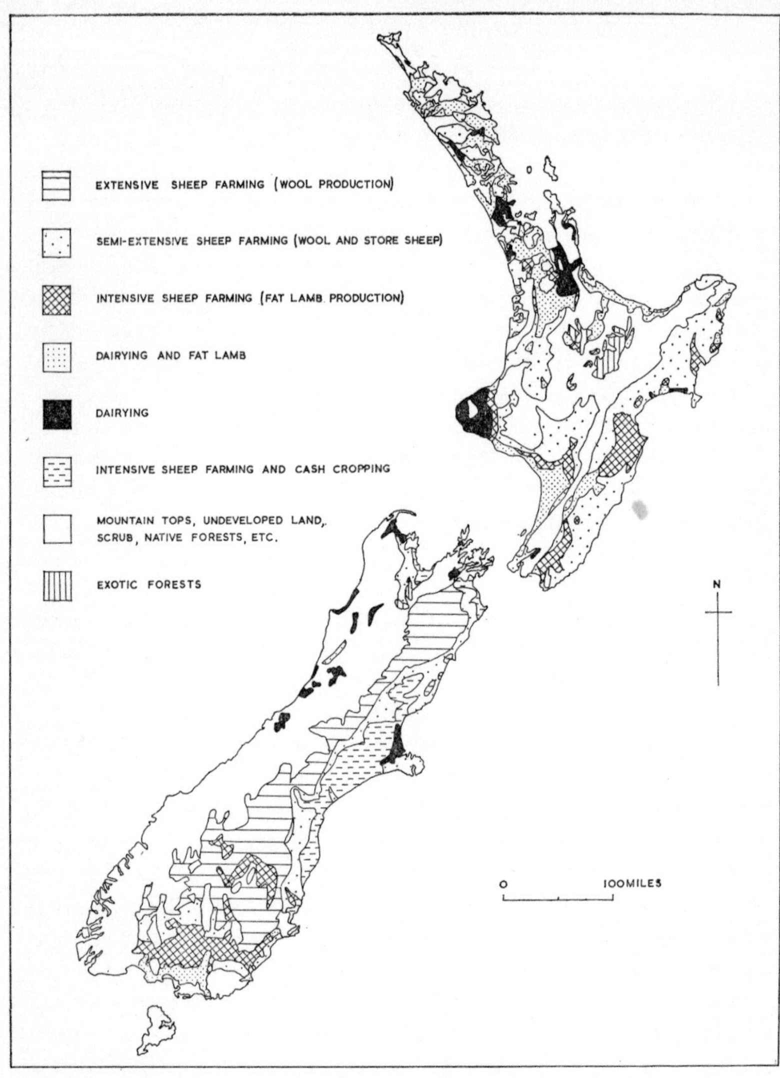

Figure 7. Types of farming, New Zealand. Intensification of production has reduced the area devoted to extensive sheep farming which is now important only in the South Island mountain zone, east of the Southern Alps. Much of the low hill country of the North Island is, however, unsuitable for enterprises more intensive than raising store sheep combined with wool production. The highly productive areas therefore represent only a small proportion of the total area. The great extent of the agriculturally unproductive land in the mountains of the South Island and on the North Island volcanic plateau is evident. The exotic forests are softwood plantations.

Source: Based on maps in *Descriptive Atlas of New Zealand.*
By permission of the Department of Lands and Survey, New Zealand.

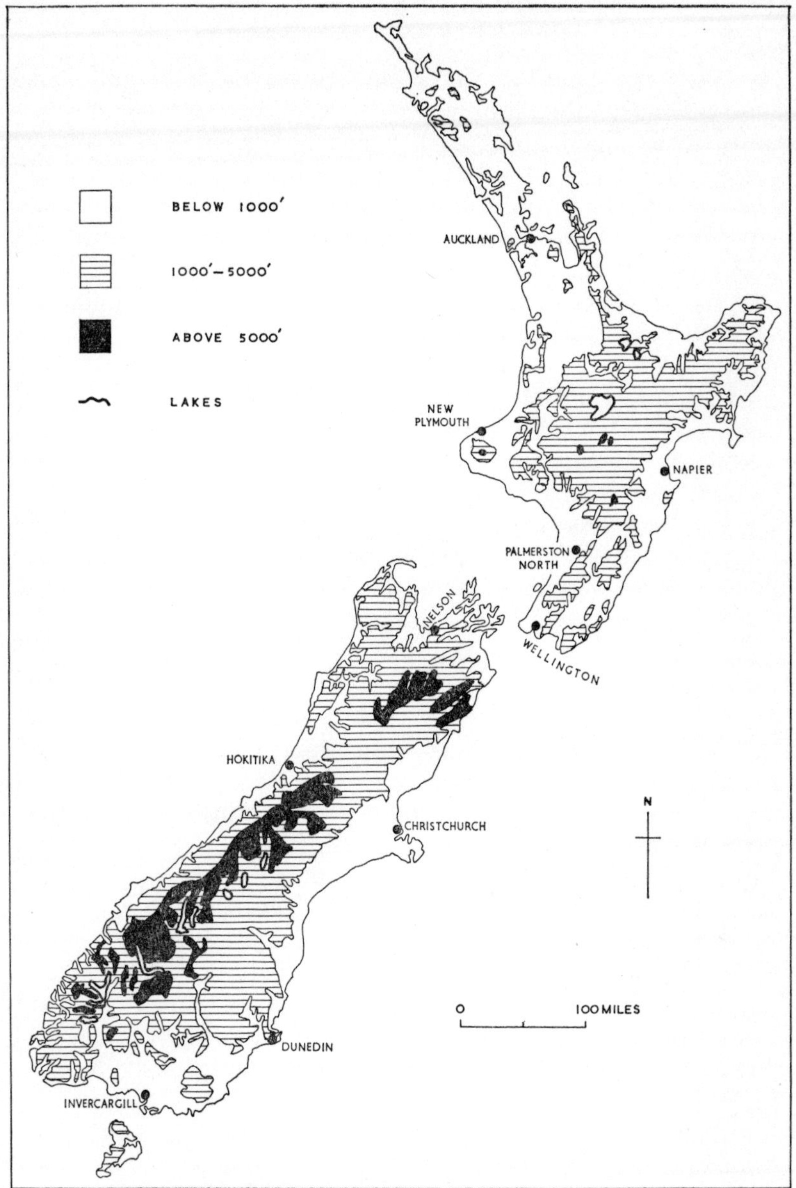

Figure 8. Relief map of New Zealand. Large areas of the North Island below 1,000 feet are classed as hill lands because of the steep slopes that are their dominant feature. Nearly all down and terrace lands are below 1,000 feet.

Source: Based on maps in *Descriptive Atlas of New Zealand.* By Permission of the Department of Lands and Survey, New Zealand.

is better developed in the humid plains of Southland, but the tendency has been in recent years for dairying to give way to fat lamb production, which has been more remunerative for farms of suitable size, and is less demanding in labour. Many farms here and in the North Island combine dairying and fat lamb production. A narrow belt of country on the sub-humid Canterbury Plains specialises in dairying, favoured by the market for liquid milk in Christchurch and the facilities for export through the port of Lyttleton.

Dairying is encouraged by the heavier soils and where these give way to lighter textures, and in drier areas without severe decline in fertility, intensive sheep farming is more generally found. Six or more sheep per acre are carried on light land which responds to top-dressing, with grass and clovers supplying almost all feed requirements in the North Island but with arable crops necessary in the South Island to supplement pastures. Irrigation is used in some cases. Fat lambs form the basis of the farm economy, with wool, ewe mutton and beef subsidiary. The larger areas devoted to this kind of farming are the valleys and lower hill country of the east of the North Island, and Central Otago and Southland in the South Island.

On the higher and steeper country, accounting for most of the rest of the occupied land in the North Island, and the foothills and lower ranges of the South Island, more extensive sheep farming is practised. Store sheep for fattening on the low-ground farms and wool production are together the main sources of income on these farms, sometimes supplemented by beef cattle. Conditions vary widely, but between one and two sheep per acre would be normal, a carrying capacity similar to that of the more productive hill farms of the British Isles.

On the highest and steepest occupied land, including the ranges of 6000 to 8000 feet on the eastern side of the Southern Alps, the high country sheep run is virtually the only feasible type of farm. On these properties, extending to many thousands of acres, hardy sheep are kept for their wool, often with only one sheep to ten acres. Merinos are the only sheep capable of utilising the high runs. They climb to the high ridges and eat down to the lower levels, thus coming into easier country before the winter snowfalls, although losses in snow are still heavy. On lower and easier ground some cattle are kept together with crossbred sheep.

New Zealand now has over 50 million sheep and more than half of its total area is devoted to sheep farming of some kind. Since nearly one-third of the total land area of 66 million acres is mountainous or otherwise at present unusable, the area in sheep farming (32 million acres) amounts to about three-quarters of the total agricultural area. From the early days, when the Merinos formed almost the entire national flock, breeds have multiplied to suit the differing conditions of semi-intensive and intensive sheep farming. Flocks on these farms are based on descendents of the English breeds, particularly Romney, Southdown, English Leicester and Border Leicester. To suit South Island conditions the Corriedale was evolved from crossing Merino, Lincoln and English Leicester breeds. However, the variety remains small compared with that in Britain, about a dozen breeds compared with nearly forty.

In cattle, dairy cows are predominantly Jersey, favoured because of the high butterfat content of the milk, and Friesian, preferred for town milk supply. Beef breeds are mainly Aberdeen Angus, Hereford and Galloway.

Livestock products account for 95 per cent. of New Zealand's export earnings. Arable crops are grown almost entirely for home consumption, and do not satisfy the domestic market. Wheat was grown for export in the early 1880s, but the specialisation that developed in North America and Australia cut prices below the level at which New Zealand farms could compete, although yields per acre were much heavier in New Zealand, and former grain farms were turned over to livestock production. Today, wheat is an important aspect of farm production only in the South Island, about 70 per cent. of New Zealand's production being grown in Canterbury, and most of the rest in Otago. Other crops, including oats, barley, potatoes and green fodder crops, and temporary pastures feature in rotation with wheat. Fat lamb production is also commonly combined with the arable farming. This is the type of farming shown in Figure 7 as intensive sheep farming and cash cropping, and is associated, of course, with flat and gently rolling terrain.

New Zealand Farming as a Type of Mixed Agriculture

Compared with most farms in Britain and much of the continent of Europe, those of New Zealand are relatively specialised. Apart, however, from holdings devoted to fruit and vegetable growing which are similarly specialised in Europe, there is rarely only one significant enterprise on the New Zealand farm, except in dairying and high country wool production. These again, are paralleled in the larger British dairy and hill sheep farms. It is probably true to say that the majority of New Zealand farms have two significant enterprises, such as dairying and fat lamb, or store sheep and cattle, where the British farms have usually four or five. Very often, the additions in the British Isles are pigs and poultry, both of which in New Zealand cater only for the limited home market. Pigs are usually kept as subsidiary enterprises on dairy farms and fed largely on separated milk, while poultry are found mainly in large specialised poultry farms, or as smaller flocks maintained on part-time smallholdings.

The regional variation in type of farming is not as great as in Britain. The latitudinal extent of the two countries is similar, and this factor induces greater variety in the case of New Zealand because it extends into a warm temperate type of climate, so Mediterranean and sub-tropical fruits, maize and tobacco can be grown commercially. Relief also is more marked, but the extensive sheep farming of the Southern Alps is not more different than hill farming in the British mountains from their low country equivalents. Some crops important in Britain are absent, notably sugar beet. But the outstanding difference is in social and economic organisation. Throughout New Zealand, conditions are comparatively uniform in the range of sizes of farms, conditions of tenure and rural land values, and marketing opportunities. The differences that exist in Britain, which have evolved with the different historical experiences of different regions of Britain, superimposed on differences of climate and relief, have no equivalent in recently-settled New Zealand. Enhancing the uniformity is the orientation of the country to distant export markets, and the need to produce essentially the commodities in which the country's advantages can most be realised. The result is the evolution of New Zealand's agriculture as a modified form of European mixed farming, with a strong tendency towards specialisation, both on the individual farm and in national output.

CHAPTER 6

Plantation Agriculture in Malaysia

The antiquity of agriculture in south-east Asia is well known as a result of archaeological investigation. The view that this region was probably the cradle of the very earliest agriculture, and the home of domestic animals, has been referred to above (Chapter 1). From these early beginnings, however, the people of the region developed their techniques comparatively little, and at the present time subsistence farming in the region is still based on the practices of hundreds and even thousands of years ago. In this chapter we shall consider some of the features of the alien plantation system of agriculture which was introduced into the region by Europeans for their own commercial gain.

Prior to the introduction of plantations, the exports of the region were confined to spices and other luxury items, which, being highly prized by wealthy society in Europe, could withstand the high cost of shipment and long duration of travel by sailing vessel. Indian traders dominated the trade in spices, perfumes, rare woods, alluvial gold and precious stones for over a thousand years before the decline in the thirteenth century of the state of Sri Vijaya, the Sumatran focus of Indian culture in the archipelago. Power became increasingly concentrated in the hands of Muslims, with Arab traders and missionaries challenging the Indian interests. Then the Europeans arrived and began to set up trading posts. Malacca was captured by the Portuguese in 1511 and a Portuguese agent was established in Sumatra in 1512. A hundred years later, supremacy in the region was passing to the Dutch, who were not seriously challenged until the end of the eighteenth century, when the British secured Penang.

Up to this time the Malayan peninsula had been of less commercial importance than the islands, even though the first

European base had been at Malacca. But the British saw the potential value of the swampy and almost uninhabited island of Singapore as the strategic centre for both peninsula and islands, and something at least of the scope for producing tropical commodities in the Malay states. They could not at that time have foreseen that the most notable contribution that Malaya would make to the twentieth century world economy would be through the production of natural rubber.

By the nineteenth century the commercial exploitation of the tropics by the European nations had of course already been in progress for several hundred years. The plantation system had been found to answer the needs of foreign producers, and had been applied successively to different crops and in numerous tropical and sub-tropical environments. The essence of the plantation system was the acquisition by Europeans of sufficient areas of suitable land to make economically attractive units, on which were established European managers and assistants to provide commercial organisation and technical direction. Plantations later established by companies were similarly organised. A number of plantation units were required to justify port and other commercial facilities essential for conveying the products to the centres of demand in Europe and, later, in North America. Manual labour had to be cheap so that the product could be sold at a price which would ensure a large and growing volume of demand. Workers had also to be capable of toiling long hours in tropical heat. In many cases the indigenous population was either too scanty to form the basis of a labour force, or was not readily amenable to discipline. Hence the wholly reprehensible system of slavery and later the objectionable practice of indenturing were introduced to deal with the labour problem. The plantations of the Americas flourished on these supplies of European and North American capital and forced labour, and most of the profits were repatriated to the sources of the capital.

A number of crops were tried with varying degrees of success on plantations in Malaya in the nineteenth century. Cloves, nutmegs and pepper were followed by more extensive plantings of sugar cane and coffee, each of which reached about 50,000 acres at its peak period. Plant diseases and competition from other producing regions led to the decline of all of these. At the turn of the century, however, rubber was being introduced and inter-planted with coffee and sugar cane.

The value of rubber had been recognised before the middle of the nineteenth century with Mackintosh's utilisation of it for waterproofing in 1823, and, much more important, the success of the vulcanising process. This, in 1842, heralded the era of road transport, though pneumatic tyres for motor cars did not go into production till decades later. The best source was found to be *Hevea brasiliensis*, which will yield a large flow of latex over many years, in contrast, for example, to the Guayule shrub (*Parthenium argentatum*), from which the natural rubber can be extracted only by destroying and crushing the plant. The scattered occurrence of *Hevea* in its natural home, the Amazon forest, and the difficulties encountered with labour in this region led to the establishment of the tree in south-east Asia, which was physically suitable. Although the indigenous Malays were relatively few in number and did not prove to be sufficiently interested in wage employment, the labour problem in Malaya was solved by recruitment in south India, where there was a large surplus population. Chinese immigrants also provided a source of labour, though for plantation work much less important.

Humid tropical conditions are essential for the commercial exploitation of *Hevea*. Even in equatorial areas most rapid growth is confined to the lowlands below 650 feet (200 metres). For every increment in altitude of this magnitude trees require three to six months longer to reach the size at which tapping is commenced, and 2300 feet (700 metres) is a practical upper limit.[1] Rainfall of between 70 and 150 inches per year is preferred, with no month normally below three inches. At the same time, wet days interfere with tapping, so that it is best if the rainfall is concentrated on not more than about 150 days.[2]

Soils need to be deep, permeable and fertile for the best growth. The fertile volcanic and alluvial soils in south-east Asia give excellent results but the widespread need to use these best soils for food crops means that lateritic soils have to be used for rubber. To maintain good physical conditions, attention

[1] Ochse and others (1961), 950.

[2] For the effects of physical conditions on rubber production in Malaya see Wycherley (1963).

has to be paid always to drainage, fertilising and control of erosion, and irrigation may sometimes be used with advantage. The soil is also generally protected by a cover crop between the trees. Soils within the range pH 4·0 to 8·0 are usable, but the best results are attained with pH held between 5·0 and 6·0.

The tree secretes its latex in tubes in the soft tissues of the inner bark close to the wood. There is no latex in either the wood or the outer bark. The latex is tapped by paring away a thin sliver of bark which severs the latex vessels. After a few hours coagulation takes place at the ends of the vessels so that the flow ceases. Tapping is repeated every second or third day, rubber and bark regenerating naturally. Regular tapping may be maintained over a lifetime of some 30 years but skilful and properly regulated tapping is essential.

Economics of Rubber Production

It is evident that scientific management is required for good results and an appreciable amount of capital is involved. Although the trees grow fast there is a lag of some five years before the first returns are obtained from young trees. Capital is invested not only in trees but in factories for processing the latex (less than one-third of which by weight is rubber), housing for the labour force, roads, vehicles and other equipment. Capital was readily attracted early in the present century, demand having forced up prices for rubber, and governments encouraged companies by allocating land and building roads and railways. Migration of workers was also encouraged, and Singapore developed as a great processing and commercial centre. The volume of shipping between Singapore and Ceylon and the consuming countries in Europe and North America, together with comparatively good internal communications, enabled the plantation product from this region to compete easily with the output from South America.

However, as with other primary products, supply and demand were never nicely balanced for long, so that prices fluctuated continuously. After the First World War prices fell to a very low level, as in other forms of agricultural produce, and to meet this situation the Stevenson Valorization Scheme was introduced to raise prices by restricting output. This could succeed only if there was full co-operation between producers, but this was not achieved. In particular, the Dutch increased their plantings and production. The situation was worsened by the world economic depression and the price fell rapidly until in 1931 it was only 2½d. per pound compared with 12s .6d. per pound at the peak reached some twenty years earlier. This situation could not continue and resulted in 1934 in the International Rubber Regulation Agreement. With excess supplies being withheld from markets some stability of prices was achieved until the second World War.

Meanwhile synthetic rubber production had been developed, arising out of Germany's needs in the first World War. It represented only 8 per cent. of world consumption of rubber in 1940, but there was a rapid increase in its production during the second World War. Consequently, the restoration in 1945 of the rubber plantations, after the wartime destruction and severance from markets, had to face new conditions in competition. The range of products in which natural rubber still held distinct advantages over the synthetic product was much reduced, and there was surplus capacity in synthetic plants. Nevertheless, the natural product has itself been developed to be more competitive, and given reasonable conditions of access to markets, has succeeded in again proving economically feasible.

For some years now prices have ranged between about 1s. 8d. and 2s. 3d. per pound. To produce profitably at this level, plantations must be highly efficient, and larger than would be practicable with higher prices. In Malaya, where two-thirds of the cropped area is in rubber (Figure 9) and rubber accounts for 60 per cent. of exports by value, considerable amalgamation of estates has taken place. Estates seem to need to exceed 1000 acres to be economically attractive to European companies. A typical company owns 16 estates varying from 1100 to 5600 acres planted area. This company expects a profit of £39 per acre of mature trees at 2s. per pound selling price, or £26 per acre with the price at 1s. 9d. per pound.

The profits of estates of this kind have to be judged in relation to the need to find dividends for overseas investors on a scale sufficient to offset the political and economic risks inherent in investment in rubber production. Smaller estates (less than 500 acres) are acceptable to Asian operators who do not have

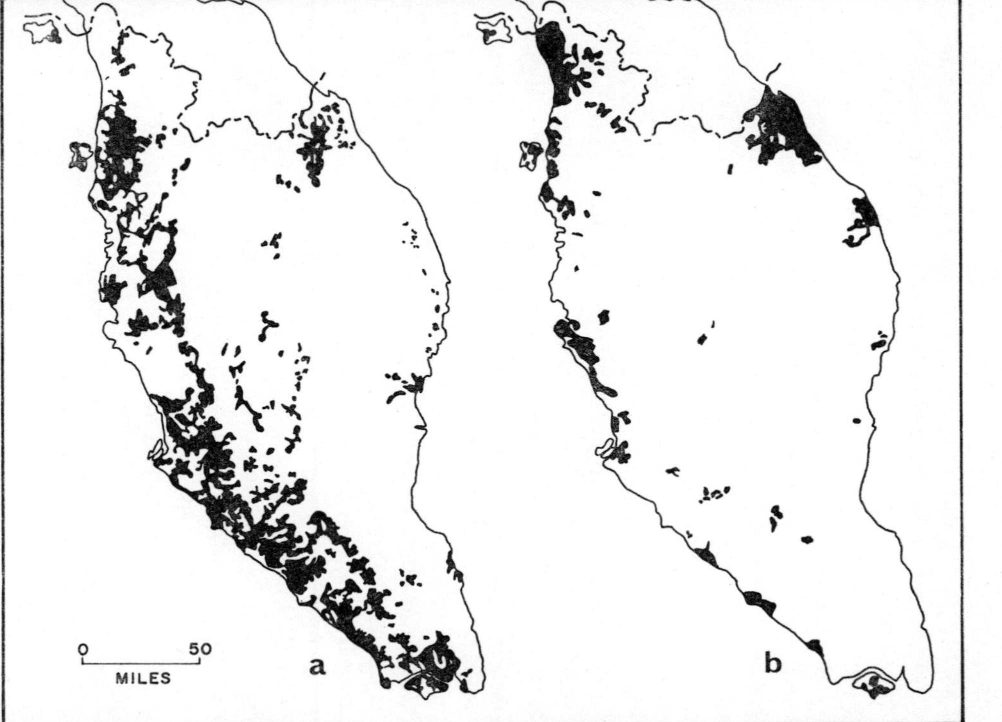

Figure 9. Distribution of land used for production of rubber (left) and other crops (right) in Malaya. The remaining land is in forest, natural jungle, or is undeveloped except for the small area of urban and industrial development.

Source: Malaya Land Utilisation Map (1:760,320, 1953), reproduced by permission of the Directorate of National Mapping, Malaysia. Copyright reserved.

this problem. In addition there are a large number of smallholdings (less than 100 acres) locally owned and worked. In most cases these have only five acres or so of rubber, integrated with other crops.

For all producers, but most of all for the large commercial estates, the problem today is to obtain the highest possible yield per tapper, because tapping is the largest single item in production costs. Increasing the frequency of tapping or the number of trees per acre may result in higher yield per acre, but lower yield per tapper, and is accordingly undesirable. Efficiency is therefore judged by the standards common in commercial farming in countries where labour is short, rather than by the criterion of yield per acre normal for food crops in tropical Asia. Fortunately, attention to plant breeding and scientific management have made possible greatly increased yields in recent years. New high-yielding strains produce 1500 to 2000 pounds per acre compared with the 500 pounds normal for older rubber. Extensive replanting with high yielding rubber has been carried out in Malaya with government assistance for both estates and smallholdings. Smallholders are subsidised to the extent of two-thirds of the cost of replanting, and the government makes clones and seedlings from its nurseries cheaply available. The cost of the scheme is met partly by a cess on exports. Over half of the total area in rubber, including a quarter of the smallholdings, is now planted with high-yielding strains. The completion of replanting should be achieved in less than 25 years.

Not all former rubber land is, however, being replanted in this way. To reduce the impact of low prices, many estates are diversifying their production to some extent, the oil palm being an alternative currently in favour in Malaya.

The Future of the Plantation System

With the rapid decline in colonial administration and corresponding freedom of choice—subject to economic pressures—of the indigenous population, the plantation system must necessarily face major adjustments. Malaya again provides a good illustration. Since independence and throughout the period including the establishment of the Federation of Malaysia, the country has been governed by a moderate coalition disposed to favour the continuation of the British connection. This government has guaranteed the integrity of the foreign-based companies and their freedom to repatriate both dividends and capital. The policy of future governments could, however, change. There is inevitably much local feeling against foreign companies, which is not met by present taxation of company profits or even by dues on exports. In addition, in south-east Asia, the persistence of civil wars, armed 'confrontations' and guerrilla warfare discourages foreign investment, particularly in a commodity, such as rubber, which is faced by competition from a synthetic product not liable to such uncertainties.

Political factors weigh almost wholly against the plantation system. Some of the economic factors which also militate against them are of major importance—high charges on capital, management costs and other overheads such as the cost of roads and social services for the workers. On the other hand, the resources of the larger companies permit economies of scale and rapid application of new methods. Economically, therefore, the plantation has features to recommend it. In land use practices, too, there are points for and against the plantation. In the past, many malpractices have been current, partly through companies trying to introduce into tropical environments procedures which were unsuitable, though successful in temperate latitudes. The introduction of clean cultivation between bushes or trees may be cited, this having led to impoverishment of the soil and increased erosion. Whether such errors have led to long-term damage has depended on how serious the damage became, and how quickly remedial measures were adopted. A fundamental disadvantage derives from the fact that plantations generally are devoted to single crops, or at least the cropping programme is orientated mainly to one crop. The dangers of soil exhaustion linked with monoculture are therefore endemic. On the other hand, reputable companies aim to stay in business and to expand, and this they cannot do with impoverished soil and falling yields. Consequently they generally try to keep up soil fertility. This is often partly achieved by growing suitable crops such as nitrogen-fixers as ground cover between the producing plants, which reduces soil erosion at the same time. The larger companies are able to devote resources to research and experiment into the most efficient methods of production. Commercial companies also sponsor independent research organisations, such as the Rubber Research Institute in Malaysia.

Some of the technical and commercial advances made under the plantation system benefit the smallholder, so that gains are diffused through the economy directly as well as through trading needs and monetary expenditure. Nevertheless, it is to be expected that the smallholder will generally be opposed to the plantation economy, which constitutes one of the main political weaknesses of the plantation system in formerly colonial, now independent, countries. The other is that most, if not all, plantation crops can be produced by smallholders, even if not as efficiently as by commercial plantations. Consequently it is hard to avoid the conclusion that the plantation system is likely to decline, and its place be taken increasingly by smallholder production, or by medium-sized estates operated largely without foreign capital. The diffusion of technical aid to developing countries facilitates this process by making the smaller producers more able to take over the role of the foreign companies. Therefore, we may expect to see continued increases, for this as well as other reasons, in the commercialisation of formerly subsistence farmers. That this process has already gone a long way is suggested in Chapter 8, and is a reason for treating subsistence production in this book as a relict form of agriculture, alien to modern forms of production rather than as a form which must be studied before current systems can be understood.

When a plantation is superseded by another form of organisation, it does not follow that this will comprise smaller units acting independently or linked only through voluntary cooperatives. An alternative form is the collective farm, in which the larger unit may be maintained, though under a kind of peasant ownership, and production directed by an elected management. Most systems of collectivisation have come about in the search for greater efficiency in peasant agriculture rather than in the course of the break-up of a plantation system, but it is an obvious alternative when this occurs. Such a form of organisation may have advantages in making available much of the efficiency of the plantation system without its social and economic disadvantages. Some of the disadvantages of large scale collectivisation, however, become evident on studying the history of the U.S.S.R.

CHAPTER 7

State and Collective Farming in the U.S.S.R.

In the forms of agriculture so far considered, the units of organisation, whether farms or plantations, are controlled by the individuals who own or manage them. In the plantation owned by a public limited liability company, ownership and management are separated and the function of shareholding does not, of itself, convey the right to participate in the day-to-day management of the company. Even long-term strategy is beyond the influence of most shareholders whose only opportunity of voicing their beliefs is at an annual meeting. Although subject to some form of government influence through manipulation of prices, subsidies, tariffs and market controls, the farm entrepreneurs in public companies are only a little less free than private farmers to make their own judgments on the disposal of their resources, planning of their production, and the sale of their output. The agricultural landscape is therefore made up of a large number of individual units not subject to overall planning control and this is commonly reflected in heterogeneity of production and physical appearance.

In recent decades, however, a very large proportion of the world's agricultural area has come under the direction of state agencies. The U.S.S.R. and China account for most of this state-controlled farming but it applies also to a greater or lesser extent in other countries with communistic forms of government.[1] True state farms—in which ownership and management are vested directly in the state—account for a comparatively small proportion of land and production in most

[1] A number of examples are given by Dumont (1954).

of these countries, the usual form of organisation being collective.

The term 'collective farm' means a holding which is jointly owned or occupied by a number of persons, and operated by them in accordance with a predetermined plan, binding on all the members of the community. It thus implies a much tighter form of organisation than co-operative farming, in which the individual units remain intact and co-operation is on a voluntary basis, whether this extends to shared working arrangements or only to co-operative purchasing and sales. It differs also from joint ownership or farming of common land in which individual holdings are not fenced, but operation—usually grazing—is on a more or less individual basis.

Collective farms are not confined to communist countries but occur also in Italy, Mexico, India, Pakistan, Japan and other countries. The Israel *kibbutzim* are probably the most-studied collective settlements, other than those in some of the communist countries. The most fundamental difference between them and the collectives of the U.S.S.R. and China is that the *kibbutzim* are voluntary organisations and are free to determine their own programmes without the necessity of fulfilling government quotas for stated products.

The central idea of the collective farm is the introduction of communal ways of living and working, as a means to satisfying an ideological concept. This concept assumes that greater social satisfaction may be derived from group life than from an individualistic family social structure. The degree of family private life permitted varies from one form of collective to another, as does the amount of property owned individually.[1] In voluntary collectivisation, there is usually an element of asceticism in the belief that the pursuit of private acquisition of property is undesirable. In the collectivisation that was forced on Soviet and Chinese peasants a similar ideology was assumed, as throughout the communist dogma, but it could not be said that there was unqualified acceptance of this ideal by the people who were being organised into collectives. A substantial part of the driving force in collectivisation in the U.S.S.R. and China undoubtedly derives from the previous inefficiency of agriculture, necessitating fundamental re-organisation, together with the advantages in communal forms

[1] Digby (1963).

of organisation for the maintenance of the control by the centralised state and the furthering of government policies generally.

In China, the communist reorganisation of agriculture was pushed ahead much more rapidly than it had been in the Soviet Union. In 1958, the Chinese assumed that full communism could be achieved almost immediately through the institution of the commune[1]. They were warned against this assumption by the leaders of the Soviet Union, who drew on the experience of over thirty years of difficulties in the collectivisation of their own peasant societies. Indeed, disagreement over Chinese policies in agriculture was one of the earliest fields in which the current ideological dispute between the U.S.S.R. and China became known to the rest of the world. The Chinese were not persuaded by the Russians and continued their policy of hasty communisation of the rural people. It is claimed by some critics that the communes have in fact failed, in that the peasants have not become reconciled to the new form of organisation and that production on the land has not increased in the expected manner, but it seems to the present writer that insufficient evidence is available at present to make a sound judgment on this important matter[2].

Collectivisation in the U.S.S.R.

In the U.S.S.R., in theory, the land of a collective farm (*kolkhoz*) is national state property but is leased permanently by title deeds to the *artel*, the official name for the association of workers of the farm.[3] All the working capital belongs to the *artel* except for dwellings, gardens, small personal plots and minor implements. Farm policy and production is decided in accordance with the national and regional plans and applied by the farm committee. Production is subject to state taxation, mainly in the form of stated quantities of produce at fixed

[1] The commune is not merely a collective farm but a social unit for the organisation of production, sometimes including industrial production, education and other services. Not all communes, however, have achieved such comprehensive functions and many are virtually collective farms. The situation remains fluid.

[2] For a recent report, see K. M. Buchanan (1965).

[3] The term *artel* was used in mediaeval Russia for co-operative undertakings, fishing, building and industrial, though not agricultural. *Kolkhoz* is an abbreviation of *kollektivnoye khozyaistvo* (collective farm).

prices. As the quantities demanded are absolute and not proportions of production, it is in the interest of the members of the farm to maximize production as they are entitled to sell the balance on the open market. The proceeds are divided among the members according to the amount of labour-days worked. There is thus a kind of piece-work system and bonuses are given to workers who exceed their work quotas. Hired labour is not normally employed.

The collective farm now owns its own machinery, the machine-tractor stations (MTS) which formerly served them having been closed since 1958. The purchase of the machinery by the collectives required considerable outlay of capital and this was in some cases the reason for amalgamation of farms. The possession of their own machinery by the farms has eliminated the difficulties that had arisen from control of equipment in other hands, including the meeting of dates on which the machines were required by individual farms. The training of farm personnel over the years had eliminated the need for the MTS on technical grounds, but Repair and Technical Stations were set up to assist in maintenance, at least for a transitional period.

The elimination of the MTS also meant the end of payments of substantial portions of produce which had to be made by the farms to the MTS for their services. At the same time further reforms raised the prices paid by the state for the compulsory deliveries of produce, which had formerly been artificially low to keep down the cost of living in the towns.

The members of the collective farms retain their personal plots which have been permitted since the early days of collectivisation. At times efforts have been made to reduce them, and it has been said that the long-term aim is so to improve the output of the collective farms and the income of the farmer that the personal plot will become unwanted. However, it continues to have lavished on it the maximum amount of attention and fertiliser that the farmer and his family can manage. This personal acre, or even half-acre, has in the past carried the family through very difficult times with intensive production of potatoes, vegetables and fruit for home consumption, and maize and roots for the personally-owned cattle, pigs and poultry.

It was calculated that in 1960 almost half the meat and milk and nearly all the eggs produced in the Soviet Union came from the personal plots of collective and other workers which accounted for only about 6 per cent. of the land in cultivation. Previously the proportions had been higher but the decrease has continued since 1960 as improvement has been effected in the public sector of the agricultural economy. Yields from the personal plots continue to be much higher than from the same unit area of the collective land, but it must be remembered that the crops sown in them are those which respond to intensive cultivation, and the vegetable garden of a commercial farm will also normally yield more highly than the broad acres in mechanised cultivation. Of the produce of the personal plots comparatively little is sold on the open market—in 1959, 19 per cent. of the crops and 23 per cent. of the livestock products, compared with 59 per cent. of the crops and 72 per cent. of the livestock products of the public sector.[1]

There has been an overall trend towards larger units since the beginning of collectivisation in 1928. The 25 million or so peasant holdings of 1928 which had averaged about 4 hectares in size had become by 1940, 240,000 collectives. By 1950 amalgamations had halved the number of units to 123,700 and further amalgamations, together with conversion to state farms, reduced the number of collectives to less than one-third of this number by 1963, viz. 39,500. The collectives then averaged over 3000 hectares of arable land and 411 households.[2] The enlarged collectives of the present day offer more scope for efficient cultivation of more diversified crops with maximum mechanisation and electrification. In 1958, only about half of the collective farms were electrified, but by 1963 the number using electricity had risen to 88 per cent.

The traditional settlement pattern is one of nucleated form, with the individual houses grouped near but separated from the communal buildings of the *kolkhoz*—the farm buildings as well as the general store, school and community hall. These vary in pattern, design and materials of construction as well as

[1] Newth (1961), 170. A number of Newth's tables of data are quoted by Lydolph (1964), 291–293.

[2] All statistics for 1959–63 are from *Narodnoye khozyaistvo S.S.S.R. v 1963 godu* (1965).

in location on valley bottom, interfluve or mountain slope, according to region.[1] The new buildings, as commonly in other parts of the world, show less regional variation, but respond to the economies of building in local materials and siting in accordance with natural advantages. Some of the enlarged collectives have been given new centralised villages in accordance with the 'agrogorod' concept.[2]

State Farms

The state farms are owned and operated by government agencies and have been generally larger and better endowed with equipment and capital than the collectives, and it has been easier to make them efficient. State farms include experimental and special farms but most are essentially devoted to normal production, the name *sovkhoz* being applied to this type of farm.

The average *sovkhoz* is probably hardly a more valuable concept than the average farm in other countries, but a few average figures for 1963 do show the great size of these farms: thus, average labour force, 775; average cropped area, 9800 hectares. The average grain *sovkhoz* had three times this area of cropland—27,700 hectares. On this type of *sovkhoz* the livestock averaged, cattle 3551; pigs, 1071; sheep and goats, 5509. To quote only one more comparison, the sheep *sovkhoz* averaged nearly 33,000 head of sheep and goats on a total area of over 132,000 hectares.

In spite of amalgamation of collectives to form larger units, presumably in search of greater efficiency, many have been made into state farms. The regional distribution of lands as between *kolkhoz* and *sovkhoz* as it was a few years ago is shown in Figure 10. Since the data for this map was compiled, the state farms have grown still more and in 1963 accounted for an area of agricultural land exceeding that of the collectives. In terms of cultivated area, in 1963 the state farms nearly equalled the collectives, compared with one-sixth ten years earlier.

A rise in importance of the state farms in grain production

[1] A very useful summary is given by Pierre George (1962), 297–301.

[2] N. S. Kruschchev, in 1950 when Chairman of the Council of Ministers in the Ukraine, advanced the idea of 'agro-cities' in which *kolkhozniki* would live centrally but the idea was not then adopted.

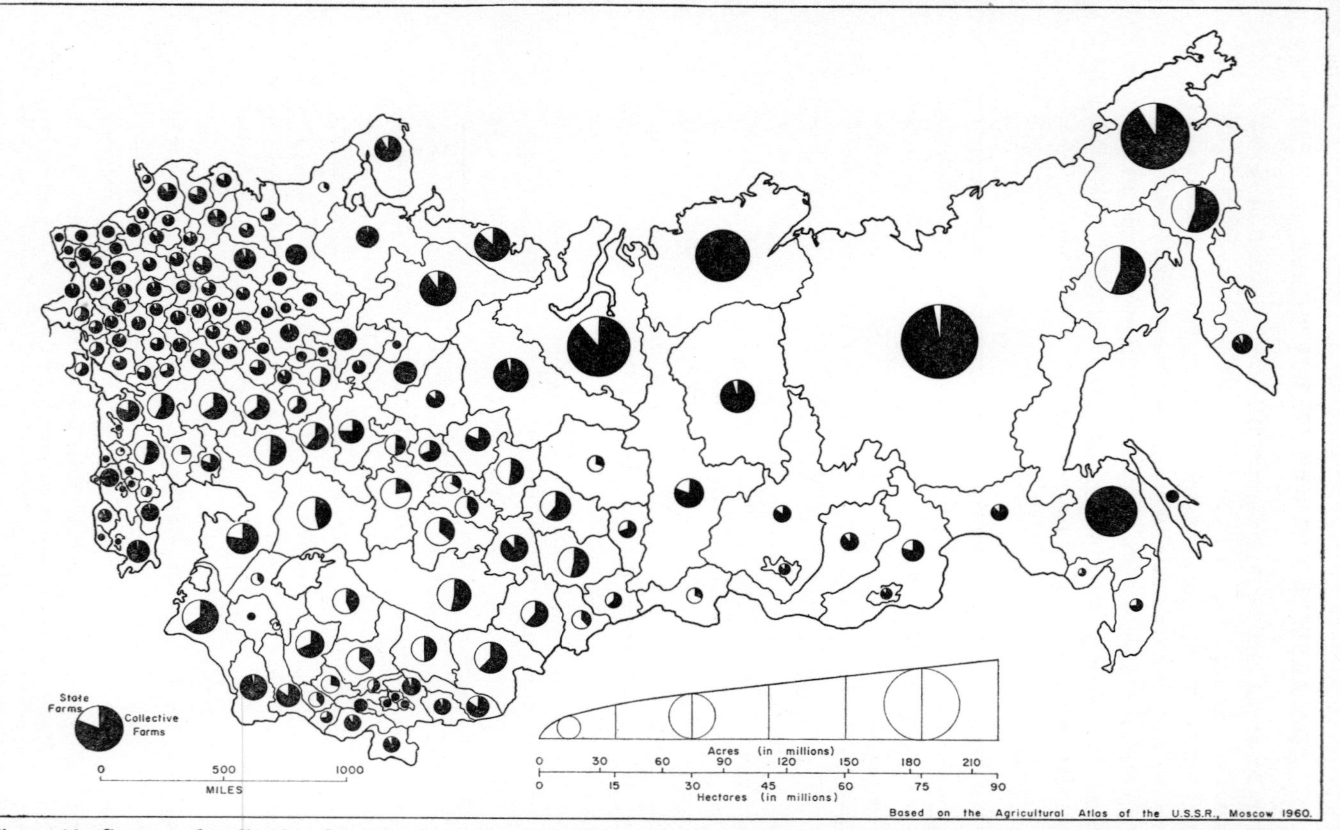

Figure 10. State and collective farm lands in the U.S.S.R. Note the higher proportion of state farms in the areas of recent development; western Siberia, central Asia and northern regions. Since the date of the data on which this map is based the

from 11 to 41 per cent. between 1950 and 1963 reflects the extension of cultivation in the 'virgin lands' of west Siberia and north Kazakhstan and for pioneering cultivation in other areas. The increase in their role in this period in vegetable production is noteworthy, from 21 to 53 per cent. The Moscow area in particular has benefitted by the increased vegetable production resulting from the entry of the state farms in this field.

These are fields of production in which the state farms have been given parts to play larger in each succeeding year, and this applies also in livestock rearing. The absolute numbers of cattle on the collectives have been increased, in spite of the reduction in the area farmed collectively, but the collectives account for fewer pigs, sheep and goats than five years earlier. Numbers of livestock on personal plots do not show any marked changes, except for a sharp decrease in goats and a more than corresponding increase in pigs, a move which suggests better husbandry.

In terms of livestock products, the contribution of the state farms rose from 21 per cent. in 1950 to 37 per cent. in 1963. In milk and wool the increase in the period was from 15 per cent. to nearly 40 per cent., and in eggs it was from 7 per cent. to 30 per cent.

The *sovkhozi* are the principal means of extending the frontiers of cultivation and of promoting advanced methods of agriculture. In the last few years they have been increasingly used to develop livestock husbandry. In the Baltic provinces, for example, the emphasis has been on dairying. Altogether in 1963 in the Soviet Union, 3,483 *sovkhozi* were devoted principally to dairying and beef production, 858 mainly to sheep, 560 to pigs compared with 1162 to grain—mostly in Kazakhstan and west Siberia—1350 to fruit and vegetables and the remainder to sugar beet, cotton, etc. Altogether they numbered over 9000 and covered 283 million hectares (nearly 700 million acres) of agricultural land.

In areas of sparse settlement, such as the mountain regions of the Far East, where collectivisation is impracticable, a small number of individual farms remain as virtually private holdings. In terms of cropped area, such farms were reduced from nearly two million hectares in 1950 to 14,000 hectares in 1959 (from 1·30 to 0·01 per cent. of the cultivated land of the U.S.S.R.).

Their continued attenuation emphasizes the thoroughness of the transition in farm organisation in the Soviet Union.

Historical Perspective

In order to assess the achievements of Soviet reorganisation of agriculture, it is necessary to consider the antecedents of the present system, the most important elements being the late survival of serfdom, continued exploitation of the peasantry, land hunger and the absence of a revolution in agrarian methods comparable with that which took place in western Europe before the twentieth century.

In mediaeval Russia there were many categories of more or less enslaved peasants. In the sixteenth and seventeenth centuries, when in England the conditions which produced the agrarian and industrial revolutions were being created, in Russia, the landowners were consolidating their control over the peasantry. There was never any clear formulation of serfdom or any code setting out the rights and obligations of masters and serfs. Ancient customs, new economic pressures and increasing control of the land by the tsars through the aristocracy facilitated the binding of the peasants to their masters. Peasant migration was a feature of the sixteenth century, which was marked by internal struggles, destruction of villages and laying waste of land, especially in the central parts of Muscovy. The rights of free peasants to leave landowners provided that their dues had been met was increasingly challenged and the landowners demanded increased rights to pursue runaways. New land grants to the middle classes and military gentry who had helped found the Romanov dynasty in 1613 were followed by the code of Tsar Alexis in 1649. This abolished time limits which had previously limited the recovery of runaways. During this period of shortage of agricultural labour, slaves, who had previously been used mainly for domestic and military purposes, were put to work more often on the land. After 1680 taxes were levied on these slaves, as on the peasantry, so that the tsars had less reason to oppose the increase in slavery.

Associated with the practice of serfdom was the commune, or *mir*, which at the emancipation of the serfs (1861) became a legal economic unit. The origins of the commune are lost in pre-history, but it seems clear that widespread collective arrangements had evolved in peasant communities for regulating allocation of land, land utilisation, admission of newcomers to the group and other local affairs. The commune was used by the central government to assist in the calculation and collection of taxes.

B. H. Sumner gives the following description of the commune in the nineteenth century:

> At the time of the emancipation most of the Russian peasantry were grouped in communes, of varying sizes, composed sometimes of one village, sometimes of parts of one village, sometimes of groups of scattered settlements. The most essential usual features of the commune from the agricultural and economic standpoint were: (i) that its membership was hereditary, though newcomers could be admitted; (ii) that its members worked land by families, but (except in a minority of communes where holdings were hereditary) periodically redistributed their strip holdings scattered in the (usually three-course) open fields, in accordance with either working strength, or taxation and other obligations, or the number of 'eaters' in each family; (iii) that the members of the commune regulated in common the use of meadows, pasture, fisheries, woods, etc., and the disposal of any communal land not already utilised and the acquisition of new land or working rights.[1]

When at last the emancipation of the serfs came in 1861, in response to economic and social pressures from industrialists and the more progressive landowners who wanted a more efficient and more progressive labour force, as well as from the largely inarticulate body of the peasants themselves, the reorganisation was based on the *mir*. Although the freed serfs had to pay for their holdings to the state, mainly by redemption annuities for 49 years, to repay the compensation given to the landowners, the title to the land was vested not in the individual but in the *mir*. This, together with the high rates of the annuities, the large areas the landowners were allowed to retain and the grazing and forest rights that were given to the

[1] Sumner (1961), 136.

landowners, resulted in the peasants feeling that they had again been cheated. Emancipation was therefore followed by further unrest and rioting, which was quickly suppressed in the usual manner developed by the tsars and their gentry.

The commune retained its old functions and added new ones, including collection of the redemption annuities. It stood between the peasant and the state and, although it represented a measure of peasant self-government, it was the object of much of the peasant's dissatisfaction because it administered so much that was unpopular. Meanwhile, the lands worked by the peasants remained for the most part in the three-field system and the strip holdings were generally still redistributed at intervals. In the areas where population pressure was highest, in the central black-earth and middle Volga provinces in particular, the peasants found themselves with far too little land. Here and in other regions, the more fortunate—and the more commercially-minded—were able to buy out their less fortunate neighbours and enlarge their holdings. Thus arose the class of *kulaks*, later the object of the hatred of the communists. The population grew more rapidly and the pressure on the land became more intense. The emancipation had in fact done little to improve the lot of the peasants. They even still had to have a passport (as they had since the time of Peter the Great, and now granted at the discretion of the commune) before they could move about. The commune, because of the manner of levying the poll-tax and other taxes, had reason to try to prevent men leaving it.

Except in Siberia, in which agricultural serfdom had not developed, and the newly colonised lands in the European and Asiatic south, the remnants of serfdom were still clear twenty years after the emancipation edict. Continued unrest culminated in 1905 in widespread riots and arson. Thus, peasant unrest was contemporaneous with, though not integrated with, the revolts in St. Petersburg and Moscow which were the main expression of the Revolution of 1905. This secured the 'October Manifesto' including the establishment of the Duma, a parliament which, though it had little power, signified the weakening of tsarist autocracy. But the peasant riots continued in 1906. Severe repression by the military and the execution of some 4000 persons was followed, belatedly as always in tsarist Russia, by some measures of agrarian reform.

The 1906 reforms were designed to enable the scattered strip holdings to be consolidated into more efficient farm units. The hitherto ineffective Peasants' Land Bank, set up in 1883, was improved to enable peasants to rent additional non-peasant land. The control of the peasant by the commune was reduced by the abolition of communal responsibility for taxation. It was made easier for peasants to leave the commune and to migrate to the new lands in Siberia and the south.

During the next ten years considerable progress was made in the modernisation of agriculture. More machinery and fertilisers helped the expansion of the cropped acreage. After the crop failures and famines of 1905–7 there were a number of good crop years. Even so, in 1917, the majority of the peasants were still living in a deplorable state of poverty, many of them bound to landlords, no longer as serfs but by debt. The situation was still particularly acute in the central black-earth and middle Volga provinces, where population pressure was heaviest. The majority of peasants in European Russia were still tied to the communes, their land in scattered strips in the open fields. Only about a tenth of the peasant households had been actually resettled on the new consolidated holdings. The success of the more prosperous peasants, the *kulaks*, in buying up holdings vacated by peasants leaving the communes, and in renting land from the gentry, did nothing to assuage the land hunger and dissatisfaction of the majority. The war, with its inevitable drain of manpower from the countryside as well as the towns, and the appalling casualities—40 per cent. of the Allied death roll was attributed to Russia—did not divert the peasants from the age-old conviction that the gentry had stolen their land, and the traditional faith in the tsar as the little father who would protect them from their immediate superiors had worn a little thin.

Agrarian Reform in the Revolution

In the deliberations of the various organizations that worked towards revolution in the latter part of the nineteenth century and until its achievement in 1917, the question of agrarian reform was, of course, well to the fore. It was intimately bound up with the assessment of the part that could be expected of the peasants in a large scale uprising. Plekhanov, the first Russian exponent of Marxism, discarded the romantic view of the *mir* or commune as evidence of the peasants' adherence to a communal way of life, stressing the need to focus revolutionary organisation on the industrial proletariat. This class was growing rapidly and was being exploited mercilessly in the factories and mines. Lenin, however, while accepting the role of the industrial workers as fundamental, did not reject the peasantry as uniformly conservative and counter-revolutionary. His first period of exile, for participating in student demonstrations, was to a rural district and his first writings were on the situation of the peasants.

After the split of the Russian Social Democratic movement into Bolshevik (majority) and Menshevik (minority) wings in 1903, Lenin pursued the thesis of joint industrial and rural proletariat action. Their combined congress of 1906 adopted the Menshevik programme of agrarian reform, with land to be held by the *zemstvo*, or district council, and leased to the peasants, but the Bolsheviks favoured collective cultivation with state aid. As already noted, the fortunes of the peasantry had improved only marginally by 1917 and when, eventually, military defeat and food shortages led to revolution in St. Petersburg in March, the provisional government that took office had still to face the need for urgent agrarian reform, as well as labour legislation for the industrial workers, and the continued prosecution of the war.

Side by side with the provisional government formed by the Duma, and competing with its authority, Soviets or councils of workers and soldiers were formed and similar groups were later formed in the rural areas. Thus, there were already in being bodies through which orders could be passed to the countryside when the Bolshevik *coup* of October 25 (November 7 new calendar) gave them control. One of the first two decrees provided for termination of private ownership of land and its immediate distribution to the peasants and workers, the other concerning the ending of the war. In fact, the peasants had already begun to seize land and were not to be easily won over to the Bolshevik cause. Their retention of food supplies worsened the supply situation in the towns and drew upon them the force of the Red Army and the secret police, re-created by the Bolsheviks. Thus the first days of the Soviet government did not augur well for relations between the new authorities and the peasants. But worse was to follow with the development of the 'white' counter-revolutionary movement and the intervention of the Allies in support. For three years armed struggle raged from the Baltic to the Bering Straits. The French organised the particularly bitter fighting in the Ukraine, Czech troops held the Trans-Siberian Railway, thousands of Japanese troops were poured into the Far East and British, American, Polish, Greek, Bulgarian and other regular and irregular forces took part. The peasantry gave up the hopeless struggle to cultivate crops which were likely to be forcibly requisitioned if they were not destroyed in the fields. Near-famine conditions prevailed in many rural areas as well as in the towns. By the winter of 1921–22 reserves had been used up and the famine of that time was estimated to have caused the death of some five million people, and many more would have died but for food distributed under international aid arrangements.

Shortly before this deterioration, Lenin in his New Economic Policy had accepted the need for compromise with capitalist interests which could revive the economy. In the following years, when the peasants were allowed considerable freedom in their sales of produce, they took the opportunity of getting high prices and the *kulak* class recovered and prospered. Meanwhile Lenin died and the struggle for power within the Communist party intensified, resulting in the destruction of all opposition by Stalin. In December 1927 the Fifteenth Party Congress sanctioned his programme for forced industrialisation and agrarian revolution, based on collectivisation.

Progress in Collectivisation

The five-year plan, accepted in 1928, required collectivisation of up to one-fifth of the farms by 1933. It was stated that the *kulaks* had withheld grain deliveries, thus re-creating conditions of food shortage, and the raids on *kulak* farms, requisitions and arrests which began in 1928 were intensified. In the next two years this class, estimated at 1½ to 3 million men, was ruthlessly destroyed, and many of the much larger group of middle-class peasants were also arrested and deported to labour camps. In their resistance the peasants hid or burnt crops, slaughtered livestock and wrecked machinery. Stalin himself saw the folly of this brutal attack and ordered an end to force, but not until 1930, by which time the damage was done to the cause of collectivisation and the economy further weakened. Later it was revealed that between 1929 and 1933 livestock numbers fell by some 30 million cattle, nearly 100 million sheep and goats and 17 or 18 million horses. Stock raising had always been less well managed in Russia than crop cultivation and it was now further weakened. Even nomadic and semi-nomadic Kazakhs reduced their stock.

In spite of the slowing down of the programme, by the end of the first five-year plan in 1933 about 60 per cent. of all holdings had been collectivised as compared with the 20 per cent. planned before the intensification of the drive.

The original *kolkhoz* was formed by the amalgamation of an average of about 75 peasant holdings administered by a chairman and his assistants. The workers were required to devote 100 to 150 days to the co-operative enterprise. The state at that time claimed all produce over the allowances for the subsistence of the collective.

An essential prerequisite for the successful cultivation of the new large farms was mechanisation. The urgency was increased by the losses in horses. Only 7000 tractors were in use at the beginning of the drive but in 1929 alone 30,000 were manufactured. The machine-tractor stations (MTS) were introduced to act as pools for machines, operators and mechanics and by 1936 there were almost 5000 of them. This relieved the *kolkhoz* management, already overburdened with the task of training the work force, of the problems connected directly with mechanisation.

Between 1931 and 1933 famine struck again, partly because of the resistance of the peasants to the collectivisation. Among the worst-hit regions were the most fertile—the black-earth lands of the middle Volga, Ukraine and the northern Caucasus regions. It is said that between ten and eleven millions fell victim.[1] In 1933 Stalin relaxed his policy further and allowed grain to be withdrawn from stores and purchased abroad. Concessions were made to the *kolkhoz* labourer, most important being the allocation of a small plot of land which he could

[1] Rauch (1957), 222.

cultivate for his own purposes. He was also now allowed to keep his own cow, a few sheep and goats and some poultry, and receive a cash share in the proceeds of the sales of the *kolkhoz*. Stalin himself announced the aim as being to make the *kolkhoz* peasants wealthy.

The *kolkhoz* was now favoured at the expense of the *sovkhoz* and many of these great farms which had also been created during the preceding years were broken up and the land distributed to collective farms. Others were retained as research, training and stud farms. As already noted, this trend has since been again reversed, the *sovkhoz* being now an important institution in the development of Soviet agriculture.

By 1940, as already noted, the 25 million or so peasant holdings of 1928 which had averaged about 10 acres had become about 240,000 collective farms, averaging about 1500 acres in size. On these lived about 75 million people with perhaps another million serving on the machine-tractor stations. By this time the collective had been able to demonstrate some advantages in working the land, especially in the more difficult areas. In arid and semi-arid conditions sowing could be completed quickly, when conditions were most satisfactory, irrigation facilities could be used more efficiently and new cultivation could be planned to best advantage. In addition, economy of labour released large numbers of workers needed in the towns and on construction projects.

During the war, which raged on Russian territory from 1941 to 1945 and caused loss of life amounting to some 20 million people and the destruction of 25 million homes, Soviet agriculture suffered a further immense setback. The 'scorched earth' policy which denied the advancing Nazi troops food, shelter and machinery meant incredible sacrifices for the long-suffering peasants. After the war a renewed drive had to be made to modernise production. In 1951 it was claimed that almost all ploughs were mechanically operated and 60 per cent. of the harvesting was by machine.

Between 1949 and 1951 an experiment was initiated with enlarged collectives, formed by the grouping of three to five existing collectives. The first formed was near Cherkassy in the Ukraine, and by the end of 1950 the 240,000 or so collective farms had been combined into half this number. Consolidation of collectives into fewer farms has continued together with conversion into state farms as recorded above.

The Problem of Productivity

Soviet agriculture under collectivisation has not come up to expectations. Official figures have consistently revealed that not only has agricultural productivity failed to rise proportionately with industrial productivity, but that absolute increases in output have been relatively small. Yields remain in general far below those of the United States of America, western Europe and other advanced economies. Compared with the U.S.A. it has been calculated that in 1960 Soviet average yields were less than 50 per cent. of the American average for maize, wheat, sugar beet and potatoes, and less than 66 per cent. for rye, oats, barley, and tobacco.[1] In livestock products the differences may well be greater. Exhortations to the farmers from the Soviet leadership are constant while successive American governments advise ways of limiting production. (To what extent this comparison, in a world of hunger, indicts the American system as well as the Soviet must not detain us here, but ought not to be ignored.)

According to the general index of agricultural production[2] there was a continued rise in output of 2 per cent. per annum from 1960 to 1962, though this was a lower rate than that of the preceding years. In 1962 the index reached its highest level, 233 (crop index 229, livestock production index, 235). Then in 1963 there was a collapse to the pre-1960 level. It is well known that prolonged bad weather was mainly responsible for this setback, but it has also been made abundantly clear by the Soviet leaders that they were not satisfied with progress prior to that setback.

Grain deliveries in 1963 were down on the previous year by over 20 per cent. and were 12 per cent. below the five-year average, accounting for a major part of the fall in the general index. Fewer potatoes also were available on the markets than in preceding years though there was some recovery from 1962. Vegetable sales in 1963 were slightly down compared with 1962, but better than earlier years. Milk and eggs showed

[1] Bell (1961), quoted by Lydolph (1964), tables, Ch. 14.

[2] *Narodnoye khozyaistvo S.S.S.R v 1963 godu* (1965), 227.

a similar picture—lower than 1962 but better than any earlier year. Wool showed a slight gain, and meat a more distinct advance, but there may have been some additional slaughter of cattle owing to shortage of fodder. In industrial crops, cotton did well, but sugar beet was down. In relation to the growth of population the position was obviously far from reassuring.

It is, of course, generally recognised that physical conditions in the Soviet Union are far inferior for agriculture generally to most of the U.S.A. or western Europe. Even in the 10 per cent. or so of the U.S.S.R. which is within the limits set to cultivation by cold, drought and relief, the more humid areas have long winters and the warmer areas are mostly dry. In such circumstances yields can never compare with those in more favourable conditions in western Europe and the U.S.A. under similar systems of cultivation. Where Soviet agriculture seems to have failed relatively is in the failure of the most fertile regions to produce as highly as might be expected, particularly with comparatively high inputs of labour.

Compared with five years earlier, however, the position does not look quite so bad, except in grain, sugar beet and potatoes. Table 8 compares the averages of 1962 and 1963 with those for 1958 and 1959. It is at once apparent that major advances have been achieved in livestock husbandry, long regarded as the greatest weakness in Russian agriculture. This is supported

TABLE 8

U.S.S.R.: PRODUCTION AVERAGES 1958/9 AND 1962/3

		1958/9	*1962/3*	*Per cent. change*
Grain	million tons	57·8	55·25	− 4·3
Cotton	,, ,,	4·49	4·75	+ 5·8
Sugar beet	,, ,,	46·2	42·7	− 8·0
Potatoes	,, ,,	13·9	12·1	−12·9
Vegetables	,, ,,	7·2	8·6	+19·5
Meat	,, ,,	5·3	7·0	+32·0
Milk, etc.	,, ,,	26·8	31·9	+19·0
Eggs	000 million	8·65	12·05	+39·3
Wool	000 tons	294·0	338·0	+14·9

Source: Narodnoye khozyaistvo SSSR v 1963 *godu, statistichesky ezhegodnik,* Moscow, 1965.

by individual advances, such as in yield of milk per cow, which for the whole of the U.S.S.R. is recorded as averaging 1584 kg. in 1963 compared with 1137 in 1950, an increase of 39·3 per cent. In the collective farms there has been an even larger percentage increase but not sufficient to overtake the state farms which still claim the higher average milk yields in all regions except Kazakhstan. The average wool clip has increased in the same period from 2·2 kg. to 2·7 kg., approximately 23 per cent.

What is not always recognised by critics of the Soviet system or even, perhaps, by the Soviet authorities themselves, is the dead-weight of the past that hangs heavily over the land to this day. It is for this reason that special emphasis has here been given to the historical antecedents of the present system. The age-old suffering of the Russian peasant, so well revealed by the nineteenth century Russian writers of the realist school, is seen to have continued into the period between the wars of the present century, the feeling of being cheated of the land is seen as a repeated theme of peasant reaction to reforms. Many of the *kolkhozniki* of today are of the generation that suffered as children under the old regime but experienced the worst years of the new when they would feel it most as young farmers and parents. They would not be the most promising people to weld into a new agrarian society.

Then, too, the U.S.S.R. has suffered from war and famine on a scale which is quite horrific. Comparison with the U.S.A. is rendered meaningless by the destruction that occurred in the second World War, which did not physically touch America. It took until well into the 1950s to effect recovery from the war and build up equipment and livestock numbers to pre-war levels. Since then, improvement has been fairly steady in most aspects of the agricultural economy.

As in other countries and under contrasting economic systems the task of raising agricultural productivity is largely that of upgrading the poor units. In 1964, in announcing details of a general pension scheme for collective farm workers with a minimum rate but graded according to past earnings, Mr. Kruschev[1] gave comparative figures for two collective

[1] N. S. Krushchev's report at the U.S.S.R. Supreme Soviet Session on July 13, 1964.

farms in the Odessa region with similar soil and climatic conditions, which are worthy of reproduction, both for illustration of the difference in productivity, and for the examples they provide of apparently typical collective farms, albeit of good and poor production achievements.

	The 21st Congress Collective Farm Centners (100 kg.)	*Suvorov Collective Farm Centners (100 kg.)*
Production of grain per hectare of ploughland	19·3	14·6
Production from livestock per 100 hectares		
Meat (slaughter weight)	98·5	25·0
Milk	480	168
Livestock per 100 hectares		
Cattle	60	36
of which, cows	23	14
Money income per 100 hectares	39,800 roubles	8100 roubles
Money income per able-bodied member in 1963	1822 roubles	506 roubles

Experiment and adjustment continues on the social as well as the technical plane. The private plot of the collective farmer is an instance. In 1955 steps were taken to reduce its importance by limiting its size and the number of livestock that could be kept privately. Late in 1964 these restrictions were declared to be 'unjustifiable' and were lifted. Private plots and livestock are now again permitted to be owned not only by members of collective farms, but by single, aged and disabled members of collectives reorganised into state farms, and by industrial workers.[1] Owners are to be helped in the acquisition of livestock and in the storing of fodder. Allocation of land for pastures for personal livestock has also been encouraged.

A massive investment programme has been announced, to give agriculture in the next five years almost as much investment as in all the years since the war. Emphasis is placed on long-term grants for capital construction, mechanisation and increase in provision of fertilisers. In mechanisation, much

[1] Information Bulletin published by U.S.S.R. Legation, Wellington, 1st December, 1964.

progress has been made with, for example, an increase of nearly 50 per cent. in the number of tractors between 1958 and 1963 but there is still plenty of scope for further improvement, and the plan envisaged an increase of 240,000, about 15 per cent., in 1965 alone. The increase in mineral fertiliser deliveries promised was no less than 30 per cent., after also having increased by 50 per cent. between 1958 and 1963. That the proposed investment is so great is, of course, a commentary on the relative backwardness of Soviet agriculture at present.

Land improvement was to take one-eighth of the year's investment. Apart from continued extension of irrigation in central Asia, which accounts for over half of the irrigated area in the U.S.S.R., the main emphasis will be on drainage in the Baltic Republics, Byelorussia, in the Ukrainian Polesye, and in parts of the Russian Federation. Better distribution of water to the fields and improvement of roads are important requirements in all areas.

At the same time, the evaluation of the land resources is being stepped up. Following their early lead in soil science, the Russians have been working on a major pedalogical survey and a general report has been translated.[1] The geographers are contributing in the work of land classification and have published some interesting articles on methods of approach. Two contributions in this field have been translated and published in English. One stressed the use of economic criteria in appraising state farms in the virgin lands,[2] the other a general methodology for physical and economic classification of agricultural lands[3] outlined in Chapter 10.

It looks as though the agricultural industry of the Soviet Union is at last to receive the financial and scientific support which is needed to put crop and livestock husbandry on a sound basis throughout the Union. The profit motive is to be exploited more, and, in conformity with this, greater freedom is to be allowed to both management and workers on the farms. In 1966 guaranteed monthly payments became part of

[1] *Soil-geographical zoning of the U.S.S.R.* Academy of Sciences of the U.S.S.R., Moscow, 1962, translated by Israel Program for Scientific Translations, Jerusalem, 1963.

[2] Kuznetsov (1963).

[3] Zvorykin (1963).

the system of remuneration on the collectives, with cash payments related to work done.

The ownership and operation of agricultural land in the U.S.S.R. is, however, probably still far from becoming stable. The problem of low productivity has stimulated amalgamation into ever-larger units, but not everyone accepts this as being the best course. Recently, the agronomist V. Zhulin has suggested a radical revision of policy and return to smaller units.[1] His suggestions do not include complete abandonment of the collective principle, but rather division of the big collectives into 'links' worked by half-a-dozen or so persons who would have full ownership of the land and would be wholly responsible for its cultivation. It is impossible to guess whether this proposal will be acceptable to the Soviet government but Zhulin states that such holdings are already being tried experimentally in the 'virgin lands'.

The Soviet agricultural worker may perhaps receive the choice of working in one of the large state farms for a wage or on one of the small collectives. As one of a small partnership he might feel that at least he has gained the ownership of the land for which the Russian peasantry struggled for centuries and which he has not found in the impersonal large collective.

[1] In *Komsomolskaya Pravda*, reported by United Press International, Moscow, August 8th, 1965.

CHAPTER 8

Subsistence Agriculture

It is customary in textbooks of economic geography to deal with subsistence economies before commercial agriculture, either because they arose first or because they represent simpler forms of production. In this study, however, subsistence agriculture is relegated because it represents today a relict form of economic organisation.

As with the term 'peasant', considered in Chapter 2, and indeed with all terms that we use, it is desirable that we should consider what we mean by 'subsistence agriculture'. It might be argued that true subsistence agriculture could be said to occur only where there is no exterior trade. Just as, however, a farmer producing essentially for the commercial market will use a little of his output in his home, any practical interpretation of subsistence agriculture must allow of at least some trade. At the simplest level, this may merely be trade by barter between nearby communities occupying areas of somewhat different physical conditions, and so having an incentive to exchange surplus goods. In these middle decades of the twentieth century, however, it may be said that commerce has affected most societies and few do not produce some article for sale outside the immediate locality, using the proceeds to purchase at least a small range of manufactured goods and perhaps some foodstuffs to supplement the local produce. How then shall we decide when to refer to an agricultural economy as 'subsistence'?

Whittlesey regarded intention as critical:

> No farming region lives wholly without exchange of surplus, but the percentage of goods exchanged in the total produced ranges from almost nothing to very nearly everything. The critical difference is the intention of the farmer. If he grows his crops or raises his animals with the

object of selling, he is a commercial farmer; if he merely sells what he happens to have left over, or what he is forced to part with by emergencies, he is a subsistence farmer.[1]

This attempt at a definition is unsatisfactory because large numbers of producers cater deliberately for both the subsistence needs of their own families and for a commercial market, i.e. the division of intention is not as simple as Whittlesey visualised. Furthermore, the divisions have almost certainly become more blurred since Whittlesey wrote, over a quarter of a century ago, during which time the social and economic emergence of the peoples of Asia and Africa has been a world issue. People engaged in all types of farming have been affected by the developments of transport and other facilities for trade which have occurred throughout the world. An example is the Chimbu people of the central ranges of New Guinea, whose society and agriculture have been effectively studied by a geographer and an anthropologist working together.[2] The Chimbu became known to the outside world only in 1933 and for centuries their only link with lowland New Guinea had been tenuous routes by which food crops, traditional feather and shell valuables and, latterly, worn steel knives and axes were traded. Since the arrival of the Europeans, and on a much larger scale since about 1950, money has become important. Small sales of foodstuffs to Europeans provided the main income until about 1959 but sales of coffee have increased rapidly. Sawn timber has become another source of cash. Outlets for expenditure are few and much is still spent on acquiring traditional valuables but between 1958 and 1960 there was a notable increase in the purchase of clothes. The few leading men, with large coffee holdings, have purchased coffee-hulling machines and building materials and have begun to employ labour.[3] The pace of change is clearly rapid.

More thoroughly revolutionary in their impact upon traditional methods and objectives of agriculture, as well as politically, are the great changes resulting from the extension of communism. When Whittlesey wrote, rural Russia was in

[1] Whittlesey (1936), 211.
[2] Brookfield and Brown (1963).
[3] Brookfield and Brown (1963), 66–68.

ferment with the aftermath of the first collectivisation programme and to the rest of the world the situation was far from clear. Now, virtually all of the peasants of the U.S.S.R. have been brought into the state economic system. Still more significant, however, is the social revolution in China. It may well be that for many years to come the Chinese farmer will be producing mainly for his own family's consumption, but only as part of the efforts of the production brigade and commune. The state has a claim on this produce and aims to derive larger surpluses from every unit to improve the food supplies of the non-agricultural areas and to stimulate the whole economy.

These great changes have reduced to a fraction the former large percentage of the world's population whose farming was based on the intention to provide for their own subsistence and sell only whatever they might 'happen' to have surplus.

In seeking a definition of subsistence agriculture, it seems more profitable to have regard to actual disposal of crops rather than to intention, and to consider cash sales relative to subsistence consumption, taking one year with another.

A working definition, then, might be: 'a subsistence farmer is one whose output is consumed almost entirely in his own home, not more than a small proportion being regularly offered for sale.'

At once another question must be posed—what is the critical proportion that may be offered for sale without the status of the farmer being considered to change? Further, it may be objected that whatever arbitrary figure is selected, only rarely will statistics be available to enable the classification to be used with precision. It is, of course, with the regions and economies about which least statistical information is available that we are here concerned.

One possibility might be the restriction of the term 'subsistence farmer' to one whose contribution to commerce is so small as to be barely measurable. To put this in terms of consumption, such a family unit will have very few purchased goods, food or services, but perhaps odd tools, cooking utensils and matches. This rather narrow definition would exclude large numbers of sedentary cultivators, especially those cultivating, as a minor interest, a cash crop such as cotton or rubber for sale to a marketing agency, and the intensive rice growers whose small individual surplus collectively helps to feed the cities and plantation workers of south-east Asia. Pending any more satisfactory term, the latter folk might be referred to as 'quasi-subsistence farmers'. When cash crops become of substantial importance in a holding which is not yet devoted preponderantly to them, the term 'semi-subsistence farming' would seem to be appropriate.

These classes may be compared with those suggested[1] by an administrator concerned with levying taxation in East Africa, namely (*a*) pure subsistence—no cash crops; no tax; no import or export of labour, (*b*) subsistence with taxes—some cash crops grown or employment sought elsewhere mainly for the purpose of paying taxes, e.g. the peoples of Ruanda Urundi, the Karamoju and the Masai. These two groups might both be considered as subdivisions of 'subsistence farmers.' (*c*) Subsistence plus cash crops, where taxes have become a minor element of cash outlay, which might be equated with my quasi-subsistence group, (*d*) subsistence plus cash, suggested with particular regard to men travelling outside their district to seek work, (*e*) agricultural labour working mainly for wages on plantations and (*f*) wage labour in an industrial economy.

The last two classes are not relevant to the immediate question but the 'subsistence plus cash' group may be equated with the mainly sedentary farmers envisaged in the term 'semi-subsistence farming'.

If this case be accepted, there still remains the problem of defining the upper limit of sales that might be included in these classes. The difficulties of relating small cash sales to the produce consumed at home are formidable. The valuation of the domestic consumption in monetary terms, or the assessment of total production and sales in terms of starch equivalent, or some other material measure, is theoretically attractive. In both approaches variation of quality of produce adds to the difficulty of obtaining sufficiently accurate figures. Perhaps preferable is the proportion of farming time devoted to products for sale. Where other figures are available they can be converted into this measure through the concept of standard man-days, calculated for particular regions and types of farming (see Chapter 9).

[1] Winter (1956), quoted by Clark and Haswell (1964), 4.

As a starting point it is suggested that 25 per cent. of farming time devoted to products for sale might be taken as the borderline between quasi-subsistence and semi-subsistence farming. The farmer who is devoting more than a quarter of his time to commercial products has a vital stake in the market, and success or failure in that market may decide whether the family lives in tolerable comfort or below whatever is a locally acceptable idea of the poverty line. As long, however, as he is not devoting more than half his time to produce for sale the term 'semi-subsistence' would seem to indicate fairly the nature of the farmer's interest in the market.

My proposed classification is then:

(1) Subsistence farming:
- (1*a*) Pure subsistence
- (1*b*) Subsistence plus earnings for taxes, etc.

(2) Quasi-subsistence farming: not more than 25 per cent. of working time devoted to cash crops.

(3) Semi-subsistence farming: 25–50 per cent. of working time devoted to cash crops.

Owing to the lack of statistical information it is impracticable to confer upon such terms a high degree of accuracy except where detailed surveys are undertaken. Nevertheless, it is suggested that use of these terms, with an indication as to the accuracy assumed in any particular case, would add a useful degree of precision to reporting on the myriad variations of what is loosely referred to as 'subsistence agriculture' at the present time. Use of this terminology would also help to destroy the over-simplification of the primary division of agricultural economies into 'subsistence' and 'commercial.' There is a gradual blend from one to another and this is better suggested by the division here proposed. It may be borne in mind that state and collective farming makes another division, for these are not wholly commercial in their objectives.

The suggested classification is one of social organisation and economic objective. Alone, the terms here discussed tell us nothing about the type of farming, which demands a separate classification. Whittlesey recognised six subsistence types in his classification of world agriculture outlined in Chapter 4.

Whittlesey's first type, *nomadic herding*, has its commercial counterpart in livestock ranching in his classification but many herders are now organised in collectives. Those remaining nomadic herders are probably mainly subsistence or quasi-subsistence in economic type. His second type, *shifting cultivation*, is mainly subsistence in my proposed classification, though some examples would be quasi-subsistence. *Rudimentary sedentary tillage* is probably quasi-subsistence as commonly as it is subsistence. The other three types classed by Whittlesey as subsistence, viz. *intensive subsistence tillage with rice dominant*, *intensive subsistence tillage without paddy rice* (i.e. wet rice) and *subsistence crop and stock farming* contain all three of my classes, but in the last one semi-subsistence and quasi-subsistence economies have probably nearly ousted the subsistence type.

In a world classification it seems best to use type of farming, or crop and livestock combinations, for the primary classification, and economic class—subsistence or otherwise—to qualify this classification. We may then modify Whittlesey's classes to suit more readily the changed and fluid conditions of the present time. For example, his class *intensive subsistence tillage with rice dominant* would no longer include the word 'subsistence' in the title. 'Intensive tillage with rice dominant' adequately identifies the type, and does not destroy its close association with the monsoonal lowlands of south-east Asia. Description can then be pursued with attention to the variation in the type from subsistence to semi-subsistence, and on to collective farms and any commercial units that may be concerned with this fundamentally unified type of farming.

Similar comments apply to the similar type without wet rice. It may be noted in passing that Whittlesey's definitions left a gap between the types 'with rice dominant' and 'without paddy rice'. It may be desirable here to distinguish intensive tillage with wet rice subsidiary, and intensive tillage with wet rice absent or unimportant.

The subsistence crop and stock farming type could disappear as such, broken up among the appropriate crop and livestock types, ranging from rarely subsistence to commonly commercial and collective types. The other three 'subsistence' types did not include this term in their titles and so may remain unaltered, at least as far as this modification is concerned. *Nomadic herding* has undergone change of a drastic kind in some regions through collectivisation, but there are still large numbers of nomads whose economy is subsistence or quasi-subsistence. Nomadic herding in its more sedentary variations merges with and may ultimately become grouped with *rudimentary sedentary tillage*, modified in title to take account of the important, probably still dominant, livestock interest. The title 'rudimentary sedentary tillage' without emphasis on livestock remains applicable to large numbers of cultivators whose arrival at this type of agriculture has not been via nomadic herding, but rather through shifting agriculture. Here again, then, there is marked blending, but shifting cultivators and those who have become more or less sedentary but still retain some of the ways of the shifting cultivator offer the clearest examples of true subsistence agriculture. Even so, many shifting cultivators already have growing interests in cash crops.

Shifting Cultivation

As an example of agriculture which regionally is still of the subsistence class, though efforts have been made to transform it into what I am calling quasi-subsistence, a form of shifting cultivation will be examined. However, we are now confronted by another problem in definition to which reference must be made, that of the term 'shifting cultivation'. Various terms are used to describe this form of agriculture which is widespread in the tropical regions of the world. The essentials of the technique are the clearing of a patch of primary or secondary forest with axe or cutlass and fire, the planting of crops for a few years in the clearing, and movement to a new site when the fertility of the soil is seriously reduced. After a period of rest or fallow, the area will in due course be cleared again. These general principles suggest some of the alternative names that have been conferred on the practice, not only 'shifting cultivation', but 'slash and burn' and 'bush fallow' agriculture. Local terms include *ladang* (Malaysia and Indonesia), *caingin* (Philippines), *milpa* (Central America and Mexico), *ray* (Vietnam), *conuco* (Venezuela), *roça* (Brazil), and *masole* (Belgian Congo).[1]

[1] Terms listed by Gourou (1961), 25.

The UNESCO Commission on World Land Use Survey[1] suggested that the term *shifting cultivation* should be used only when settlements as well as fields are moved frequently. They suggested *land rotation* where villages are fixed and the lands around farmed in a somewhat erratic rotation. The use of the word 'rotation' appears to the present writer to risk confusion with farming systems in which systematic rotation is practised.[2] A more immediate difficulty in the UNESCO terminology is pointed out by Nye and Greenland[3]:

> In fact, the two practices merge: thus among forest tribes, the Boro of the Amazon basin shift their settlements every few years; the people of Sa'a in Melanesia move when buildings become dilapidated, the cultivated land too remote, or if death and other misfortunes seem to dog the place;[4] the Ashanti in Ghana live in towns or villages that have endured for generations or even centuries. Recognition of a clear division between nomadic, semi-permanent, or permanent cultivators is also blurred by changes of population within a settlement. A family or clan will frequently move to found a new village or to expand an existing one. Nevertheless, so far as the soil is concerned what matters in all these cases is that the fertility of the land is improved by the natural regrowth of vegetation that springs up when cultivation 'shifts' to a new patch. ...

Nye and Greenland make it clear that it is this process of fertility with which they are concerned, and they therefore use the term 'shifting cultivation' to describe cultivation practices rather than patterns of settlement. It is, however, obviously undesirable to use a term based on cultivation to describe a settlement pattern and therefore for this reason and that mentioned above, the term 'shifting cultivation' will here retain its general meaning, as interpreted by Nye and Greenland and other authorities. If further precision is required in terms

[1] UNESCO, *Report of the commission on world land-use survey* (1952).

[2] In such cases the usual term *crop rotation* is not wholly satisfactory, because it is not only crops that are rotated but complex systems of crop, grass and animal husbandry.

[3] Nye and Greenland (1960), 5–6.

[4] Forde (1934).

of settlement the obvious distinction would seem to be 'shifting cultivation without movement of settlement' and 'shifting cultivation with movement of settlement' or as appropriate for intermediate forms.

To an observer unacquainted with its detailed composition and history an area of shifting cultivation presents a chaotic appearance:

> The first sight of native subsistence farming in the semi-deciduous forest region, e.g. in Ghana, presents an appearance of bewildering confusion to any one familiar only with the pattern of well ordered fields under single crops characteristic of more advanced systems of farming. There are no clear boundaries, individual fields can scarcely be discerned, and while some patches of land are definitely under crops, and others are under a thick regrowth of forest, there is a middle group in which perennial crops survive amidst a regrowth of forest which is gradually choking them. Some patches of land carry only one kind of crop, yet others appear to carry a mixture of up to half-a-dozen kinds in a seemingly haphazard arrangement. A pattern emerges from this higgledy-piggledy confusion if one follows the history of a single plot of land over a number of years.[1]

In the example to which we may now proceed for illustration of subsistence and quasi-subsistence agriculture, de Schlippe's valuable study of the Azande of the southern Sudan,[2] apparent confusion is again seen by patient study to be underlain by order:

> When one enters a Zande homestead for the first time, the impression is that of complete chaos. The courtyard is shapeless or roughly circular or oval. . . . Crops, food and household belongings may lie about the courtyard, or be piled on to the veranda of a hut in what seems to be a most disorderly fashion. Worst of all, no fields can be seen. The thickets of plants surrounding the homestead seem as patchy and purposeless as any wild vegetation. It

[1] Nye and Greenland (1960), 1–2.
[2] Schlippe (1956).

is impossible to distinguish a crop from a weed. It seems altogether incredible that a human intelligence should be responsible for this tangle.[1]

The tangle extends to family and group relationships, obligations and duties, and rights of ownership, including the ownership of land and crops. Individual ownership of land gives way, as commonly in such communities, to occupation of such areas as may be indicated from time to time by the tribal chief. The individual, however, owns the crop. Even this is complicated. Man and wife have fields of their own. The family is fed mainly from the fields belonging to the woman, so these crops go into her granary. The crops from the husband's fields go into his granary and are used mainly for entertaining guests. For most fields the wife has the main responsibility, but if she wants to sell any of these crops she must have her husband's permission and he decides on the distribution of the profit, but the husband has complete jurisdiction over his own crops. A second or third wife does not usually help the first in the fields, but daughters and small children help their mothers. Adolescent boys have small fields of their own for crops which do not require processing.[2]

Zande crops were found to be grown in associations of certain crops, sometimes sown simultaneously, sometimes successively. Each 'field type', as these associations were called, requires a particular ecological background.[3] A former refuse heap provides a specially favourable site for bananas, coco-yams, maize and eleusine (finger millet), the overhanging thatch of a kitchen roof shelters a tobacco nursery and hashish is sown in some corner of a field, where weeds help to conceal it from European eyes.

De Schlippe stresses the importance of the status of the woman as an economic 'atom' possessing her own equipment and field types, which he suggests may be a key to the understanding of an African system of agriculture.[4] 'In the Zande system of agriculture, and, I believe, in many similar systems at subsistence level, each smallest economic unit, in this case the

[1] Schlippe (1956), 101.
[2] Schlippe (1956), 104–5.
[3] Schlippe (1956), ch. 3.
[4] Schlippe (1956), 106.

woman, possesses a complete set of fields belonging to definite types in the same way in which it possesses complete sets of definite types of pots, mats, tools and buildings'. (Figure 11).

The number of field types in the Zande system is smaller than at first appeared to de Schlippe and his team, and can be summarised as follows:[1]

(1) The *öti-moru*, or *main eleusine association*, may be established either on virgin land or in a second shift, that is on land which has been cultivated the year before. Work on this field type begins with clearing (May to July) and hoeing, followed, some twenty days later, by burning. This is called the 'hoe and burn' opening method. In grassless forest, hoeing is replaced by slashing of undergrowth with a machete. This is the 'slash and burn' opening method typical of the whole equatorial forest belt. On the very day of the burning and hand cleaning, or very soon after it, maize is sown in widely spaced holes and cassava cuttings may be planted. Two to seven weeks later the mixture of seeds of the eleusine association is broadcast and hoed in. Sesame and sorghums are commonly sown with the eleusine, less common associates being deccan hemp, oil-seed, water melons and cucumbers. A single weeding operation is carried out two to three months after broadcasting, one to two months before harvesting. The different crops become available for harvesting from September to January.

The main eleusine association can be established far from the homestead. It needs no guarding, only the maize and sorghum being liable to destruction.

(2) The *baawande*, 'place of groundnuts', is referred to as the *groundnut-eleusine succession*. With variations, the general procedure is similar, the hoe and burn or slash and burn opening being earlier, however, than in the previous case. Sowing of groundnuts follows at once (early April to late June), with maize or cassava as associate crops. This is the only big field type which needs constant guarding, jackals, guinea fowl, squirrels, pigs and monkeys all offering hazards at one time or another. A small guard hut is built in the main field and a man sleeps out armed with spear and grass torches. Groundnuts are the

[1] Schlippe (1956), ch. 9., my summary. These are the 'field types' of the 'green belt', exceptionally rich lands.

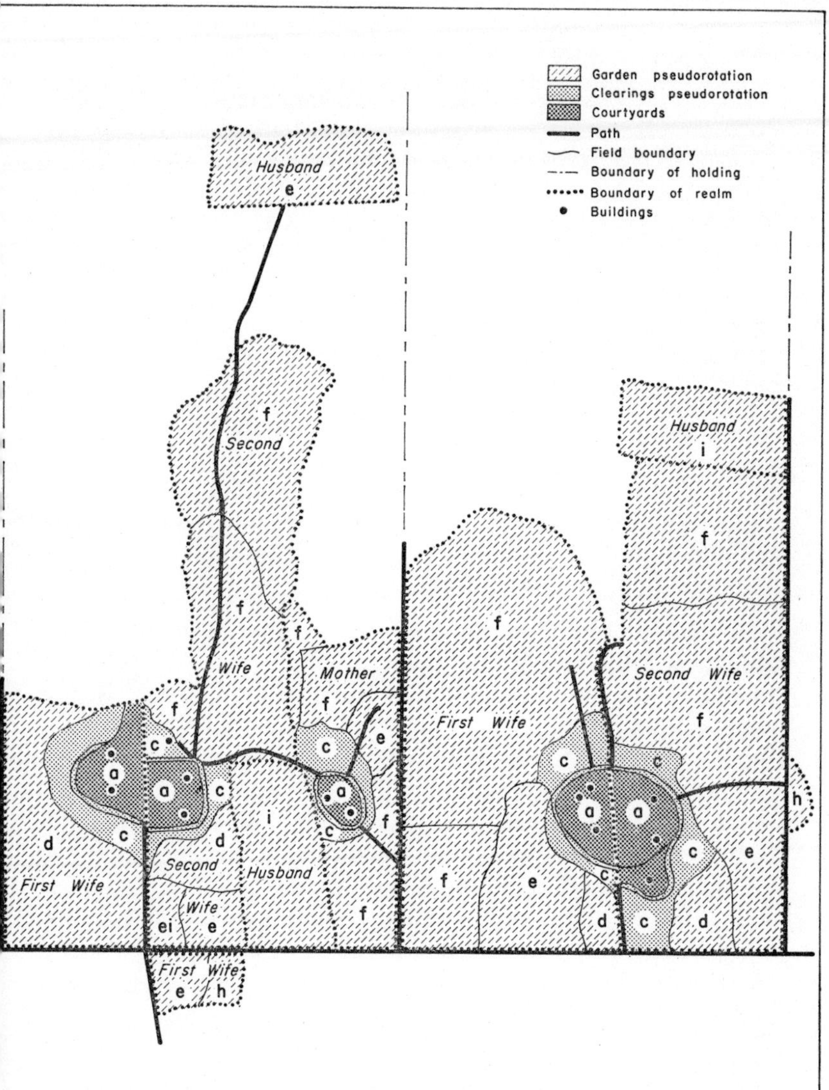

Figure 11. A map of two adjacent holdings in the eastern green belt of the Zande country in 1949, showing the distribution of fields and realms. On the left, Kaimbaga's, a bigamous family, with a courtyard divided into two by a hedge of cassava and with a separate courtyard for the mother. On the right, a bigamous homestead with a courtyard which is not visibly divided into two realms. Key to field types: *a*, courtyard; *c*, maize through sweet potatoes association; *d*, maize and oil-seed gourd association; *e*, groundnut-eleusine succession; *f*, main eleusine association; *h*, bean patch; *i*, cotton field. The *ei* field is an experimental association of groundnuts and cotton.

Source: P. de Schlippe, *Shifting Cultivation in Africa.*

first crop available to end the seasonal food shortage, harvesting beginning late in June. Eleusine is sown as the groundnuts are harvested through July, August and September.

The broadcasting of eleusine through groundnuts utilises efficiently labour and the season. It also reduces to a minimum the period in which the soil is exposed to the heavy rains.

(3) The *bamvuo* or *eleusine through grass* association utilises the third shift or semi-exhausted land of a recent grass fallow. In the main eleusine association the period of rest from burning to broadcasting is meant to establish a low cover of grass through which the eleusine is broadcast and which is destroyed by the hoeing. Pre-sowing cultivation is unnecessary in the *bamvuo* but a thorough hand cleaning follows germination as in the main eleusine association. Sesame is the most usual associate crop and may be the more important crop or even the only one, replacing eleusine in this field type.

(4) *Beans.* Patches of beans are very similar to the preceding field type. The seeds are sown through grass without pre-sowing cultivation and in this case hand cleaning is not needed. No guarding is needed so beans can be grown at a distance from the homestead.

The preceding four types are all independent of the homestead, being established in rapidly shifting clearings. The first two make use of land either newly cleaned or cropped the previous year, with appropriate variations. Type 3 is associated with a second phase and type 4 with second or subsequent phases. The next three are garden types, associated with the homestead.

(5) *Ridge cultivation.* The courtyard of a Zande homestead is usually surrounded by a ridge of earth, made up in February and March. Maize and pumpkins are sown here at this time along the crest. The pumpkin vines creep down the inward slope into the courtyard and in June and July cuttings of sweet potato vines are planted on the outward slopes. This field type, which produces the earliest crops along with groundnuts, is the only one on which manures are applied, consciously by applying chaff and residues from salt preparation, and unconsciously through refuse sweepings. Other ridges are also made in the courtyard for yams, vegetables, rice and bananas. With this category go the old refuse heaps.

(6) The *baabangbe*, 'place of sweet potatoes', is generally a strip one to ten metres wide, along the ridge on the outside. It is referred to as a *maize through sweet potatoes* field type. Maize is grown between crops of sweet potatoes, usually with cassava as an associate crop, and it may become a cassava grove.

(7) *The maize and oil-seed gourd* association is similar to the *baabangbe* and extends from the ridge into neighbouring areas. It requires little labour but produces low yields. The oil-seed gourds, like the pumpkins and sweet potatoes, provide a good vegetative carpet during the heavy rains.

(8) *The cassava fallow* 'can be considered in a certain sense as a field type'. Cassava is interplanted from May to August in Types 1, 2, 6 and 7, but rarely in a first shift. In the following year the land reverts to fallow and no further attention is paid to the cassava. It is harvested according to needs in the first two years of fallow, and most is never harvested.

It has been noted that each field type occupies land at a particular stage, or one of two stages of the 'rotation'. Likewise each has its particular ecological background, higher or lower steps on the catena, transition forest or built-up ridge. Other special ecological situations are used often for specialised crops not included in the main associations, for example, the previously mentioned refuse heap and thatch overhang. Others are ash accumulations, living trees for climbing yams, and termite mounds for sorghum, rice and cowpeas.

Cotton and 'The Zande Scheme'. All the field types so far mentioned have been concerned with subsistence crops, even if a little surplus might be sold from time to time. The introduction of a cash crop into the Zande system of agriculture followed the belief that economic development was necessary for progress, and that social progress of 'remote areas' could not be indefinitely financed by the economic development of the coastal belt.[1] The Zande district was selected for an experiment because it has the most reliable rainfall and the richest vegetation in the southern Sudan, together with the most disciplined population. Resettlement of the Azande people had already been undertaken in the 'twenties to facilitate control of sleeping sickness.

[1] Schlippe (1956), 20.

The new project acquired the name of 'The Zande Scheme' and it aimed at the complete social emergence and economic stability of the people. The central project was to be a cotton industry, providing for growing, spinning and weaving in the district and an industrial centre was established between 1946 and 1949. Also during these years resettlement was undertaken and 60,000 cultivators were given new, dispersed, holdings. It was hoped that this would be the beginning of a transition from shifting to fixed cultivation, and in any case would facilitate supervision of the cotton crop. Each Zande cultivator received a holding some 800 to 1000 metres long and 150 metres wide, with a frontage on a common path. Fifty to sixty holdings formed a settlement under one elder. The Azande were allowed to erect their homesteads at any point within their holdings.[1] A homestead is not moved without good cause, such as marriage, death of a wife, repeated family misfortunes or persistent crop failures.[2] The early years, particularly the first, in a new homestead are difficult because of all the extra work to be done.

In the cotton field the opening (May) is similar in all respects to the hoe and burn method of the main eleusine association. Opening and sowing of fields quickly is encouraged to limit the breeding season of insect pests. Sowing is, however, often delayed because the Azande are reluctant to abandon all other activities to concentrate on cotton. Much weeding is required, in contrast to the customary field types which require none, or only one weeding. Picking, which should begin 140 days after sowing and be finished some 70 days later, is also often delayed and is very inefficient. Cotton clashes with the customary field types in labour utilisation, especially the main eleusine association.[3]

Earnings from the cash crop were small, partly because yields were low, averaging about 400 kg/ha. compared with over 800 kg/ha. in similar conditions and without manures at the Yambio Experimental Station. In 1950, because it promised higher yields, it was decided that cotton should be grown in a second shift, after a groundnut-eleusine succession.

[1] Schlippe (1956), 21.
[2] Schlippe (1956), 192.
[3] Schlippe (1956), 137–138.

It proved, however, impossible to induce the Azande to come home from fishing and hunting sufficiently early to make a clearing of the necessary shape and size for a groundnut-eleusine succession. This led to successive crops of cotton and to overcultivation.

De Schlippe had to conclude that the conception of a holding, including a cash cropping interest, to which a cultivator's family would be confined had not proved an antidote to shifting cultivation.[1] In fact, overcultivation near the homestead resulted in homesteads established in 1946–47 reaching premature senility in 1952–53. Many people, if allowed, would move to new sites. They might, of course, be induced to move within their holdings, but transition to sedentary cultivation remained far off.

This summary of the very detailed survey made of Azande cultural adaptation has covered only what appeared to the present writer to be particularly relevant to this theme. Much else that is relevant has had to be omitted, but perhaps sufficient has been preserved from the original to indicate the complexity of a typical system of shifting cultivation and the risks inherent in interfering with it, however well-meant the scheme devised. Only by patient enquiry can a system be thoroughly understood and even then to prescribe remedies for the undoubted evils of an existing system may still be fraught with peril. Long term education so that the indigenous people may be able to be largely responsible for their own approaches to development—an acceleration of the process of change that affects all peoples in some way—may be the only answer.

It is no longer as customary as it used to be for scientists and other specialists to condemn shifting agriculture, though as recently as 1957 the Food and Agricultural Organisation of the United Nations was responsible for the statement that:

> Shifting cultivation in the humid tropical countries is the greatest obstacle not only to the immediate increase of agricultural production, but also to the conservation of the production potential of the future, in the form of soils and forests.[2]

[1] Schlippe (1956), 232.
[2] FAO staff, Shifting cultivation, *Unasylva*, 11, No. 1, 9–11, reprinted in *Trop., Agric. Trin. 34*, 159–164.

Opposing views based on the past success of shifting cultivation in sustaining growing populations and the dangers of disrupting tribal life and organisation have received some support from the technical investigations of soil scientists. Nye and Greenland show that the question of whether or not shifting cultivation leads to a squandering of resources of the land admits of no simple answer.[1] Much depends on the particular environment, there being far less to be said in favour of the system in savanna than in forest regions. Improvement of the system may be possible, but there is no evidence yet that a planted fallow will restore the fertility of a forest soil any faster than the natural woody fallow. In particular, the nitrogen status maintained beneath a forest fallow is good. In other respects much depends on variations in the system. Useful elements in the fallow may be employed, such as bananas, a semi-perennial crop, while in savanna regions livestock may provide an answer. Greater availability of cheap fertilisers may be the key to evolution of farming systems here, as in temperate latitudes.

Again one is reminded of the variety to be found within a seemingly simple label. Watters has suggested a classification[2] based on predominant and subsidiary ways of producing food by combinations of shifting agriculture, permanent cultivation, pastoralism, hunting, fishing and gathering. The potential for development will vary enormously from one type to another as well as from one region to another. What is common to all types and all regions, with insignificant exceptions, and forcing changes in the agricultural system, is the growth of population at rates much more rapid than in the past. Even the modest aids to health and longer life-span that reach the communities of the forest and savannah are having this effect.

The low level in population supported by typical shifting cultivation systems has been demonstrated by many writers. Gourou[3] quotes a number of studies indicating that 30 to 50 persons per square mile is typical, with lower optimum figures in many cases. In contrast, a population of 1400 per square mile has been estimated for the alluvial rice lands of the Tonkin delta of Vietnam.

[1] Nye and Greenland (1960), esp. chapter 8.

[2] Watters (1960).

[3] Gourou (1961), 38.

One cannot, of course, expect that lands used for shifting cultivation will necessarily have a very high potential under any other system, so that the above contrast may be regarded as illustrating inherent land potential as well as the productivity of a system of agriculture. Shifting cultivation land may, however, be suited to a variety of uses, including plantation agriculture, and the alienation of tribal lands for this purpose or for resettlement of other tribes has been the cause of privation for some communities. It was not always in the past realised how large an area might be needed for the maintenance of a family, and that land found apparently unoccupied might be part of their bush fallow though miles from the homestead.[1]

On the other hand, formation of plantations or the introduction of settlers of more advanced techniques may ultimately have beneficial effects on a primitive tribe. Similarly, sedentary cultivators may be affected for either good or ill by the establishment of plantations in their locality. An initial impact is the attraction of the plantation in providing regular employment. This may act as a disrupting force to local cultivation, but if there is surplus labour it may, on balance, prove economically beneficial.

Peasant Farming in Malaya

In Malaya, the plantations have not been as great a disruptive force as might have been expected from their rapid growth to their present extent. Prior to the colonial era the peasantry was composed of Malays, whose culture was based on rice supported by fruits, coconuts, vegetables and spices. This truly subsistence economy was disturbed by British rule, or British protection of the native ruler, because it spread a monetary economy, largely through the introduction of the plantation system. Fortunately, the requirements of rubber led to the development of the rolling, well-drained lands, with much clearance of forest. The low, wet lands suitable for rice were left in the hands of the indigenous farmers and legislative control over the transfer of land helped to maintain this position. Moreover, the Malays were largely indifferent to the demands of the plantations for labour, preferring their independent, rather casual farming to the regular and monotonous

[1] An outstanding case is described by Bower (1952).

plantation employment. Hence, the labour force became based mainly on Indian and Chinese immigrants. But the growing markets for crops and more stable conditions, particularly the suppression of banditry, made it more attractive to grow surplus crops for sale. The growth of the rubber industry provided outlets for peasant as well as plantation. The enthusiasm with which Malay peasants turned to rubber growing[1] is a measure of the attraction of a commercial economy, in spite of the small size of farms.[2] It might be expected that unless a holding amounted to 20 acres or so, it would be used for intensive crop production. In fact, even in Johore, where 94 per cent. of the peasant holdings are under 15 acres in size, rice cultivation is unimportant compared with cash cropping based on rubber, coconut and pineapple.[3] In the peninsula as a whole, rice is the most important food crop (occupying nearly a million acres compared with 3½ million acres of rubber), but coconuts are second to rubber as a cash crop from peasant farms. Pineapples and bananas are fairly important in trade while other crops are grown by Malays mainly for domestic consumption.

The main areas of paddy growing are the northern coastal plains and it is estimated that the growers in Perlis and Kedah sell about half their crop, while in other coastal plain areas paddy farmers have about one-third of their crop for sale. During the annual fallow, selected areas of the paddy fields are planted with maize, groundnuts and vegetables mainly for domestic consumption. Inland, small paddy fields occur widely in the valley bottoms with tree crops on the interfluves (Figure 12). In these areas paddy is a subsistence crop while cash is obtained from rubber and some of the coconuts and other fruit grown.

Even the Malays of remote jungle areas purchase some goods from the proceeds of nipah palm leaves (for thatch) rattan (for baskets, mats and furniture) gums, resins and other forest products. Hence, it can be said that an entirely

[1] Ooi Jin-Bee (1963), 202, 204.

[2] Peasant farms (under 100 acres), in 1960 numbered 449,510 of which 10 per cent. were under one acre, 45 per cent. under 2¾ acres, and 96 per cent. under 15 acres.

[3] Ooi Jin-Bee (1963), 193.

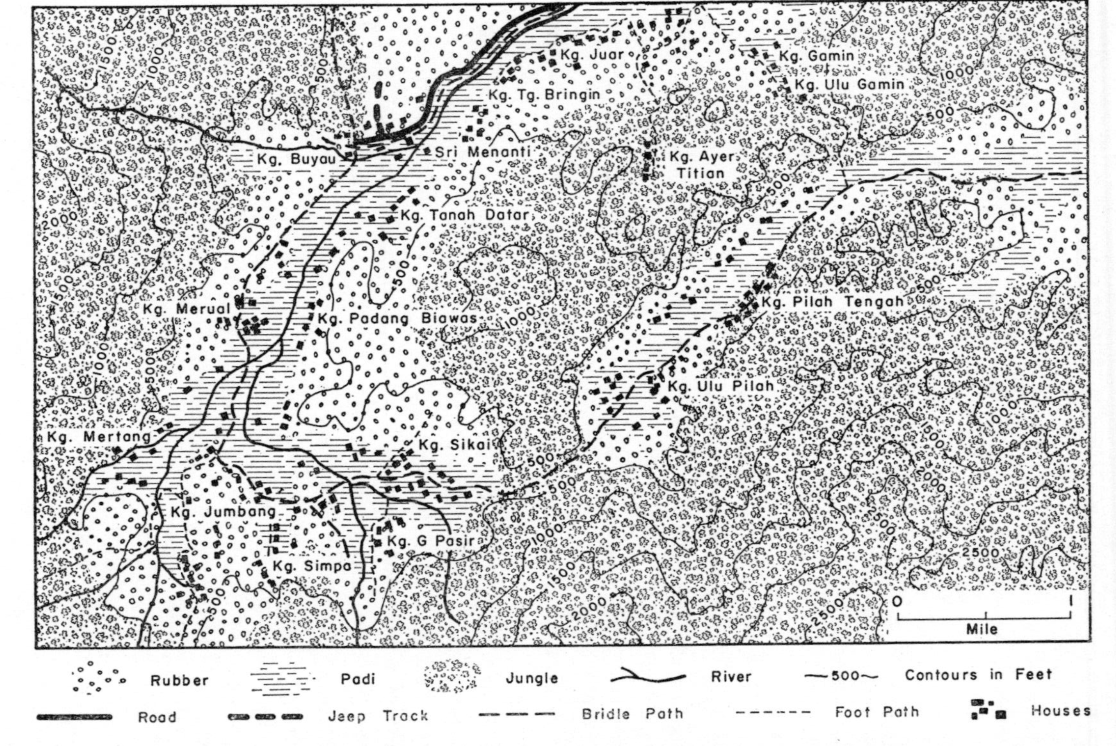

Figure 12. An area of peasant holdings in Malaya with the valley bottoms occupied by paddy and the valley sides by rubber.

Source: Ooi Jin-Bee, *The Journal of Tropical Geography*, Vol. 15, 1961.

subsistence economy does not exist today among the Malays.[1] Most would be, in terms of the classification proposed above, quasi- and semi-subsistence rather than subsistence farmers.

If the Malay is firmly attached to the money economy, this is even more true of the Chinese peasant in Malaya. The Chinese, who migrated to the Malay peninsula in large numbers after the establishment of British rule, sought occupations which would enable them to make profits and eventually return to China. They therefore grew cash crops in high demand, notably vegetables in intensive market gardening. No doubt, the success of the Chinese immigrants encouraged the Malays to pay more attention to producing for sale, but they have never rivalled the Chinese in intensive farming. One reason is that the Moslem objection to the pig prevents the Malays from integrating pig and crop farming as the Chinese do, using pig manure for the crops and crop residues for the pigs. Indian and Pakistani peasants are far fewer in number but are also engaged mainly in production of cash crops, notably rubber.

From the national point of view the preference of the smallholder for cash crop production has some unfortunate results. The demand for rice is not satisfied by home production and large sums of hard-earned foreign exchange have to be spent on imports. But from the point of view of the individual smallholder it makes good sense. The wet and cloudy climate does not greatly favour rice growing and the smallholder can normally buy more rice with the proceeds of an acre of rubber than he can grow on the same area.

For examples of true subsistence economies in the Malay peninsula it is necessary to turn to the aboriginal population. This comprises Senoi, Aboriginal Malay, Negrito and many lesser groups, totalling in all perhaps 100,000 people. The numbers of such people in the Indonesian islands and New Guinea are much greater. Many of these tribes have not changed their way of life during the thousands of years since man first entered the region and they remain virtually in the stone age. Since hunting and gathering are not regarded in this book as agriculture, little space will be devoted to comment on the economies of these people, who use spear, trap, and

[1] Ooi Jin-Bee (1963), 163.

blow-pipe to add to the berries, roots and fruit collected in the jungles. It may be remarked, however, that even these groups are being slowly affected by contact with more advanced cultures and may plant a few food crops in places which are convenient for them to return to for such harvest as may survive. In Malaya, shifting cultivation is practised by many of these folk and some establish rubber trees, which, with the proceeds of collected forest products, enables them to make a few purchases. As many as, possibly, 15 per cent. of these aboriginals in Malaya now live a settled life, cultivating paddy and rubber.

PART III

REGIONAL ANALYSIS

CHAPTER 9

The Agricultural Region: Concepts and Methodology

The concept of the region is of fundamental importance in geographical studies.[1] A region may be defined for the present purpose as a part of the earth's surface having certain characteristics which enable it to be recognised as a unit, distinguishable from other units which surround it, and which may themselves be identified by similar or different characteristic features. A region may be defined in physical terms, e.g. a volcanic plateau, a river valley; in climatic terms, e.g. a tropical monsoon region; or by economic and social criteria, such as a textile-manufacturing region, or a nomadic herding region. A single point in space may thus be included in several regions, differently defined, the boundaries of which will rarely coincide over much of their length, except where some marked physical feature such as a seaboard or steep mountain wall sets a limit.

It is partly because of this variability of boundaries that the methods by which regions may be defined have been examined and re-examined repeatedly during the past half-century, and ever more complex procedures evolved. Not only will the limits of a region differ according to the criteria by which it is defined but, at least in some cases, these limits will change with time. It remains true, however, that different areas in the world are clearly distinguished one from another, and not only geography but other sciences—agricultural, biological and anthropological—require attempts to delimit these areas of variation.

Boundary lines are in themselves unsatisfactory. Most regional variations occur in a more or less gradual way, so that

[1] See, for example, Hartshorne (1939, 1959), Whittlesey (1954), Bunge (1962) and Grigg (1965).

zones rather than lines should be used as boundaries. On a small-scale map, of course, even a fine line does, in fact, represent a broad zone, though it may still be too narrow to suggest accurately the real width of the transitional area. Provided, however, we remember that boundary lines can be interpreted only as more or less accurate indications of zones within which marked changes in the regional pattern occur, a map of regions can add greatly to knowledge without seriously misleading the careful interpreter.

The nature of the task has been stated by Buchanan:[1]

> Establishing the pattern of agricultural regions involves finding the best possible boundaries to the individual regions, which in turn implies both definition and delimitation. My first proposition is that definition must be in agricultural terms—a crop, a crop association, a crop-and-livestock association, a system of organisation of farm processes will serve as convenient examples. . . . Delimitation, the actual fixing of the boundary, implies that the criterion or criteria must be capable of being mapped.

If we keep in mind the need to define agricultural regions in agricultural terms we shall be making a good start. Thus, we shall take criteria like spring wheat growing, which is the indicator of the Spring Wheat Belt of the United States and Canadian prairie provinces, and the association of wheat, alfalfa and cattle for the Wheat-Alfalfa-Cattle Crescent of the Argentine pampas. Many such regions are readily recognisable on the ground even to the untrained eye, at least in core areas. Two such areas long recognised in the United States are the Corn Belt and the Cotton Belt. When we come to fix boundaries to these regions, however, we soon find need to clarify observations by resort to theory supported by mapping and statistical analysis. Thus, we may decide to define a particular crop region as the area in which a certain percentage of farms have not less than a specified percentage of their area in that crop. A theory is essential to guide the analysis but the approach remains empirical.

[1] R. O. Buchanan (1959), 5.

Before proceeding to examine methods used in identifying and delimiting actual agricultural regions we should note that approach to the problem of recognising and explaining regional variation may be essentially theoretical, with a minimum of observed facts. The ultimate aim of such theories is to build up a general theory which can be used to elucidate any situation. We are far from such achievement at present, but it is instructive to review some of the theories affecting the study of agricultural regions and the location of agricultural production, and this will therefore be done, in so far as it is possible in the limited space available.

Theories of the Location of Agriculture

An attempt to offer a theory which could explain the location of different types of agriculture according to economic principles was made by Johann von Thünen in the first half of the nineteenth century.[1] Von Thünen, who managed an agricultural estate in Mecklenburg, near the city of Rostock, observed the disposition of different agricultural activities in his area and related these to the farm accounts he managed. The theory he produced has provided the starting point for many discussions of regional location by economists and geographers. It must be realised at the outset that von Thünen's theory can be judged only in the restrictive conditions he postulated and in the historical conditions of his time. There are obvious discrepancies between the theory and observed fact, but to criticise the theory on this account, neglecting the postulations, is improper, as with any theory.[2] Essential to the theory were the postulations that surrounding one central city in an 'isolated state' was an area of uniform physical conditions suitable for tillage, and all surplus produce of the region had to be sold in the city. On the assumption, further, that all transport was by one means (horse-drawn) and transport costs were proportional to distance and borne by the farmer, then the result would be a series of concentric rings or belts of differing production around the city. (Figure 13A). The boundaries of each belt would be defined by the principle of

[1] von Thünen (1826).

[2] For sympathetic discussion of von Thünen's theory see Grotewald (1959), and Chisholm (1962).

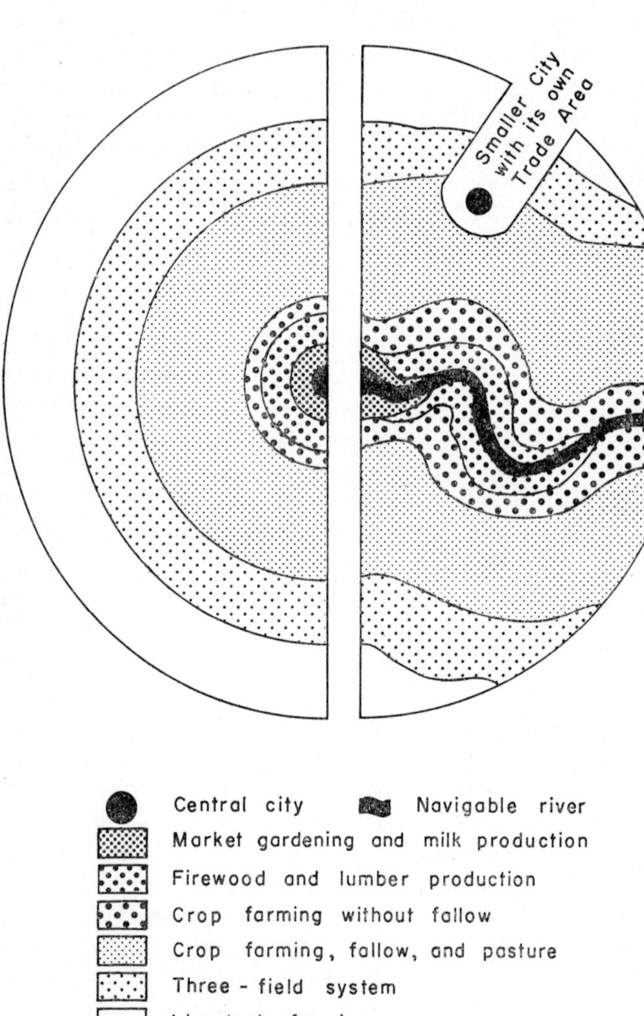

Figure 13. Von Thünen's agricultural zones.
Source: A. Grotewald, *Economic Geography*, Vol. 35, 1959.

greatest rent,[1] in effect the maximum profit per acre having regard to transport costs. In von Thünen's time, wood, in great demand in a city for fuel, could return higher profits per acre than rye, provided transport costs were low, but cost of marketing limited the zone within which this would apply. In fact, in von Thünen's model, the wood-producing zone was nearest to the city excepting only for the zone of market gardening and milk production, of which the location was fixed by slow transport and consequent high prices for perishable goods. Beyond the wood-producing zone were belts of arable production, of decreasing intensity. Higher costs of transport were offset by lower production costs. Beyond the third zone was an area of the least intensive system, livestock farming.

Although the stipulated conditions of the isolated state and one form of transport do not occur in practice, and competitive marketing and variable transport costs, to say nothing of differing soils, complicate the position in every area, some traces of the type of distribution envisaged by von Thünen can still be found. A practical reason applicable in any circumstance is that it costs more to obtain goods from further afield or to cultivate land further from a farmstead or settlement than nearer, unless transport costs are outweighed by differences of soil fertility, climate, land prices or other variants. Except where mechanised transport is available, even short distances to be traversed to work in the fields greatly reduce the time and energy available for productive work. Hence, nearer fields are preferred for the more intensive forms of cultivation. Impressive zoning around agricultural villages has been observed in many countries and a number of examples are cited by Chisholm,[2] together with consideration of the background of costs and time expenditure.

[1] In orthodox economic theory rent is the surplus or excess payment obtainable for a factor of production on account of its inherent qualities, e.g. land of special productivity or in a particularly desirable position. It is an unearned payment to the owner, which is not necessary to bring the land into production but which the user is willing to pay because yield is greater than on alternative land. The concept, propounded by Ricardo early in the nineteenth century, is discussed in all textbooks of economics and a clear description in relation to von Thünen's theories is given by Chisholm (1962), Chapter 2. Later in the nineteenth century Jevons and Marshall made the more exact proposition that rent should be determined by the marginal productivity of land. Analysis by production functions is now favoured, see Clarke and Haswell (1964), Chapter 6.

[2] Chisholm (1962), Chapter 4.

Summarising the evidence, Chisholm notes the frequency with which distances of similar magnitude appear critical among peoples of widely different technical achievements and inhabiting areas with markedly different physical characteristics:

> Any distance up to about a kilometre from the dwelling is of such little moment for any but specialised systems of irrigation and garden farming that little adjustment is called for in either the pattern of settlement or of land use . . . at a distance of 3–4 kilometres the costs of cultivation necessitate a *radical* modification of the system of cultivation or settlement—for example by the establishment of subsidiary settlements—though adjustments are apparent before this point is reached. . . . Over much of the world, the present spontaneous tendency is to modify the patterns of rural settlement and land holding in such a manner that the distance separating the farmstead from the lands cultivated is reduced to something in the order of 1 or 2 kilometes, if the farmstead is not actually on the farm.[1]

Of the many examples adduced by Chisholm two only must suffice here to illustrate the argument that distance, irrespective of natural fertility, exercises a strong control over intensity of cultivation. The first example is from Sardinia:

> From whichever side one leaves a village, one is struck by the rigorous disposition of the various elements of the countryside into concentric zones. Around the village . . . there is a first zone in which the view is restricted, where the parcels are small and bounded by hedges of prickly pear, growing vegetables, olives, almonds and vines. But this pleasant labyrinth constitutes only a narrow belt, and suddenly there opens out a landscape which is flat and bare, without walls, without hedges, without trees; these are the arable lands. . . . Completely cultivated in the area nearest the village, this territory becomes poorer in the distance, the amount of fallow increases. . . .[2]

[1] Chisholm (1962), 148.
[2] Chisholm (1962), 61, quoting M. de Lannou, *Pâtres et paysans de la Sardaigne.*

The second example to be quoted, from India, illustrates two reasons why the nearer lands tend to be the more fertile—selection of the site for the homestead for convenient tending of fertile land, and the availability of manure.

> The most fertile, heavily manured, and irrigated land surrounds the village. Beyond this lies another zone given over to the chief food crops and irrigated from wells or canals. An outermost zone, the poorest in fertility, is used for dry cultivation, usually millets and fodder crops. . . .[1]

The pattern is, of course, disturbed by routeways, as von Thünen recognised in his modification of the concentric bands consequent on existence of a waterway. Exploitation of land is naturally facilitated by roads and railways, and development is frequently found to be restricted to narrow bands on either side, and is begun only when the route is developed or in anticipation of early improvement.[2]

Olof Jonasson, the Swedish geographer, developed von Thünen's model, relating it to the distribution of agriculture in Europe.[3] He prepared a diagram (reproduced as Figure 14A), which in effect represented an adaptation of the von Thünen model to the agriculture of Europe in 1925. The zones of production he postulated were:

I Horticulture.

Zone 1. The city itself and immediate environs. Greenhouses, floriculture.

Zone 2. Truck products, fruits, potatoes, and tobacco (and horses).

II Intensive agriculture with intensive dairying.

Zone 3. Dairy products, beef cattle, sheep for mutton, veal, forage crops, oats, flax for fibre.

Zone 4. General farming; grain, hay, livestock.

III Extensive agriculture.

Zone 5. Bread cereals and flax for oil.

[1] Ahmad (1952), 232.
[2] Some cases are considered by Chisholm (1962), Chapter 5.
[3] Jonasson (1925).

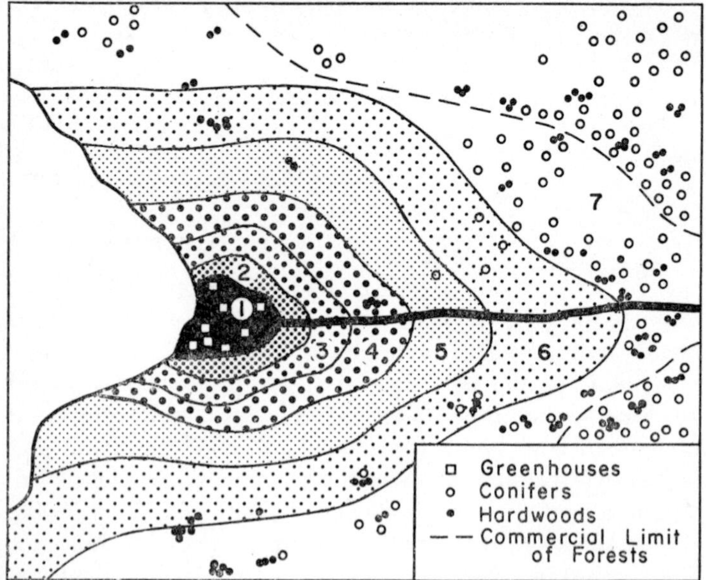

Figure 14A. Model of the zones of production about a theoretical, isolated city in Europe. For key to zones see text.

1. City market.

2. Floriculture.

3. Truck and fruit farming.

4. Dairy and poultry.

5. Grain and cotton.

6. Stock farming.

7. Ranching.

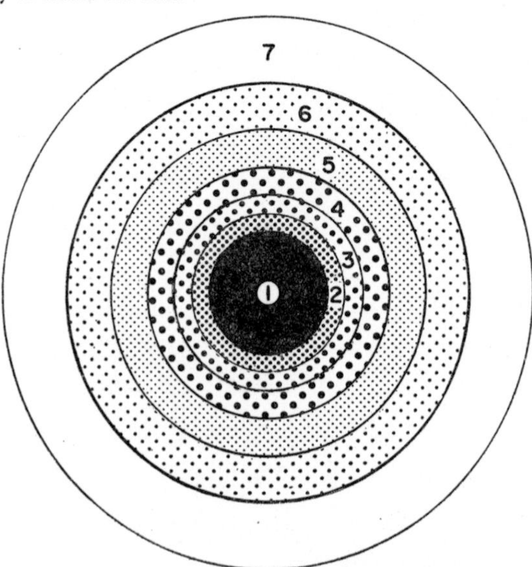

Figure 14B. Zoning on the Edwards plateau of Texas, assuming uniform productivity.

Source: O. Jonasson, *Economic Geography,* Vol. 1, 1925.

IV Extensive pasture.

Zone 6. Cattle (beef and range), horses (range), and sheep (range), salt, smoked, refrigerated and canned meats, bones, tallow and hides.

V Forest culture.

Zone 7. The outermost peripheral area. Forests.

Jonasson recognised that an actual case of such effect of distance from market upon the gradation of land utilisation did not exist but cited examples which offered parallels. He quoted Moscow, Indianapolis and Buenos Aires in this context. He was evidently impressed by the finding of conditions not far from the ideal on the Edwards plateau in Texas,[1] and his reproduction of these conditions is again reproduced here. (Figure 14B).

The most regularly occurring element in this pattern of concentric agricultural regions is the zone of market gardening found adjacent to many cities. This survives because people are prepared to pay prices for fresh vegetables which yield often a higher return to the grower, given short hauls and therefore low transport costs, than is available from selling vegetables for freezing or canning. Thus, there is an incentive for growers to locate close to city markets. Furthermore, as noted in Chapter 3, the return is sufficient to enable the market gardener to pay higher prices for purchase or rent of his land than could be sustained by other forms of agricultural production. Surrounding, or interwoven with, this zone is commonly also found specialisation in producing fresh milk for the urban areas. Although rapid transport enables cities to draw milk from great distances today, intensive dairying can return higher revenues than less intensive forms of farming and therefore can tolerate higher land values.

One must, however, be wary of generalising too much in speaking of the economic qualities of market gardening or dairying as if there were no differentiation between different types of vegetable or milk. Chisholm has examined the distribution of twenty-nine vegetable, fruit and flower crops in England and Wales by counties.[2] He used the coefficient of

[1] Youngblood and Cox (1922), cited by Jonasson (1925), 285.

[2] Chisholm (1962), 92–97.

localisation, as used for industrial location analysis,[1] substituting the area under each crop for the number of employed persons. If a particular crop were distributed among the counties proportionate to its acreage in all the specified crops, the coefficient of localisation would be zero. On the other hand, a value approaching unity indicates a very high degree of localisation. The lowest degree of localisation among the crops examined is found in beetroot, onions, broad beans, turnips and swedes and runner and French beans, in ascending order of localisation, from 0·27 to 0·36. All these are crops which form part of an arable rotation, tolerate a wide range of physical conditions and are not highly perishable. At the other extreme is celery, with a coefficient of 0·61, requiring a well-drained and deep soil and grown mostly in Norfolk, the Isle of Ely and adjacent areas. More in keeping with the idea of localisation in the London area is the growing of tomatoes in the open, with a strong localisation in Essex, Kent and Middlesex. Of the crops occupying larger areas (over 10,000 hectares) the most localised (coefficient 0·48) is Brussels sprouts, of which a quarter of the country's acreage is in Bedfordshire.

It was noted in Chapter 3 that the market gardening industry of Bedfordshire has changed in character with the end of supplies of manure from London, and the improvement of communications that has made it possible to supply Brussels sprouts and other crops to more distant areas, as well as other factors encouraging change. The pattern is not as simple as at first may appear. As an example of a much smaller city, which is nevertheless dominant in the South Island of New Zealand and comparatively isolated from other large towns, Christchurch has a zone of market gardening land straddling its boundaries. The smaller transport costs that growers close to the city have to incur offset the advantages of climatically more favoured areas such as the Nelson district. The zone is far from complete, however, around Christchurch, as fat lamb production, the dominant activity on the adjacent Canterbury Plains, is carried on immediately to the west of the city, where soils are light and dry. The difference in different kinds of dairying enterprises is also marked. Town milk supply obtains much higher prices per gallon for milk than the alternative

[1] Florence (1944).

outlet provided by the butter or cheese factory. Hence, farmers who undertake dairy production near towns do so for town supply, whereas those more distant cannot compete in this and have to accept butterfat prices. Fat lamb production is more attractive to these farmers than milk production for manufacture and so is interwoven with town milk supply, and dominates the areas beyond. In the more distant hill country are farms producing store sheep. The low-intensity store sheep farming in the hill country is maintained there, however, not because it can withstand high transport costs, but because of the low physical productivity of the land, which necessitates extensive grazing.

Thus, in this region there is some zoning in the pattern of agricultural land use reminiscent of that postulated by von Thünen, but soil and climatic factors in this case limit the play of transport costs.

The search for a general theory of location of industry which has occupied many economists since von Thünen's day has been concerned mainly with the distribution of manufacturing industry rather than of agriculture. The theories of Weber,[1] Hoover,[2] Lösch[3] and others who have investigated the advantages to be derived by the manufacturing firm from locating at the point where its costs will be least and/or revenue will be at its maximum are, however, relevant to the study of the theoretical best location of agricultural enterprises. Isard[4] has attempted to integrate industrial and agricultural aspects of location through land use, and Dunn[5] has applied location theory specifically to agriculture.

A location theory should provide the answers to a number of questions. For the individual farmer there should be guidance on where he should locate his farm to produce given products, how large the farm should be and how intensively it should be cultivated. Regional and national authorities should be able to obtain solutions to problems of economic and regional planning. So far these objectives have not been achieved, in spite of growing complexity in the methods of economic

[1] Weber (1909).
[2] Hoover (1948).
[3] Lösch (1940, 1954).
[4] Isard (1956).
[5] Dunn (1954).

analysis employed, which demand a considerable mathematical knowledge for their full appreciation. No model can yet cope with the complexity of background, the intricacy of human reasoning and the constant change that affects all economies. Dunn aims to provide, and to some extent succeeds in achieving 'a general framework of analysis that will serve the dual function of aiding in the evaluation of existing techniques in the field of agricultural economics, and suggesting new approaches to the study of agricultural phenomena.'[1] Understanding of the orientation of production and of the fact that the spatial orientation is an inseparable part of the total economic problem is carried a little further than previously. But it is not suggested that a model is offered which is capable of direct application to the solution of location problems. 'One cannot insert data into a machine and receive an answer sheet that defines the optimum geographic distribution of agricultural production. There are too many sources of discontinuity and elements of indeterminacy in the realistic case'.[2]

Because of the space that would need to be devoted to this type of approach for an evaluation to be useful, the analytical procedures that need to be mastered first, and the lack of practical applications, it will not be pursued here. But we must note that the development of such theories may eventually make them of practical application, and meanwhile they can help empirical investigation to proceed more critically and perhaps itself contribute ultimately to a general theory of location.

It should also be noted that the work of von Thünen and the later location theorists has been mainly devoted to the problem of how to decide what are ideal locations, given certain fixed assumptions, or, especially in von Thünen, how to explain observed distributions. The task of defining actual agricultural regions, with reference to which we began this chapter, and with which geographers are particularly concerned, is different. This problem is essentially one of recognising what exists and delimiting the distinctive areas. Location theory may then help to explain these patterns, and to suggest how they should be

[1] Dunn (1954), 93.
[2] Dunn (1954), 93.

modified, or why different patterns ought to be built up for maximum economic advantage (though other considerations may conflict with these). The central geographical problem of defining regions is essentially attacked on empirical lines.

Empirical Studies

As Grotewald[1] has pointed out, facts actually observed and generalisations derived from them are likely to be more valid than *a priori* theories, because they do not rest upon propositions and therefore their relevance to reality cannot be doubted. There are many differing methods of empirical analysis that deserve attention by the student who would understand what is meant by an agricultural region.

The pioneer work by O. E. Baker and his co-workers first calls for comment. O. E. Baker, economist in the U.S. Bureau of Agricultural Economics, stated the physical and economic principles which explain the distribution of crops in the first issue of the journal, *Economic Geography*:[2]

1. The crop or other agricultural product which is most limited in climatic or other physical requirements of production will, if the demand for it be sufficient, have first choice of the land. It possesses, so to speak, a sort of natural monopoly and consequently commands a price which gives it an advantage over other crops or products.

2. The crop or other agricultural product which has small bulk or weight per unit of value can best bear the cost of transportation and will be grown, consequently, in those regions offering the most favourable physical conditions; but not to the exclusion of more bulky crops, because a certain quantity of these bulky crops that cannot bear the cost of transportation must be grown locally to meet the local demand.

3. The varying seasonal requirements of the several crops and agricultural products for labour tend to diversify the agriculture of a region.

4. Not only is it desirable to grow such a combination of crops as equalises the seasonal requirements of labour, but

[1] Grotewald (1959), 347.

[2] Baker (1925). The summary here is from Jonasson (1925).

also it is important to grow such a combination of crops as will maintain soil fertility and promote freedom from insects and disease.

5. Opposed to these tendencies toward diversification is a tendency to grow the most productive crops (value per acre) on the most valuable land, and as population increases and land becomes relatively scarcer this tendency becomes stronger, since the more expensive land and more abundant labour must be profitably employed.

6. Lastly, but not least important, is the character of the farm population and the accumulated community skill and experience.

Between 1926 and 1934 *Economic Geography* published twelve articles by O. E. Baker in which he analysed the agricultural regions of North America, while other contributors dealt later with other continents. Baker did not, so far as we know, begin by looking for regions which theory told him should exist, but rather by accepting such as were already widely recognised and by relying on practical knowledge and statistics to reveal others. Baker's concern was to locate and to describe, not to set the regions in their economic relationships, internal or external. Thus, 'Baker's descriptive treatment of the Corn Belt as a going concern stands unrivalled . . . but should, it would seem, better be regarded as a contribution to regional than to economic geography'.[1] The Corn Belt, recently re-christened the Corn and Soy Bean Belt to take account of changing cultivation patterns[2], is a good example for the illustration of problems of delimitation.[3]

In some cases Baker was able to use boundaries beyond which the appropriate crops were not cultivated at all, for example the northern boundary of his cotton belt. Corn, however, is the most widely grown crop on the continent and what was required was a valid method of accurately distinguishing the area of corn-growing par excellence, *the* Corn Belt. He defined it as including 'that portion of the east central United States in which corn (maize) is produced in great quantities and is

[1] R. O. Buchanan (1959), 10.
[2] Haystead and Fite (1955).
[3] Summary based on Buchanan (1959).

more important than any other crop.' This definition would, however, include much of his Corn and Winter Wheat Belt. It has been suggested that what he really meant was the dominant crop, in the sense that corn provides the focus for the whole farm organisation including the crop rotation, but he does not say this.

On the quantitative measure of relative importance of corn that could be mapped he says 'The yearly average production along the southern margin is 3000 bushels per square mile and this is generally also true along the northern and eastern margins.' We are not, however, told by what method he arrived at the figure of 3000 bushels, nor whether he applied it strictly.

A rigorous procedure which is appropriate in a case like this is to make a farm-by-farm investigation along a series of transects from well outside the approximate boundary to well inside it. Correspondences noted between any line joining the points at which corn ceased to be the dominant crop and other boundaries, physical or economic, would have validity as firm correlations, established *after* the extent of the belt had been fixed. No correlation can have any value at all unless the variables it relates are completely independent. Baker's methods may have been sound but he has left no way of judging them. In spite of this failing his contribution was important in furthering the use of statistics.

Realisation of the value of the work being carried out by Dr. Baker led to the initiation of a more detailed study of the farming types of the United States. Data were obtained through the 1930 census of agriculture and all farms were classified into twelve types and five subtypes on a basis of farm income. Further processing led eventually to the drawing of boundaries defining 812 type-of-farming districts, which were subsequently grouped into regions and provinces.[1]

Also in this period Hartshorne and Dicken classified the agricultural regions of North America and Europe, using statistics for delimitation.[2] This appears to have been the first attempt to analyse the agriculture of the two continents on a basis of statistical measurement. The limiting criteria were

[1] Elliott (1933), quoted by Renner (1935).

[2] Hartshorne and Dicken (1935).

selected from a range of isopleths based on a method suggested by W. D. Jones:[1]

> For any particular limit, that isopleth was selected which seemed to represent most closely the change from one definite type to another. In a number of cases that one was selected which conformed most closely to the boundaries based on value of products . . . the ratio based on acreage was regarded as more significant geographically than one based on value, not only because it is an actual area measurement but also because it fluctuates much less widely from year to year.[2]

The table of criteria used for this classification is given below. It is instructive to study the basis of the delimitation of the regions and also to compare the types of agriculture with those defined by Whittlesey and discussed in Chapter 4.

TABLE 9

CRITERIA FOR TYPES OF AGRICULTURE

		Major Crop	*Others*	*Limits*
	All types	......	......	Crop-and-pasture land > 10% total area.
I	Mediterranean	wheat,	barley, vines, fruits	Vine and sub-tropical tree crops > 15% cropland.
II	Corn-wheat-livestock	corn	wheat, oats, hay	Cotton < ½ corn acreage. Tobacco < 20% cropland. Corn and wheat > 30%, corn alone at least 20% cropland.
III	Small grains-livestock	wheat, rye	oats, barley, potatoes, hay	Tilled crops > hay and pasture. Wheat and rye > 10% of crop-and-pasture land.
IV	Hay-pasture-livestock	hay	oats, barley, potatoes, silage corn	Hay and pasture > tilled crops. Wheat and rye > 10% crop-and-pasture land.
V	Extensive commercial grain	wheat	rye, corn, barley, oats	Livestock < 20 units per 100 acres of cropland. Large farms; low yields. Cropland > 20% total area.
VI	Commercial orchard and truck	......	......	Orchards and vegetables > 20% cropland.

In its use of statistics to provide a scientific, measurement basis for classification in agricultural geography, applicable to

[1] Jones (1930).

[2] Hartshorne and Dicken (1935).

diverse regions, this article represented another major step forward. On the other hand, it failed to recognise the difficulties inherent in combining crop and livestock data and the importance of distinguishing the object of crop growing, e.g. for sale or consumption as fodder on the farm.[1]

British geographers began using statistical data to assist in the delimitation of types of agriculture, which had hitherto been discussed mainly by reference to physical or 'natural' regions, as early as the first World War period. The first Agricultural Atlas of England and Wales[2] used parish statistics,[3] which were depicted as dot distribution maps. In the following decades a number of studies were made on this basis and both dot and density shading maps based on parish statistics featured as a standard method in the reports of the Land Utilisation Survey of Britain.[4] In these reports statistical methods supplemented field enquiries in the interpretation of the land use maps prepared in the early 1930s. Unfortunately, the boundaries of parishes do not coincide generally with significant physical features, but rather run from river valley on to surrounding upland or even mountain regions. Hence, although England is but a small country, and parishes numerous, the subdivision is not fine enough for satisfactory micro-geographical work. Parish statistics permit the clarification of distributions over broad regions and changes within these areas over time, but for study of agricultural regions in detail in areas where there is great physical and cultural diversity the network of statistical units must present a very fine mesh.

Such a fine mesh exists and has been put to use in Northern Ireland. There, the agricultural statistics were formerly collected by the police and returned by enumeration districts of which there were 550 in the six counties of Northern Ireland, an average size of 6048 acres. The statistics are published[5] only in lesser detail but for years in which this method was used the details by enumeration districts have been accessible to research workers. By their aid quite detailed distribution

[1] Chisholm (1964).

[2] Howell (1925), 2nd ed. Messer (1932).

[3] Collected by the Ministry of Agriculture and Fisheries, also by Department of Agriculture for Scotland.

[4] Stamp (ed.) (1937–44).

[5] Regular publications of the Ministry of Agriculture for Northern Ireland.

maps could be constructed and the maps in the report of the Land Utilisation Survey of Northern Ireland[1] were compiled on this basis. Even with this degree of detail there were still difficulties, such as enumeration districts, like British parishes, including both lowland and hill areas, but the error in the resulting maps was small compared with those constructed with parish statistics. Unfortunately, this method of collection and processing of statistics is no longer used and similar detail is not available for research purposes. The maps in Figure 15 show the degree of detail obtainable with the enumeration district basis as compared with the present rural district basis.

In surveys like those carried out by the government departments responsible for agriculture in the United Kingdom, statistics of crops, livestock, labour employed and many other details are required under legal duress every year from every farmer. But the law also requires that such statistics shall be regarded as completely confidential so that they may not be disclosed to even a *bona fide* research worker. This is unfortunate, since they would provide excellent material for analysis. Since the farm, not the parish or enumeration district, is the unit of operation and the financial unit, it is obviously a desirable point of departure for research in economic geography as well as in agricultural economics. Many studies based on selected farms and random samples of farms have been carried out by agricultural economists but comparatively few by geographers. Most of the surveys which have used data for a large number of farms have been official,[2] and consequently access to the official statistics has been permissible, though details for individual, identifiable, farms are never published.

Realising the limitations of parish statistics, even when interpreted with the aid of fieldwork, Birch[3] for a survey of farming-type regions in the Isle of Man decided to base this on a sample of farms selected for the purpose. He notes that any such survey must incorporate (i) an objective method of making a representative selection from the total of farms in a

[1] Symons (ed.) (1963).

[2] For example, *National Farm Survey of England and Wales (1941–1943)* Summary report, H.M.S.O. 1946; *Types of Farming in Scotland*, H.M.S.O. 1952.

[3] Birch (1954).

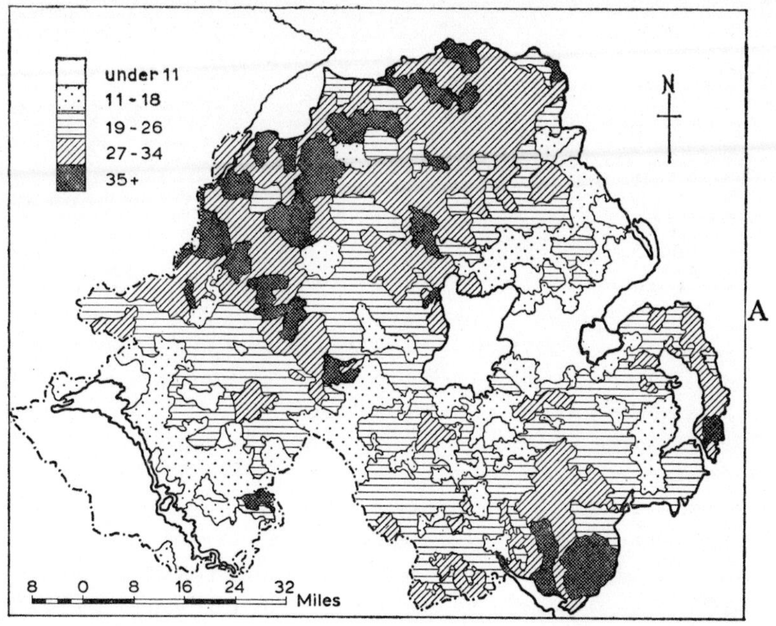

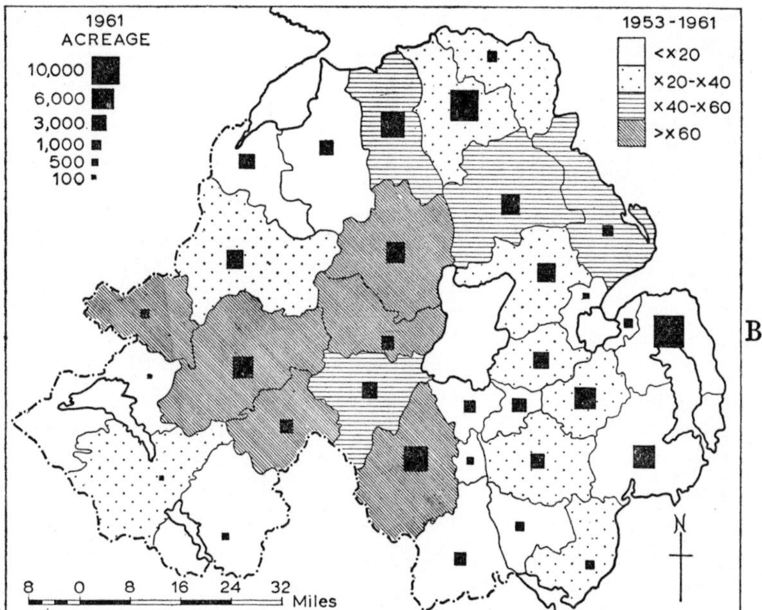

Figure 15. A comparison of detail in density maps obtainable with former and current agricultural census data for Northern Ireland.

(A) Ploughed land as a percentage of crops and pasture, 1953, by special enumeration districts, subsequently discontinued.

(B) Increase in cultivation of barley, 1953–61, by rural districts.

Source: L. Symons, *Land use in Northern Ireland.*

given landscape; and (ii) a method of obtaining from those farms a standardised body of quantitative and qualitative data.[1] He used the one-inch and six-inch to one-mile maps as 'statistical frames'[2] and 232 farms out of the total population of 1160 Manx farms were selected.

> They were spaced, as far as possible at regular intervals, over the farming landscape. Of this original selection, 14 farms or 6 per cent., proved unco-operative. A further 24 farms were added as the survey proceeded. This was necessary because the original density of selection did not appear adequate to define what were emerging as localised areas of dominant milk production adjoining the smaller centres of population, and equally localised pockets of store cattle raising near the moorland edge.

This illustrates the commonly experienced need to modify the statistical sample as experience is gained in the field in spite of careful reconnaissance survey. Birch continues with a statement of the two qualities in the sample ensured by the systematic selection of farms from areal frames:

> (i) An adequate spatial distribution of the farms of all sizes. This is essential.
>
> (ii) The greater proportional representation of the large holdings. This accords with the design of the sample used in the National Farm Survey. It was made possible in this case because the probability of a selection of a farm, by this method, is proportional to its size.

Each farm selected for the sample was visited and if the farmer agreed to co-operate, a questionnaire was left for completion. '110 questionnaires, for 45 per cent. of the total farms, were completed in this way, though in some cases after as many as three visits to each farm, extending over a period of two years. For a further 55 farms, 23 per cent. of the total questionnaires were completed in full by students or by the writer'.[3] Some data were collected for most farms for which the full questionnaire was not completed.

This report indicates the difficulties experienced by the

[1] Birch (1954), 144.
[2] Birch (1954), 145.
[3] Birch (1954), 146–147.

private research worker, with limited time and resources, in obtaining data from a sample of farms by individual interview and questionnaires. It goes a long way towards explaining why such investigations are not common.

This problem was encountered in a marked form in the compilation of the report of the Land Utilisation Survey of Northern Ireland. It was felt that the interpretation of the land use map made in 1938–39 and further analysis of the land use pattern demanded information on a large number of individual farms. Although Northern Ireland is a small area, only about 5200 sq. mls. (3,326,400 acres), the number of farms amounted in 1957 to about 74,000. Workers engaged in the different areas were given freedom to use their own methods to achieve this object. Postal questionnaires were not expected to be of great value, but the research workers concerned with some counties tried using them. 441 questionnaires were sent out to two counties, but of these only 87 were returned completed. Reliance on personal field enquiries was therefore continued.

Advances in Statistical Analysis

While the collection of data on the farm-unit scale continues to lag, national and international statistics on crop acreages, numbers of livestock and other details of agricultural land occupance grow rapidly in bulk. It is therefore fortunate that the digital computer makes possible the handling of an amount of data that would have been impracticable without its aid. This permits the combination of data relating to different variables to resolve the patterns of complex distributions. An advance in this type of work was made by Weaver in his assembly of data for several different crops produced in association in the Middle West of the United States.[1]

Basing his work on acreage statistics, Weaver computed the percentage of total harvested cropland occupied by each crop that held as much as 1 per cent. of this total in each of the 1081 counties covered in his work. Ranked by size within each county, many critical crop combinations were obvious, e.g. corn (C) 33 per cent., hay (H) 33 per cent., oats (O), 30 per cent., mixed small grains 1 per cent. in Houston County,

[1] Weaver (1954).

Minnesota. Other counties, however, as would be expected, showed all gradations between distinctive crop combinations. It was necessary to devise 'a rigorous approach that would provide objective, constant and precisely repeatable procedures and would yield comparable results for different years and localities'.

To provide a standard measurement a theoretical curve was employed as follows:

monoculture	=	100% of total harvested cropland in one crop
2-crop combination	=	50% in each of two crops
3-crop combination	=	33·33% in each of three crops and systematically through to
9-crop combination	=	11·11% in each of nine crops
10-crop combination	=	10% in each of ten crops.

To measure the actual occurrence of percentages against the theoretical curve, the standard deviation was used

$$\mathrm{SD} = \sqrt{\frac{\Sigma d^2}{n}}$$

where d is the difference between the actual crop percentage in a given county and the appropriate percentage in the theoretical curve and n is the number of crops in a given combination.

In fact, the relative, not absolute, values being significant, square roots were not extracted so the actual formula used was

$$\sigma^2 = \frac{\Sigma d^2}{n}$$

To demonstrate the technique, the example given by Weaver is reproduced below. The actual distribution of crop percentages in Keokuk County, Iowa, in 1949 was C 54, O 24, H 13, S (soybeans) 5, W (wheat) 2. This pattern measured against the theoretical base curve yields the results given in Table 10.

The deviation of the actual percentages from the theoretical curve is seen to be lowest for a three-crop combination. This result established the identity and the number of crops in the basic combination for the county as COH.

The figures thus derived for the years 1949 and 1939 were

TABLE 10

STANDARD DEVIATION ANALYSIS FOR KEOKUK COUNTY, IOWA

	MONO-CULTURE	*2 CROPS*		*3 CROPS*			*4 CROPS*				*5 CROPS*				
	C	C	O	C	O	H	C	O	H	S	C	O	H	S	W
% of cropland occupied	54	54	24	54	24	13	54	24	13	5	54	24	13	5	2
%, theoretical, base curve	100	50	50	33⅓	33⅓	33⅓	25	25	25	25	20	20	20	20	20
Difference	46	4	26	20⅔	9⅓	20⅓	29	1	12	20	34	4	7	15	18
Difference squared	2116	16	676	427	87	413	841	1	144	400	1156	16	49	225	324
Sum of squared differences	2116	692		927			1386				1770				
Sum divided by number of crops	2116	346		309			347				354				

plotted on maps for the two years. Boundaries were then drawn around blocks of counties with the same number and identity of crops. The percentage rank of crops within any given group was not considered, e.g. COH, OHC, HOC being consolidated into a common crop-combination region. The problem of small-area speciality crops was dealt with by adding a symbol, e.g. Pc for popcorn, for any speciality crop attaining or exceeding 3 per cent. of the total harvested cropland.

The results reveal significant diversity within the long-accepted agricultural 'belts' of the area, to which reference has been made in connection with the work of O. E. Baker:

> . . . So far as the identity of the major crops and the relative amounts of cropland devoted to their use are concerned, the practices in 1949 of the so-called 'Dairy Belt' farmers in southeastern Wisconsin were more nearly akin to those of the 'Corn Belt' hog and beef-cattle feeders of southeastern Iowa than to those of dairy farmers in southern Michigan. In turn, the crop-association use in that year of cultivated land in an average county in southern Michigan found its most clearly defined counterparts in such widely separated 'Corn Belt' lands as northeastern Indiana, northwestern Missouri, and southeastern Nebraska.[1]

These are useful findings which are not made less desirable to have by the fact that the crop associations, like other aspects of the economic scene, are not static but always changing. But, as Weaver himself reminds us, the regions presented pertain only to crops, and only to the land-use associations of crops. They are not substitute agricultural regions.

Weaver's crop combination methods were adapted by Scott[2] to a survey of both crop and livestock combinations in Tasmania. Modifications were made to make the procedure even more 'objective, constant, and precisely repeatable', one being to include speciality crops in the statistical definition, and Scott's aim was to employ the results to help define agricultural regions. He noted that:

[1] Weaver (1954), 189–190.
[2] Scott (1957).

> . . . a study of the crop and livestock patterns in Tasmania reveals that both the grouped combinations and the ranked combinations are relevant, since it is the ranked combinations rather than the grouped combinations which define the major crop regions and the grouped rather than the ranked combinations which define the livestock regions. This stems from the fact that crop associations are by no means so strong in Tasmania as livestock associations.

A further important step in combining dissimilar data for the indentification of regions has been taken by Coppock, also using a modified version of Weaver's method to produce not only crop and livestock combinations, but also combinations of agricultural enterprises in England and Wales.[1] Coppock did not attempt to use parishes as the basis of his work, as there are over 10,000 of them in England and Wales and even when using a computer there are limitations to the amount of data that can be handled, because extraction from records and punching cards or tape is time consuming. He used National Agricultural Advisory Districts, of which there were 350, each comprising 30 or 40 parishes and several hundred farms. As already noted, the parish itself is regarded as too large a unit for detailed regional work, but some compensation in using still larger areal units was claimed by Coppock in that the advisory districts were fairly homogeneous in size. Nearly 90 per cent. fell in the range 80 to 280 square miles, and they often contained at least no greater variety of physical conditions than the parishes.

To arrive at the various combinations of crops and livestock, Coppock used the adaptation of Weaver's method developed by D. Thomas.[2] Thus the data for the full range of crops under examination were fitted to ideal values and the squares of the differences then summed. Weaver mapped crop combinations without regard to rank. Regions in the Middle West could be distinguished by the different crops, but in England and Wales it is the different ranking of a few crops that reveals the differences, e.g. on southern chalkland, barley, wheat and oats,

[1] Coppock (1964a).

[2] D. Thomas (1963).

in that order; on east Midland clays, wheat, oats and barley. Full account of rank of all crops examined would have been too complex but Coppock did take into account rank in recognising the leading crop. Minor crops had to be disregarded in map construction but the resulting map of combinations, reproduced in Figure 16 and a corresponding map of livestock combinations provide a valuable basis for identifying regional types of agriculture. Greater detail of the combinations appears in the *Agricultural Atlas of England and Wales*.[1]

Coppock aimed, however, at not merely plotting the combinations of crops and livestock separately, but the grouping together of these to reveal distribution of types of farm enterprise, which in British farming usually include both crops and livestock on one farm. This involved comparison of unlike units—livestock with crops, and, indeed, different crops, the relative importance of which is not fully reflected by acreage e.g. potatoes and grain. The equating of different classes of livestock, as required for the map of livestock combinations, is, however, fairly simple. Feed requirements provide the normal basis for this type of comparison, and represent a modern equivalent of the souming arrangements employed for centuries by mountain townships with common grazings.[2] Livestock units with slightly varying equivalents are widely used today in calculations of fodder requirements and farming intensity. The factors used by Coppock were: horses, cows, bulls and other cattle two years old and over, 1 unit; other cattle between one and two years old, 2/3; other cattle under one year, 1/3; breeding ewes, 1/5; rams, 1/10; other sheep, 1/15; sows, 1/2; boars, 1/4; other pigs, 1/7; poultry six months old and over, 1/50; poultry under six months old, 1/200.

In order to combine different enterprises other conversion factors are necessary, enabling both crops and livestock to be equated. Monetary values are an obvious possibility but depend on adequate financial information being available. Coppock considers two alternatives: (*a*) standard outputs, in which monetary values are ascribed to each crop and class of livestock; and (*b*) standard labour requirements, in which the

[1] Coppock (1964b).

[2] Scottish examples appear in Darling (ed) 1955.

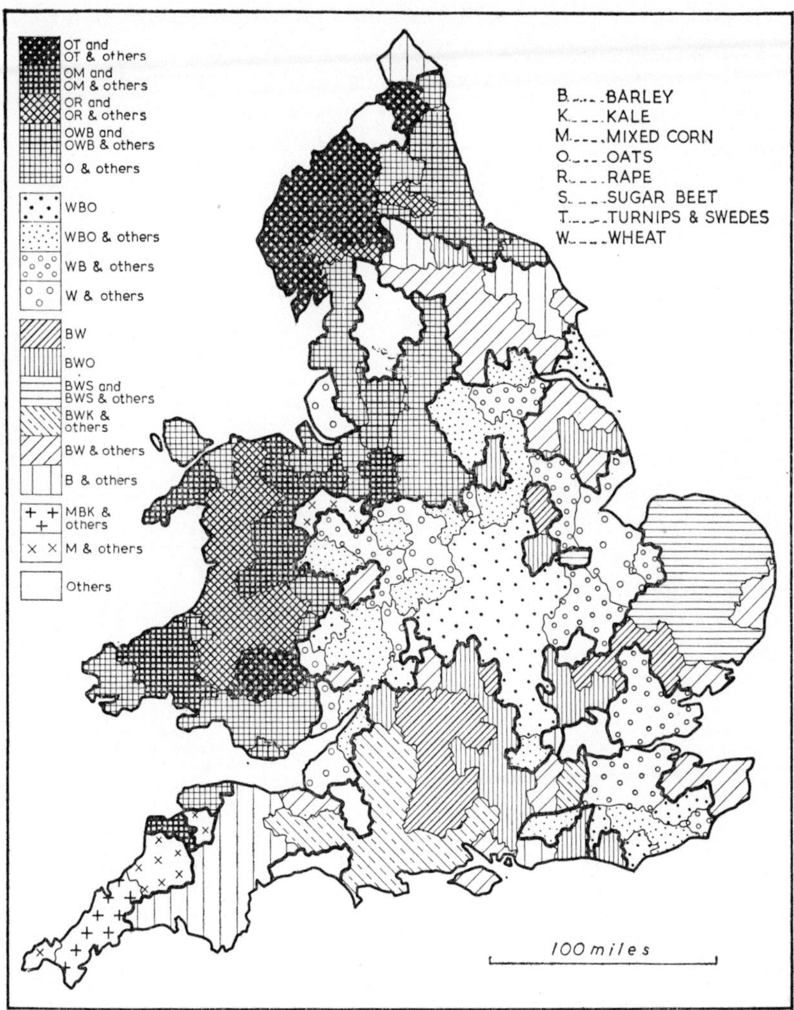

Figure 16. Crop Combinations in England and Wales.
Source: J. T. Coppock, *Economic Geography*, Vol. 40, 1964.

annual man-days necessary for each crop or class of livestock provide the common measure. Both measures have to make assumptions based on standards which cannot in fact apply to all farms or all districts. Standard labour requirements were used as the yardstick to measure eligibility for participation in the scheme to assist small farmers.[1] They have many uses, for example in comparing output in a given region with the size of its agricultural labour force.[2] Coppock decided to use these factors, with some modifications, as reproduced in Table 11.

TABLE 11

STANDARD AGRICULTURAL LABOUR REQUIREMENTS

	Man-days per acre
Wheat, barley, rye	3·5
Oats, mixed corn	4·5
Pulses for stock	4
Potatoes	20
Sugar beet	17
Turnips, swedes	12
Mangolds, fodder beet	21
Other crops	7
Vegetables, brassicas	20
Vegetables, roots	21
Vegetables, pulses	12·5
Other vegetables	40
Hops	100
Small fruit	45
Orchards with small fruit	55
Other orchards	25
Flowers, nursery stock	50
Glass	1320
Bare fallow	0·5
Grass for mowing	2
Grass for grazing	0·25
	Man-days per head
Dairy cows	15
Dairy heifers	9
Beef cows	4·5
Bulls	7
Other cattle	3
Sows and boars	4
Other pigs	1·2

[1] Cmd. 553, H.M.S.O. London (1958).

[2] For example, in Northern Ireland, Symons (ed.) (1963), 56–57.

Upland sheep one year old and over	0·5
Lowland sheep one year old and over	1
Other sheep	0·25
Poultry 6 months old and over	0·3
Poultry under 6 months old	0·1

Once man-days had been calculated for individual crops and classes of livestock it was necessary to allocate them to appropriate agricultural enterprises before enterprise combinations could be identified. Seven enterprises were recognised, viz. dairy cattle, beef cattle, sheep, cash crops, fruit, vegetables, and pigs and poultry, the last two being treated together because they depend largely on purchased feeding stuffs. Lack of detail in the census made it necessary to make certain decisions on apportionment of cattle to the beef and dairy enterprises, and as to what should be classed as cash crops—wheat, barley, sugar beet and potatoes being so considered. Man-days for fodder (other crops) and grass were then allocated to the different classes of livestock enterprise according to the nutritional requirements of these classes of stock as expressed in livestock units.

A series of maps shows the distribution of leading enterprises assessed in several ways, and combinations of enterprises. In this last (Figure 17) the enterprises are shown in rank order, but in combinations with three or more enterprises only the first two are named. Districts with the same leading enterprise are distinguished by similar shading and a heavy surrounding line. Anomalous features appear in the map; for example, the classification of the Lake District as dairying-with-livestock reflects the layout of large districts, each comprising both upland rough grazings and lowland plain.

Some of the limitations of these maps spring from the coarseness of the mesh provided by the districts, but others derive from the methods used. Coppock suggests three possible lines for improvement; firstly, in the allocation of crops and livestock to different enterprises; secondly, in improving the techniques for determining combinations and, thirdly, in cartographic representation of the combinations. Coppock claims no more than that his maps should be regarded as reconnaissance sketches, but his paper demonstrates the great scope that exists for improvement in the analysis of agricultural distributions and takes a firm step in a promising direction.

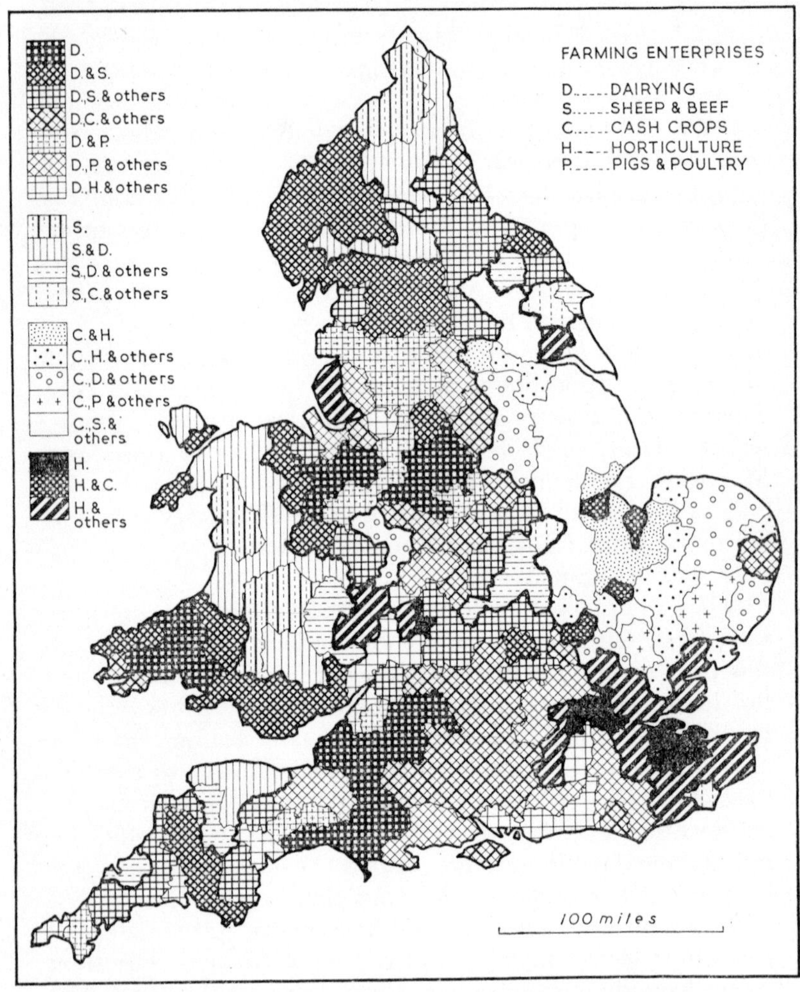

Figure 17. Enterprise Combinations in England and Wales.
Source: J. T. Coppock, *Economic Geography*, Vol. 40, 1964.

Types of Farming and Agricultural Regions

Coppock also points out that his enterprise map is not a type-of-farming map, as it is based upon the district totals and not upon individual farm records. If it were based on individual farm records and boundary lines were drawn on it to distinguish regions, would this be a map of agricultural regions? To put it another way, is an agricultural region the same thing as the type-of-farming region? Whittlesey, in his classic paper[1] set out to indicate the major agricultural *regions* of the earth, drawing boundaries for this purpose which enclosed the major *types* of agriculture, as summarised in Chapter 4. Whittlesey, however, considered that the functioning forms of a type of agriculture included not only the crop and livestock association, but also methods, intensity, disposal of products (subsistence or commercial) and the ensemble of structures used to house and facilitate the farming operations. It thus includes more criteria than would be included in analyses similar to that carried out by Coppock into crop and livestock associations (but applied to individual farms), which he would appear to require to discern type-of-farming regions.

The types of region are different, involving in one case more and wider criteria than in the other. But use of the terms as employed by the respective authors would imply different definitions of 'type of farming' and 'agriculture' which would probably not be generally acceptable.[2]

It is evident that there is need here for attention to terminology with the dual objectives of removing ambiguities and focusing attention on the exact objectives of research projects and their limitations.[3]

Such studies, seeking to define agricultural regions by reference to varied aspects of the agricultural environment are also undertaken by specialists in fields other than geography and if there is common ground in terminology it should be retained. A recent example is the study of agricultural regions in the European Economic Community.[4] In this survey, which aimed at mapping the major agricultural regions of the six E.E.C. countries on a common basis, time was an important factor. Therefore, the study group eliminated 'the idea of

[1] Whittlesey (1936).

[2] Compare the case of the terms 'land use' and 'land utilisation' discussed in Chapter 10.

[3] Work in progress by Commissions of the International Geographical Union may assist in this direction, hence further suggestions are not offered here.

[4] *Agricultural Regions in the E.E.C.*, Organisation for European Economic Co-operation, Paris, 1960.

carving out too many elementary geographical cells as a basis for analysing existing conditions preparatory to regrouping into agricultural regions'. Gaps in available statistics forced restriction to a limited number of criteria, and these were supplemented by subjective elements drawn from the experts' own experience. It was claimed that 'Agricultural regions marked out in this way are, if the agricultural conditions have been adequately translated into figures, markedly nearer the reality than regions determined purely on a statistical basis.'

Many geographers would agree with this claim, partly because statistics of different countries are often not comparable in detail, and in many cases few series are available. Also, statistics are not themselves necessarily as accurate as one may be tempted to suppose[1] and the design of any analysis demands subjective judgments in classification. But it is also true that statistical procedures alone provide us with the means of presenting classifications which other workers can reproduce for comparative purposes or to extend the area of enquiry.

Progress in Regional Delimitation

The methods which have been reviewed in this chapter go some way to satisfying the needs of regional division. However, while the hypothesis of Chapter 4 that types and systems of agriculture may be grouped spatially as regions need not be totally rejected, it may be felt that the techniques described above do not deal adequately with this difficult task, i.e., the evidence suggests that we have not yet mastered the problems of delimiting regions. More advanced methods, however, beyond the scope of this introduction to the subject, have already been tested by some workers. Examples include the linear programming type of production model,[2] in which limiting assumptions may be relaxed as the models are improved, the use of chi-square analysis for testing regional boundaries[3] and the quantification of similarity as a basis for multifactor regionalisation.[4] As mathematical models approach the stage of refinement where they can embrace the complexities of functioning and dynamic economic relationships

[1] Best (1960) illustrates this in detail.
[2] Henderson (1957).
[3] Zobler (1957).
[4] Berry (1958).

they must be utilised increasingly in our spatial analysis.[1] Meanwhile, when we use the word 'region' we should bear in mind the limitations of the processes which we have employed to define the areas distinguished by this convenient but rather over-worked term.

[1] Progress in this field is recorded and analysed by Haggett (1965).

CHAPTER 10

Land Use and Land Potential

Land use is an important aspect of geographical studies, particularly relevant to agricultural geography. Land use survey has become the spearhead of the advance of geography into the applied sciences, maps of land use having become recognised as essential tools of regional planning and development.

Once again we must clarify our concepts before proceeding to consider methodology and application. The term 'land use' is virtually self-explanatory, but complications have arisen over interpretations of the meaning of 'use' and the alternative, 'utilisation'. The present writer stresses at the outset that he does not believe that these terms should be given different meanings. Although shades of difference may be found in dictionary definitions of the two words, their employment in the English language suggests that they are interchangeable, preference being given to 'use' because it is shorter. It is necessary to make this point simply because this usage differs from that of some writers. Thus, Fox[1] gives the following definitions:

> *Land use* is the actual and specific use to which the land surface is put in terms of inherent land-use characteristics. The study of land use is concerned primarily with the vegetative cover, or its lack. . . . It is a formal concept within the field of geography as a whole.
>
> *Land utilisation* is the process of exploiting land use—that is, land applied to a specific objective. Areas undeveloped by man are negative from the viewpoint of land utilisation, which, therefore is a functional concept within the field of cultural geography.

The majority of land use surveys embrace both of these concepts, finding that it is an arid and valueless exercise to

[1] Fox (1956), 42.

examine the vegetative cover—from the point of view of use—without integrating consideration of the functions it performs. There is, however, value in a term which encompasses no more than the variation in cover, whether it be vegetative or erected structures. For this purpose, the term *land cover* suggests itself. This term has been used by the Hunter Valley Research Foundation in Australia together with 'utilisation' as follows:[1]

> *Land cover*—the setting in which this action (using or employment) takes place, i.e. the vegetation and artificial constructions (if any) covering the Land Surface (which is composed solely of rock outcrops and soils).
> *Land utilisation*—the action, i.e. the employment of the Land Surface through the medium of the Land Cover.

In this book, similarly, the term 'land cover' is used for the elements of the surface cover, whether natural or induced by man, and 'land use' (or utilisation) has the wider meaning, implying inclusion of the land cover.

In a comprehensive study of land use it is proper to include all forms of use, whether agricultural, sylvicultural, industrial or urban, though many studies are concerned with only one or another. We are here concerned only with agricultural land use, which in most occupied regions of the earth is the greatest user in terms of areal extent, though in some regions this is surpassed by the forestal use, and, locally, by urban use. Following the dominance among areal uses of agriculture, many land use surveys have been concerned almost entirely with agricultural use, even though this has not been specified.

As a result of land use survey, areas are grouped into regions in much the same way as has been discussed in relation to agricultural regions, but using different criteria, such as the respective proportions of the different classes of land use, including forests, urban areas, transport installations, industries and unused land. They may coincide closely with agricultural regions, even exactly (if there are no uses of land other than agricultural in the particular region) but the criteria used for definition and delimitation are different—they are land use criteria.

[1] Burley (1961), 4.

For practical purposes, especially where a study is addressed to a wide variety of readers of varied technical backgrounds and interests, it may be desirable to integrate agricultural and land use regions, to avoid tedious repetition and unnecessary pedantry. This was done deliberately in the report of the Land Utilisation Survey of Northern Ireland. Thus the description of the Lough Neagh Lowlands (given here in Chapter 5) as a region of small, mixed farms, is derived from the wider description of land use regions. Similarly, from a land use region which contained a significant element of forests, one could abstract the information relevant to forestry.

Land use surveys should always be prepared with the needs of a wide range of specialists and laymen in mind, for a land use survey is an expensive undertaking and everyone today is in some way concerned with land use. Although it was the first of the modern land use surveys, that of Great Britain undertaken in the 1930s achieved this quality, and the value of a broad interpretation was proved over and over again in the uses found for it in planning wartime agricultural development and post-war reconstruction.

The Evolution of Land Use Survey

Concern with the uses to which land is put must be as old as agriculture, and the systematisation of knowledge relating to land use dates back at least as far as the application of taxes to land according to its use. One of the best ancient examples was the Norman Domesday Survey of England. Centuries later the agrarian revolution led to surveys which examined usually both agricultural techniques and general aspects of land use county by county,[1] and settlement in the 'new' countries stimulated interest in assessment of land resources. It was not, however, until 1919 that the idea of a map portraying the use of land systematically was put forward[2] and not until another decade had passed was there an attempt to initiate such mapping on a national basis. Steps to formulate a scheme applicable to the

[1] The first *Statistical Account of Scotland*, which provided systematic studies of this kind, was begun in 1791, similar *Statistical Surveys* of the Irish counties appeared in the early years of the nineteenth century, and many volumes appeared on the English counties, giving in all a most valuable record of the eighteenth and nineteenth centuries in the British Isles.

[2] Sauer (1919), 48.

whole of Great Britain had been made successfully by 1930 and the fieldwork began in 1931.[1]

In this pioneer scheme costs had to be kept to the minimum and it was essential to use a scheme that was simple and readily understood by voluntary workers with varied or with little training. The scheme evolved, nevertheless, made possible the presentation of a vivid picture of the contrasts in land cover throughout the country. The field mapping was done on Ordnance Survey maps on the scale of six inches to one mile (1:10,560) which were subsequently reduced to one inch to one mile (1:63,360). Most one-inch sheets were printed and published, the exceptions being some of the sheets of the Highlands of Scotland where almost all of the land was used as rough grazing and deer forests.

The classification used, with the letter placed on the field sheets and the colouring used on them and on the published maps, was as follows:

(1)	Forest and woodland ...	F	Dark green
(2)	Meadowland and permanent grass ...	M	Light green
(3)	Arable or tilled land, fallow, rotation grass, and market gardens ...	A	Brown
	[market gardens, where clearly so, ...	A	(M.G.)]
(4)	Heathland, moorland, commons, and rough hill pasture ...	H	Yellow
(5)	Gardens, allotments, orchards, nurseries, etc. ...	G	Purple
(6)	Land agriculturally unproductive, e.g. buildings, yards, mines, cemeteries, etc. ...	W	Red
(7)	Ponds, lakes, reservoirs, ditches, dykes, streams and anything containing water ...	P	Blue

Forests were subdivided into high forest, coppice, scrub, any cut down and not replanted, and whether coniferous, deciduous or mixed.

[1] Stamp (1948, 1962).

The classification of rotation grassland as arable was correct in terms of land management but gave rise to some difficulties in interpretation. In the subsequent survey of Northern Ireland in 1938–39 all grassland, whether in rotation or in permanent pasture of good quality, was grouped together. A category was also introduced for lowland bog, which was not a significant feature in Britain but of considerable extent in Ireland.

Reports were written describing the land use of each county in Britain and published in 92 parts between 1936 and 1946. The time between the beginning of the field work and the completion of the reports may appear excessive, but to appreciate the difficulties before and during the war which had to be overcome it is necessary to read the account of the history which introduces the summary volume, *The Land of Britain, its Use and Misuse*.

It is instructive to compare the new land use survey of England and Wales with the old. A sample area is compared, with the addition of soil and relief maps, in Figure 18. The new land use map is much more detailed, with mapping on the scale of 1/25,000 for publication on the same scale. Thirteen main groups are used, with a crayon number specified for each to avoid confusion:[1]

(1)	Settlement (residential and commercial)	Grey
(2)	Industry	Red
(3)	Transport	Orange
(4)	Derelict land	Black Stipple
(5)	Open spaces	Lime Green
(6)	Grass	Light green
(7)	Arable	Light brown
(8)	Market gardening	Purple
(9)	Orchards	Purple stripes
(10)	Woodland	Dark green
(11)	Heath and rough land	Yellow
(12)	Water and marsh	Light blue
(13)	Unvegetated land	White

[1] Coleman and Maggs (1961).

All classes except (3), (4), (5) and (13) are subdivided. The arable group is subdivided into six—ley legumes, cereals, root crops, green fodder, industrial crops, all further divided into individual crops with letter symbols, and fallow. Market gardening is divided into (*a*) the 'ordinary' type, mapped under 'mixed crops', potatoes, brassica crops, etc., (*b*) nurseries, (*c*) allotment gardens, (*d*) flowers, (*e*) soft fruit and (*f*) hops. Orchards are recorded with underculture and grazing as well as the tree crop itself. The complications of grassland management led to all grass being included in one class, with modifications for grassland infested with scrub or rushes.

The subdivisions are represented by variations of tone within the main colour, or other subdued cartographic devices. The subdivisions are distinguishable with moderate scrutiny of the maps but they do not interfere with the clarity of the 13 main groups. These main groups are not only similar in most respects to the classes of the original survey, but differ only in minor details—the adoption of grey for settlement as used on the base maps, and addition of classes (3), (4), (5) and (13)—from the scheme recommended for the Old World Division of the World Land Use Survey.

The World Land Use Survey

The World Land Use Survey is a scheme fostered by the International Geographical Union to build up comparable maps and reports of land use throughout the world. At its meeting in Lisbon in 1949, the I.G.U. appointed a commission to inquire into the possibilities of carrying out a land use survey on a world scale and three years later the commission published a report making proposals and summarising the state of land use mapping in the different countries which had reported.[1] Further reports appear from time to time in the I.G.U. Newsletter.

One of the aims of the World Land Use Survey is to promote the making of a world land use map on the scale of 1:1,000,000, and the limited number of basic classes proposed in its scheme is intended to obtain the necessary degree of comparability in surveys, with subdivision as required for detailed local purposes. Even the basic classification of nine

[1] International Geographical Union (1952).

categories presents considerable problems in simplification of surveys for reproduction. The reduction of the original land use maps of Britain to a scale of 1:625,000 showed the degree of generalisation required. At this scale the smallest area that could be shown separately was about 100 acres, so adjacent blocks of fields had to be run together, with the proportions being preserved.[1] On a scale of 1:1,000,000 generalisation would have to be undertaken to produce minimum unit areas of at least 200 acres, or, say, 100 hectares.

A large number of countries have now produced, or are working on, land use maps on a variety of scales. Only a few of these are directly based on the major classes of the World Land Use Survey. Lack of standardisation arises from the multitude of authorities involved, and the different methods and objects of individual national surveys. Some of these surveys are being produced by private companies under contract to governments for national planning purposes and are not intended for publication.

The methods of land use survey cannot be discussed here in detail but it may be noted that there is still a place for field-by-field survey on the ground for detailed mapping of crops and multiple uses of land, even though large areas can now be mapped through the medium of air photography at a fraction of the cost of ground survey.

That land use survey has a value for practical purposes is no longer questioned. Accounts of its application to physical planning are numerous. An interesting volume which makes possible comparison of the British survey with the development and aims of land use mapping in a planned economy has been produced from the proceedings of the Anglo-Polish Geographical Seminar.[2] The essence of the Polish approach is contained in the following extract:

> Research connected with land utilisation has two objects, scientific and practical, but it is difficult to separate them. The most general scientific aim is, above all, the study of the ways in which man's economy utilises its natural environment. This is essentially a geographical study,

[1] Stamp (1948, 1962), 33.
[2] Polish Academy of Sciences (1961).

> which can be greatly helped by land utilisation survey . . . the survey can serve as an important foundation for the drawing of conclusions aimed towards a more rational utilisation of the geographical environment. This is its great practical significance . . . also . . . if the proper methods are used, they provide a good foundation for research on the geographical typology of agriculture. . . . Agricultural geography is still in the stage of development in which, for instance, botany, or rather phytosociology was years ago (before) . . . species or associations were grouped in proper units of a higher order based on uniform foundations, in the period of the scientific classification of phenomena which before were only described. . . . It is precisely the elaboration of such a typology of Polish agriculture which is one of the aims of Polish research on land utilisation.

The Polish map is designed to show four aspects of the work:

(1) The *form* of land utilisation, the actual use of the land (for which the term land cover has been adopted in this book) following the World Land Use categories as far as possible.

(2) The *subject* of land utilisation, i.e. the farm holdings, are shown by property boundaries.

(3) The *way* of land utilisation, such as methods of crop rotation, the use of fertilisers and mechanical aids to cultivation, shown by black symbols.

(4) The *directions* or *orientation* of land utilisation, the objects of production, e.g. fodder crop orientiation with preponderance of animals, by colour gradations within the main forms.

Thus it will be seen that the Polish survey takes a broad view of the scope and purpose of a land use survey, and shows not only land cover and land use in the sense that these terms are used here but also background data such as size of farms. Normally, such data are presented in separate maps, often as transparent overlays which can be used together with similar overlays of physical conditions, transport capacity and costs, etc. to facilitate understanding of interrelationships. The presence of such details on the basic land use map indicates the

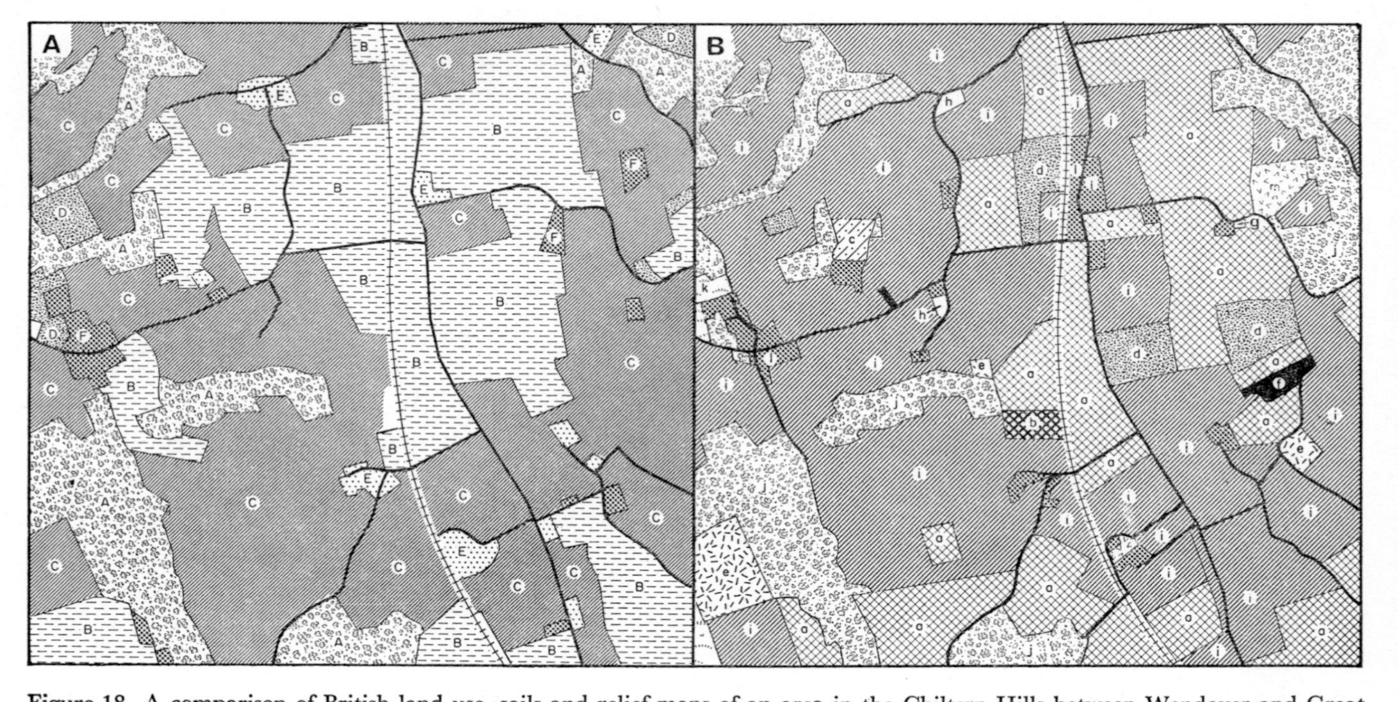

Figure 18. A comparison of British land use, soils and relief maps of an area in the Chiltern Hills between Wendover and Great Missenden to show the growing detail recorded in contemporary land use mapping and the relationships between land use and physical conditions. (Scale of these reproductions is approximately 2 inches to 1 mile).

A Part of Sheet 106 of the Land Utilisation Survey, surveyed 1931–2: A, Woodland; B, Arable; C, Permanent grass; D, Heath and rough pasture; E, Gardens and orchards.

B Sheet 264 of the new survey of 1960: *a–e*, Arable (*a* cereals, *b* ley legumes, *c* roots, *d* green fodder, *e* fallow); *f–h*, Market gardening (*f* field food crops, *g* soft fruit, *h* orchards with market gardening); *i*, Grassland; *j*, Woodland (mixed); *k*, Heath and rough land; *l*, Settlement.

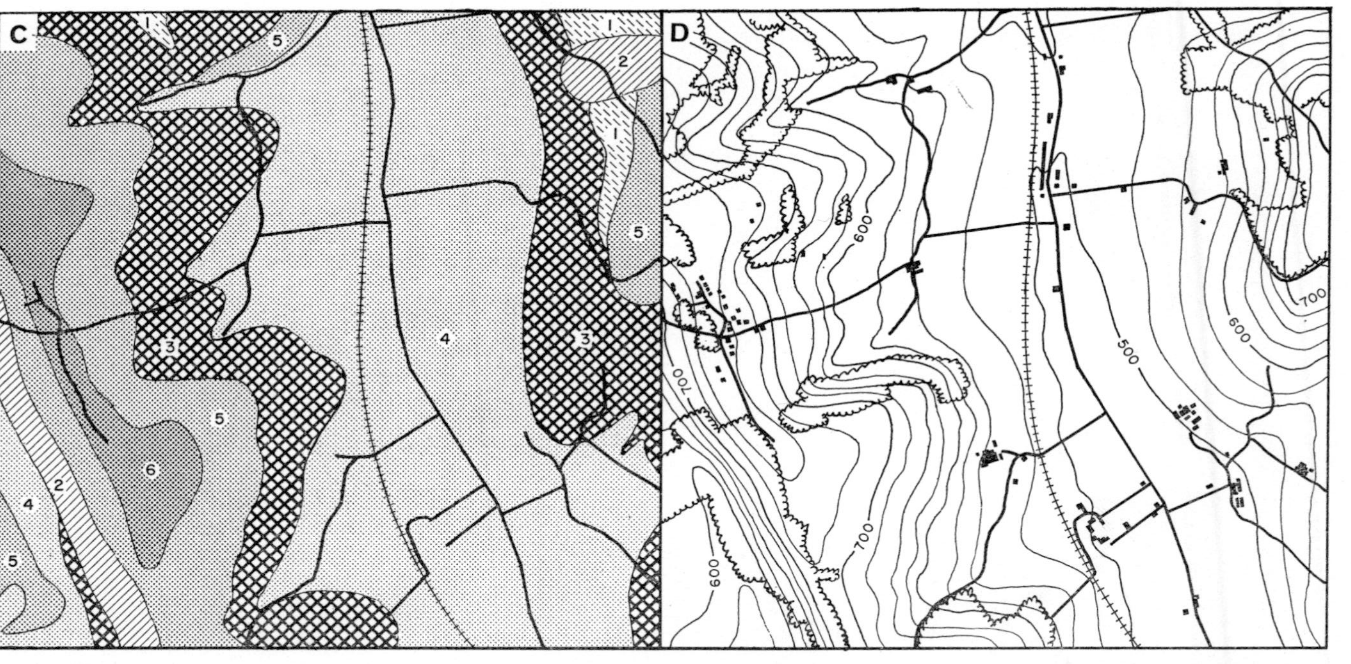

C Soils Sheet 238, 1961: 1. Rendzina (parent material, Chalk); 2. same, steepland phase; 3. Brown Calcareous Soil (on flinty and chalk Head over Chalk); 4. and 5. Brown Earths (4. on loamy and gravelly Head over Chalk, 5. Clay-with-flints over Chalk); 6. Gleyed Brown Earth (on Plateau Drift). Crown Copyright reserved.

D Topography, abstracted from the Ordnance Survey Map, New Popular Edition Sheet 159, 1945 (full revision, 1930). Crown copyright reserved.

pre-determined object of the Polish map to assist in practical planning.

A feature of land use maps which must be stressed is that the presentation of material on them is objective, i.e. they record facts with a minimum of interpretation on the part of the surveyor and cartogapher. This is so even in a broad survey like the Polish one. But, because land use maps record the land use only at a moment of time, they cannot do more than present a synoptic picture of the landscape. A field which is under grass this year may be growing a cereal crop next year. Hence, in one sense the map is out of date before it is printed. This failing of the land use map has sometimes been offered as a reason for not undertaking such mapping, but as a criticism of technique it fails to take account of the stability of the pattern in a larger area, such as the farm unit, or a typical square mile of territory. The change in the individual field is often merely an expression of crop rotation, and is offset by corresponding changes in other fields. The stability of the pattern even in a country of fairly rapid technological change like Great Britain is proved by comparison of maps of different dates. A land use map may be considered a valid document for a number of years, just how long being dependent on the nature and rate of change. Sample surveys of land use in restricted areas and the interpretation of census statistics are necessary to determine when a new survey is needed. Re-survey may be needed very frequently on the fringes of urban development, but only at long intervals in stable agricultural regions.

The feature of objective recording means that there is on a land use map no indication of whether or not the land is being used in a way appropriate to its quality, except in so far as this may in extreme cases be obvious from, say, relief relationships. Thus, the colour yellow, depicting heathland and rough grazing on mountains in the Highlands of Scotland, may be taken to indicate satisfactory utilisation at 3000 feet, but in the valleys between the mountains it poses the question of whether here might not be conditions suitable for cultivation. Again, there is nothing on a land use map, normally, to indicate whether an area of grass is very fertile or poor, without being poor enough to be classed as rough grazing. Nor is there any indication of whether the natural conditions are such that substantial improvement of the land is practicable.

Land Potential Maps

It is a matter of general knowledge that some land is better than other land in the same use, and with the pressure of growing population in relation to a more or less fixed supply of land it is important that variations in land quality should be studied and mapped. This is partly the prerogative of the soil surveyor, and a full inventory of land resources can be achieved only with detailed soil survey. Soil survey, however, is often directed to pedological rather than productive aims, and in any case needs re-interpretation to serve the needs of the planner. Soil, too, is not the only physical factor in the productivity of land. To meet the need in assessing land resources many schemes of classifying land potential have been developed.[1]

In classifying land potential the object is to establish the fertility or potential fertility of each tract of land examined. The surveyor seeks to answer the questions

(1) For what use is this land most suitable?

(2) What is the potential productivity of this tract of land compared with other tracts?

Classification may be of (*a*) a general nature or (*b*) specific. A general classification provides basic information which will assist planning of various kinds, e.g., in questions of land use involving choice between one use and another whenever they may arise. Thus the classification might be used at one time to help decide whether a particular tract being used for low intensity grazing should be used for a reafforestation scheme or for improved agriculture or left undeveloped, and at another time as a guide to whether the same tract should be reserved in its existing use, or whether building construction should be permitted. The essence of such a classification is a summary of the inherent physical characteristics not only of the tract under consideration but of other areas which could provide alternative sites for development. Such a classification has the

[1] Jacks (1946).

advantage that once it is completed it can be referred to without delay to assist in the solution of many planning problems. Indeed, no country can be considered to be adequately mapped until a land classification map of this kind on a sufficiently large scale is available. Nevertheless, such a classification must be to some extent vague and imprecise because of the many factors involved, and other classifications are needed.

A group (*b*) classification is prepared with a specific object in mind, e.g. to classify land into grades of suitability for afforestation, or for agricultural development, or even for a single species of tree or crop. Such classifications are easier to make than a general classification and may be made first but a general classification should be regarded as a further objective. Thus, given a map showing suitability of land for cattle grazing, it can be seen whether a given tract is classified as suitable or unsuitable for that purpose. If, then, there is available a general classification map this will show whether, compared with other areas, its general fertility is rated high or low. Although not suited to cattle grazing the tract may be rated as first class land because of suitability for arable crops. This type of single-subject potential map will not be discussed separately here. The problems it poses are similar to those of the general map in restricted form. It may, however, be noted that many classifications do not fall with complete exclusiveness into either category.

The land capability classification devised by the United States Soil Conservation Service is an example of a classification which is concerned mainly with the erosion hazard, but which introduces other aspects of land potential and aims at a qualitative assessment of land for agricultural and watershed protection purposes. Eight classes are recognised, with a primary division into land suited and land not suited to cultivation[1] and here given in summary form:

Land Suited to Cultivation

Class I. Very good land that can be cultivated safely with ordinary farming methods.

[1] U.S.A. Department of Agriculture (1951), (1954), summarised in standard conservation texts.

Class II. Land that may be cultivated safely with moderate precautions. Soils may lack depth, be liable to wetness or present other problems but not to a serious extent.

Class III. Land which has considerable limitations of use, but which may be cultivated regularly if hazards are guarded against. Characteristics include moderately steep slopes, high susceptibility to erosion, hardpan or claypan, and very impermeable or sandy soils.

Class IV. Land with very severe limitations in use. Cultivation should be limited to occasional crops with extreme care being exercised. A long rotation of 5 or 6 years in grass followed by a crop of grain or lucerne is often practicable. In some semi-arid regions the best land is in Class IV. Most Class IV land in humid regions is well suited to forestry.

Land Not Suited to Cultivation

Class V. Land which although nearly level is not suitable for cultivation because of wetness, stoniness or other factors. Forestry and grazing are suitable uses with few limitations.

Class VI. Land which is steep, rough, dry, wet or otherwise unsuitable for cultivation. Some Class VI land can be tilled just sufficiently to establish pastures and some can be used safely for tree crops. Grazing must be restricted to safe numbers of stock and to appropriate periods. Gully control, contour furrows, ridges, water diversions and other conservation measures may be needed.

Class VII. Severe limitations or severe erosion hazards under grazing or forestry uses characterise this land. Depletion of cover leads to more rapid erosion than on Class VI land, and structures such as contour furrows and ridges cannot be used because of steep slopes, shallow soils or other unfavourable factors. Forestry is preferred to grazing for conservation purposes.

Class VIII. Forestry as well as grazing and cultivation are regarded as unsuitable on this class of land. It includes marshes, deserts, badlands, and high mountain land, and is suited only for wild life preservation, recreation and water catchment, with appropriate watershed protection measures.

This classification has evident value for land where soil erosion or other hazards limit cultivation, but has little relevance elsewhere or to the assessment of productivity in any but the most general terms. To aid in the comprehensive planning of land use it is necessary to have classifications derived from all significant factors of the environment. A land classification scheme normally seeks to express the inherent, natural quality of the land. To the extent, however, that the effects of past cultivation have modified the natural fertility of the soil they may be taken as having become absorbed into the inherent quality of the land. The comparative quality of land may be assumed to be assessed at its normal, existing level, which could only be upgraded, if at all, by abnormal investment, such as major reclamation schemes.

The primary or physical factors which should be taken into account in assessment of land have been summarised as follows.[1]

1. Site

(*a*) *Surface Data*
- (i) Elevation.
- (ii) Degree of slope.
- (iii) Aspect—with regard to insolation.
- (iv) Drainage.
- (v) Micro-relief.
- (vi) Liability to erosion.

(*b*) *Climatic Data*
- (i) Precipitation.
- (ii) Temperature.
- (iii) Exposure.
- (iv) Frost-free periods, etc.

2. Soil

(*a*) *Physical Properties*
- (i) Depth.
- (ii) Texture.
- (iii) Stoniness.
- (iv) Structure.
- (v) Drainage.

[1] After North East Development Association (1950).

(vi) Consistency.
(vii) Organic matter.

(*b*) *Chemical Properties*
(i) More or less permanent factors—carbonates.
(ii) Temporary factors—phosphate and potash status.

With regard to the soil, it can be safely assumed that physical soil factors are of more importance than chemical factors in assessing the potential value of the land. The nutrient status of soils may be entirely artificial, i.e. depending on the system of management and fertiliser practice. If the more permanent characteristics of depth, texture, drainage, etc. are satisfactory, then the nutrient status of an inherently poor soil may be built up.

Land Classification in Britain

In Great Britain, the Land Utilisation Survey played the major role in the production of the first national map of land potential, completed in answer to urgent wartime needs. The subject was discussed at a series of meetings held in 1943 by specialists in several sciences, including geographers, agriculturalists and soil scientists. Representatives of the Soil Survey estimated that fifty or sixty years would be needed for a complete soil survey of the country, whereas the urgent need was for a simple classification of land which could be used as a basis for national planning, especially for the delimitation of the tracts of good agricultural land to be avoided, if possible, in building developments.[1] The Soil Survey's definitions of good, medium and poor quality land—Major Categories I, II and III were accepted by all. The original definitions of the three Major Categories were:

Major Category I: Good Quality Land

Highly productive when under good management. Land in this category has the following characteristics:

Site (i) Not too elevated.
(ii) Level, gently sloping or undulating.
(iii) Favourable aspect.

[1] Stamp (1948, 1962), 353.

Soil
(i) Deep.
(ii) Favourable water conditions.
(iii) Texture, mostly loams, but including some peats, sands, silts and clays.

Major Category II: Medium Quality Land

Land of only medium productivity even when under good management. Productivity limited by reason of the unfavourable operation of one or more of the factors of site or soil character, e.g.

Site
(i) High elevation.
(ii) Steepness.
(iii) Unfavourable aspect.

Soil
(i) Shallowness.
(ii) Defective water conditions.

Major Category III: Poor Quality Land

Land of low productivity by the extreme operation of one or more factors of site and soil.

The Land Utilisation Survey had already adopted ten classes for a provisional map of England and definitions of each of these were agreed in terms acceptable to the soil scientists. The ten classes, grouped into the three Major Categories, were used for the maps of the whole of Britain then prepared by the Land Utilisation Survey and published on the scale 1/625,000.[1] Some of the classes were based on land use characteristics, to distinguish classes which were different from, though not necessarily better or worse than, other classes. Thus, the best grassland, which is not equally suited to arable cultivation, is distinguished from the best arable land, which is not necessarily of higher overall productivity.

Regional classifications have been prepared for various parts of Britain on larger scales. These have been generally based on the three major categories.[2] The Land Utilisation Survey of

[1] See also Stamp (1948, 1962), Chapter 17, and *Applied Geography*, Penguin Books.

[2] For example, by the West Midland Planning Group in *Conurbation*, the University of Bristol in *Gloucester and Somerset, A land classification*, and by the North East Development Association (1950).

Northern Ireland[1] found that four rather than three major categories were desirable for conditions in Ireland and evolved a scheme which was similar to that used by the Department of Agriculture for Scotland. Though it was evolved independently the degree of coincidence is not surprising in view of the physical similarities of Scotland and Ulster. In both areas there is much medium class land which could not have been subdivided adequately for practical purposes within the British classes, and clear distinction was needed between poor hill land and very poor mountain land. The main difference was found to be in the classification of some land in Ulster as first class land which would not have been so classed in Scotland, but the standard was not raised, because of the need to distinguish the best areas in Northern Ireland whether or not they equalled those in Scotland.

It should be added that classification in the Scottish lowlands has been pursued on a field-by-field basis whereas this was not practicable in Northern Ireland. The vast number of fields in even a small area and the variations in management in Ulster made it essential to interpret the general characteristics of the land in larger tracts and to map according to the dominant class. The mapping was carried out on the 1/63,360 ('one-inch') scale, with some sample surveys at larger scales, and reduction to 1/500,000 to meet publication needs.

N.I. System		Scottish System
Category A: High Quality Land		*A*
Category B: Medium Quality Land		*B*
Class B1	Medium quality, light.	B+
Class B2	Medium quality, but rather heavy or with high water table.	B/B+
Class B3	Medium, but with adverse factors of slope, shallow soil, etc. and unevenness of quality.	B−/B
Class B4	Medium, with adverse factors more adverse than B3 and/or unevenness of quality more marked.	B−/C

[1] Symons (ed.) (1963).

Category C: Poor Quality Land		*C*
Class C1	Poor—marginal hill land, rocky, or steep lowland.	C
Class C2	Poor—peaty and ill-drained lowland.	C
Category D: Very Poor Quality Land		*D*
Class D1	Very poor, mountain.	D
Class D2	Very poor, lowland bog, marsh, sand-dunes, etc.	D

Land Classification in Tropical Regions

The formulation of a land classification system for use in tropical regions must obviously have regard to the fact that very different conditions prevail from those in the temperate regions where land classification has hitherto been most developed. Systems used in temperate lands can give guidance to surveyors in the tropics in general principles only. Certain factors will have very different effects in their operation, e.g. increasing altitude is generally detrimental in temperate regions but may be advantageous in the tropics. Nevertheless, though its effects will be different, altitude can be used to make certain broad delineations, and may be a good starting point once its effects are determined. Vegetation is, of course, often a valuable index of climate and soil and may sometimes be used as a short cut given adequate knowledge of the habitat factors of species and associations involved.

In the assessment of the productive capacity of soils it is considered in the temperate lands that physical characteristics are much more important than chemical status. This is largely because phosphates, nitrogen, potash and lime can be applied economically in large quantities and on a regular basis in commercial farming for lucrative markets. This assumption must be examined with caution before it is applied to any tropical conditions, partly because of the very high rate of leaching typical of the tropics and partly because application of fertilisers in most tropical economies is of extremely limited practicability.

The rapid decline in fertility of tropical soils under cultivation has been reported from many sources.[1] Decline is particularly rapid in humid forest regions. In Ghana, trials for 8 years under a continuous 2-year rotation of maize and cassava resulted, in the absence of fertiliser effects, in the yields in the fourth cycle being only half those of the first cycle in both crops. The first cycle followed clearing of mature secondary forest.[2] Virgin land in Malaya has been estimated to produce 1500–2000, 1200 and 880 lb. of paddy per acre in successive years.[3] Applications of manure commonly have an effect lasting only for a few months as compared with two or three years in temperate regions. Hence, a practical classification of tropical lands may have to distinguish classes for which shifting cultivation or land rotation is necessary for physical reasons.

The importance that can be assigned to soil texture is probably not yet adequately evaluated, though Gourou[4] has written 'tropical agriculture is satisfied with the poorest soils, provided that they have a suitable texture, that is to say, that they are sufficiently friable'. This is a generalisation which cannot apply equally to all cultivated, tropical plants but may help in evaluating criteria for classification.

Further, the very fact that long-term chemical changes are hard to achieve artificially but are closely related to the age and maturity of soils will assist in classification. Of exceptionally high grade will be typical fluvial alluvium of very recent deposition which comes from regions not subjected to the regime of tropical weathering, such as that of the Red River in Tonkin, quoted by Gourou. Recent marine alluvium and recent basic volcanic ash are two other highly fertile groups of parent materials. On the other hand, fluvial alluvium of the early Quaternary period in tropical lands is generally infertile.[5]

As in the temperate regions, it should not be difficult to establish classes for the types of lands of lowest fertility, bearing in mind that the minimum distinctions that will be of value must separate land types capable of improvement from those

[1] Nye and Greenland (1960), summarise a number of examples.

[2] Nye and Stephens (1960), Chapter 7.

[3] Grist (1953), 331.

[4] Gourou (1961), 14.

[5] Gourou (1961), 18.

which have no significant potential. Laterites, and soils in which lateritic processes are far advanced must be regarded as among the worst. Gourou reports on many areas where lateritic soils are almost useless and records that in Madagascar relatively friable laterites have been transformed by irrigation only into a compact puddled clay, whereas water has enabled crops to be forced from the pure and almost sterile sand of the coast strip.

It is with the subdivision of the medium quality classes that the greatest difficulty can be expected. This is especially likely in tropical conditions where there is a wide range of land types and where subsistence and commercial agriculture are often intermixed. In these circumstances, the need for a map which can be produced quickly for practical planning purposes may suggest priority for the type of classification which states the use for which each tract of land is suitable, without, at any rate in the reconnaissance stage, attempting to put a comparative label on it.

An example of this type of classification is that produced for British Honduras. The land potential map is coupled with soil maps and issued with a comprehensive report.[1] Its approach to the problem of classification is to set out the following main categories:

Land adapted to forest use—protection forest, mahogany forest, pine forest.

Land adapted to agricultural use—orchard crops, long rotation pasture, short rotation pasture and arable crops, swamp rice, market gardening, bananas, sugar cane.

Problem soil which will become useful only if main drainage or desalinisation projects are expedited.

Subdivisions are made according to the particular crops or crop combinations recommended.

It is difficult to see how a land classification of either kind can be of value in the urgent task of increasing output unless it has regard to practical limitations imposed by institutional factors, land tenure, social habits, marketing opportunities, etc. It may be necessary for a classification to be multiple,

[1] Romney (ed.) (1959).

e.g. a long-term optimum and a more immediate aim for a given area. This is well brought out in the report of the land use survey team in British Honduras. It was the conclusion of the survey that the highest production values per acre are likely to be achieved through forestry on a sustained yield basis, with the next best sustained return per acre from grass farming. The second conclusion is interesting, applying as it does to regions of over 170 inches annual rainfall and high mean temperatures. But equally it was recognised that the forest resources and grass farming would take time to develop, and meanwhile other forms of production would have to be developed to meet the urgency of the economic situation. It was suggested that for one or more decades special efforts should be put into producing rice, citrus fruits, beans and cacao since these could be sold in export markets to finance long-term developments. Soils ideal for these crops are not extensive enough to yield a worth-while volume of produce, so it was suggested that there would have to be some deliberate misuse of land for a time, using for these crops soils which would be more productive under well-managed grass.

The Punta Gorda sub-region in the southern area illustrates this dilemma. Here it is suggested that the long-term plan should concentrate on cattle raising and this is shown on the example from the land potential map (Figure 19). The farmers would, however, need instruction on sowing pastures. Marketing arrangements would be necessary to give confidence in the future of the industry, but the immediate need is for a reliable cash crop which might not necessarily be retained in the economy of the district except as a subsistence crop. For this purpose upland rice is recommended for this region.

Immediately to the south is a region where bananas and pineapples have provided useful income in the past but have failed to find regular markets. Near Barranco, swamp rice is grown in the coastal depressions. In this region also it is recommended that attention should be given to the possibilities of establishing pastures for cattle raising. The construction of a wharf would facilitate exports of cattle, nuts, rice, etc., until which time attention should be concentrated on crops least likely to suffer damage through handling and transit. Potential ricelands could become very productive, given polders, and

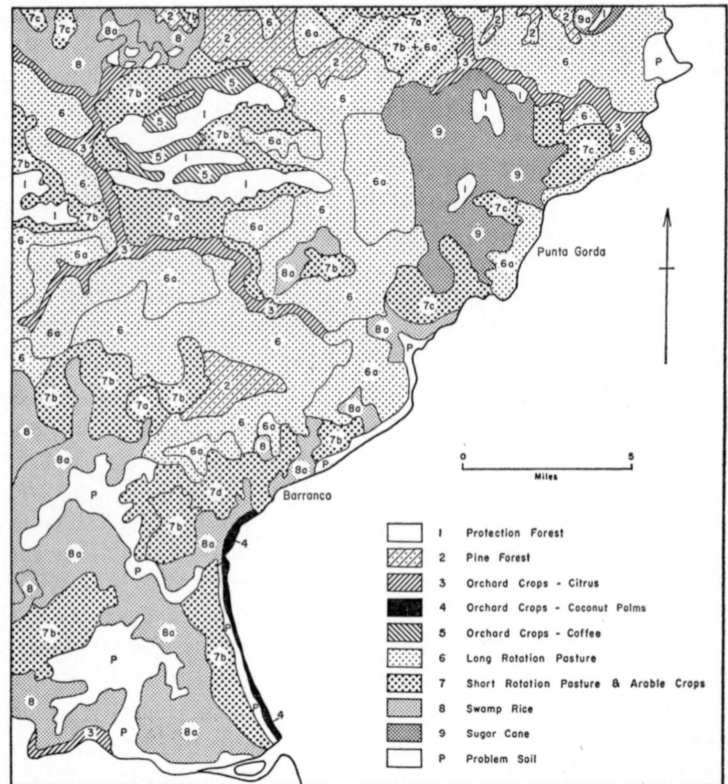

Figure 19. Potential land use, British Honduras. An extract from one of the maps in the survey report of 1959. Subdivision of classes: 6, Long rotation pasture with beef cattle; 6a, With dairy cattle; 7a, Leys with corn, beans; 7b, Leys with upland rice; 7c, Leys with swamp rice; 7d, Leys with cassava, pineapple; 8, Swamp rice, suitable for early development; 8a, Swamp rice, restricted by engineering problems; 9, Sugar cane; 9a, Sugar cane in rotation with grass.

Source: Land in British Honduras, HMSO, 1959. Crown Copyright reserved. Reproduced from Directorate of Overseas Surveys' map (Misc.) 241C by permission of the Controller of Her Majesty's Stationery Office

irrigation and engineering advice was called for in the report.

Unit-area Land Classification

Land classification schemes vary from reconnaissance to detailed field surveys, the former suffering from obvious doubts regarding applicability in detail, the latter from time and cost problems. To try to bridge the gap more effectively a unit-area method of land classification was developed for the Tennessee Valley Authority.[1] In this method the relevant factors of both physical and human environment are tabulated and numbered, and the numbers for each unit area of land are expressed in a fractional code. The denominator contains the digits representing the physical conditions, while the numerator shows the human data. A new unit-area is delimited whenever a change occurs in one or more of the items recorded.

The complete symbol for each land unit is in three parts—a Roman numeral, a short fraction and a long fraction, for example III $\frac{3}{4}$ $\frac{2B233}{4122234}$.

The Roman numeral shows the severity or absence of problems in the area, as revealed by the details that follow, in five classes; I problems insignificant; II problems not critical; III moderately critical; IV very critical; V so critical that a radical change in land use appears desirable.

The short fraction is a summary of the long fraction:

Numerator

Areas classified on the basis of:

Class 1. EXCELLENT—Medium to large fields; little or no idle land; complete agricultural utilisation of the land under a regime especially well suited to the land.

Class 2. GOOD—Medium to large fields; little or no idle land; efficient agricultural use under a regime well suited to the land.

Class 3. MEDIUM—Small to medium fields; limited idle land; moderately efficient agricultural use under a regime moderately well suited to the land.

Class 4. POOR—Small to medium fields, in many cases interrupted; considerable idle land; low-grade, inefficient, or destructive agricultural use under a regime ill-suited to the land.

Class 5. VERY POOR—Very small, interrupted fields; excessive idle land; very low-grade, inefficient, or destructive agricultural use under a regime in most cases entirely unsuited to the land.

[1] U.S.A. National Resources Planning Board (1941), 119.

Denominator

Areas classified on the basis of the present quality of the land for arable farming.

Class 1. EXCELLENT—Lands exceptionally well suited to intensive arable farming.

Class 2. GOOD—Lands well suited to arable farming and moderately suited to intensive forms of arable farming under proper land management.

Class 3. MEDIUM—Lands suited to less intensive forms of arable farming or to general farming under proper land management.

Class 4. POOR—Lands for the most part poorly suited to all forms of arable farming even under proper land management; in many cases best suited to grazing.

Class 5. VERY POOR—Lands not suited to either arable farming or grazing; in most cases suited to forest production, recreation, etc.; in some cases, waste land.

The criteria used in the long fraction are given in Table 12.

The suitability of this method of classification and mapping depends on availability of facilities for detailed field work, aerial photographs or detailed base maps and sufficient staff. It has been successfully used with the necessary modification of the digits in some areas in New Zealand.[1] The classification is not, however, well suited to distinguishing potential from existing productivity and the varying requirements for different uses are not recognised adequately.

Quantitative Classification

In the examples of land classification so far discussed there is no attempt to relate one class to another quantitatively, but many such attempts have been made to devise an objective and quantitative form of land classification. Jacks[2] says 'The methods used may be classed generally as inductive (e.g. by adding or otherwise integrating "marks" awarded to certain properties of the land or soil that influence productivity) or deductive (e.g. deduced from yield data), but many methods in actual use are a combination of both types.'

[1] Cumberland (1944).

[2] Jacks (1946), 68.

Table 12

UNIT AREA LAND CLASSIFICATION CRITERIA FOR DELIMITING HOMOGENEOUS LAND USES

A. Major land uses, shown by the numerator of the long fraction

First Digit	*Second Digit*	*Third Digit*	*Fourth Digit*	*Fifth Digit*
Major Land Use	Agricultural Emphasis	Field Size	Amount of Idle Land	Quality of Farmsteads and Equipment
1. General farming	A. Corn	1. Large	1. Little	1. Excellent
2. Animal industry	G. Grain (small)	2. Medium	2. Limited	2. Good
3. Cash-crop farming	B. Beef cattle	3. Small	3. Considerable	3. Medium
4. Part-time farming	D. Dairying	4. Very small	4. Excessive	4. Poor
5. Subsistence farming	S. Sheep			5. Very poor
6. Forest land	H. Hogs			
7. Recreational area	M. Mules and/or horses			
8. Rural-village area	P. Poultry			
9. Urban area	T. Tobacco			
10. Manufacturing and mining areas	C. Cotton			
	W. Truck			
	O. Orchard			
	N. No emphasis			
	F. Forage			

B. Major physical conditions, shown by the denominator of the long fraction

First Digit	*Second Digit*	*Third Digit*	*Fourth Digit*
Slope	Drainage	Erosion	Stoniness
1. Relatively level	1. Thorough	1. Little or no observable erosion	1. Free from stones
2. Relatively level to undulating	2. Adequate	2. Little denudation by erosion	2. Moderately stony
3. Undulating to moderately hilly	3. Poor	3. Sheet erosion and ephemeral gullies	3. Stony
4. Hilly	4. Very poor	4. Excessive sheet erosion and gullying	4. Very stony
5. Steep	5. Excessive	5. Excessive gully erosion	

Fifth Digit	*Sixth Digit*	*Seventh Digit*
Rock Exposure	Soil Depth	Soil Fertility
1. Little or no rock exposure	1. Deep (6 feet or more)	1. Exceptionally fertile
2. Limited rock exposure	2. Moderately deep (3 to 6 feet)	2. Fertile
3. Considerable rock exposure	3. Shallow (1 to 3 feet)	3. Moderately fertile
4. Excessive rock exposure	4. Very shallow (less than 1 foot)	4. Low in fertility
5. Rock exposure dominant		5. Very low in fertility

Summary after Jacks (1946): for details see U.S.A. National Resources Planning Board (1941), 121.

Jacks summarises several methods which indicate the range of approaches. The U.S. Soil Survey *productivity ratings* illustrate the deductive type of classification. An example is given as follows:

Soil type: Miami loam

Corn		*Wheat*		*Rye*		*Alfalfa*		*Sugar Beet*		*Productivity grade*	
A	B	A	B	A	B	A	B	A	B	A	B
70	90	70	100	80	100	70	90	60	70	3	1

Space is not available here to discuss the scheme in detail but, briefly, the A columns show the yields of crops with the common practices of management in the area, and the B columns those with the best practices, as percentages of standard yields. Standard yields represent average yields 'on the more extensive and widely developed soils of the regions in the United States in which the crop is a principal product.'[1] Thus, the standard for corn is 50 bushels per acre, and in the example given the average yield under average management is 35 bushels and under the best management, 45 bushels. The 'productivity grade' is obtained by a simple percentage weighting of the crop ratings according to each crop's local importance. Soils with a weighted average between 100 and 90 are graded 1, between 90 and 80, 2, and so on.

The 'Storie index' is an inductive method which has been used in other countries as well as in the U.S.A. It is based on the soil profile.[2] The main characteristics of the profile are expressed in three 'factors', one being the surface texture. Each is quoted as an estimated percentage of the optimum conditions of that factor for plant growth, and the factors are then multiplied to give the rating as a percentage of the possible 'score'. Multiplying instead of adding the figures for the characteristics enables any one very detrimental factor to bring down the index for the soil as a whole, e.g. $100 \times 100 \times 10 =$ ratio 10, i.e. $\left(\frac{100{,}000}{1{,}000{,}000}\right)$ whereas $100 + 100 + 10 =$ ratio 70, i.e. $\left(\frac{210}{300}\right)$ by addition.

[1] Ableiter (1940).
[2] Storie (1933).

It will be evident that although quantitative, such schemes have not been able to avoid a high degree of subjectivity in the allocation of the points, or in deciding what constitutes normal management, optimum conditions, etc. It is possible for a greater degree of comparability to be obtained than through the type of classification previously discussed, but additional caution is necessary lest the presence of a statistical valuation leads to an uncritical acceptance of its validity.

A Russian Approach to Land Classification

In the U.S.S.R. there has been growing realisation that increased production from the state and collective farms necessitates greater attention to yields and costs on different classes of land. K. V. Zvorykin[1] has outlined the steps he considers necessary to arrive at an evaluation in monetary terms of the worth of individual areas of land. The mapping of the land according to its physical attributes and quality of existing cultivation is visualised as the first stage in the work. Suggested indicators are:

(1) Relief and slope.

(2) Soil variety (with indication of bedrock and degree of erosion).

(3) Land use type.

(4) Vegetation (cultivated crops where appropriate).

(5) Tillage condition of the land (especially presence of weeds in cropped land).

(6) Depth of water table.

Established land use is then mapped according to the practices of the previous few years, recording features such as type of cropping, actual rotation of the last five to ten years, application of fertilisers, irrigation, drainage and terracing.

The third stage is the collection and processing of data on crop yields, and on the labour and cost required to grow crops on various kinds of lands with unlike natural properties. This helps towards selecting the most economical land use methods for particular lands.

[1] Zvorykin (1963).

The fourth stage consists of research and description of the properties of the land that may help to explain differences in fertility and workability, additional to those examined in the first stage. Climatic, soil water and chemical properties of the soil are typical subjects of this stage of the work. Dates when the land is ready for work in the spring, the length of the period during which it is worked most easily, flooding risks and other aspects of its working are also considered at this stage.

In the fifth stage the actual land classification is worked out. All the land units or 'modifications' found in the first stage are combined on the basis of information from the later stages of the work into higher rank classification units. Modifications with similar observed properties and fertility (yields and production costs within 5 per cent.) are grouped into a *land class*. Land classes suitable for identical uses but differing in fertility and workability are grouped together as *land types*. Land classes that favour different combinations of crops would thus be assigned to different land types.

Difficulties arise with such a typology where parts of the farm territory contain a frequent alternation of small plots of land belonging to different types and classes. For these cases the purely typological scheme is replaced by composite groups and sub-groups[1] called agro-production land groups.

The principal characteristic of all these land categories, whether types and classes or agro-production groups and sub-groups, is their relative suitability for a given kind of land use and for growing various crops or groups of crops. They are thus similar to the land potential classes recognised in the British Honduras survey referred to above. The British Honduras survey relied, it would seem, to a greater extent on the interpretation of the soil pattern. This was probably necessary in the conditions in which this survey was working, but Zvorykin argues that a solution of the problems of classification and land appraisal is hindered by undue emphasis on soil types. For example, he cites three soil types of which a podsolised chernozem and a weakly-podsolised chernozem belong together

[1] The problem of very variable areas was met in the British land classification scheme by the allocation of a separate class to varied, but in general medium quality land. Drumlin belts, for example, may vary repeatedly from first to third category land in short distances. This was Stamp's Class 6, Northern Ireland B3 and B4.

pedologically, while the dark-grey soil belongs to a different type. He finds, however, that the dark-grey soil and the podsolised chernozem are not only of the same land type, but of the same land class, and accordingly not only of the same agro-production group but of the same sub-group. The weakly-leached chernozem belongs to the same type or agro-production group, but to another class or sub-group.

Soil survey may in fact produce a complexity of detail which is unnecessary and possibly even misleading from the point of view of land potential, but if reliable values can be attached to each unit of the soil classification, then, of course, the soil map will be of great assistance to the land classification. Similarly with relief and landform data, of which practical data such as slope and micro-relief characteristics are needed rather than genetic interpretations.

An inventory such as proposed by Zvorykin has been pursued in local and regional investigations in varying detail by many workers. It is helpful, however, to have the form and content of land potential classification discussed from all points of view, and study of Zvorykin's scheme, elaborated where relevant by reference to the factors in physical land classification enumerated in connection with the British classification, provides a fairly comprehensive idea of the scope of land classification.

CHAPTER 11

Conclusion

The study of agricultural geography reveals the varied patterns of man's work on the land. The delimitation of agricultural regions and the classification of farming types pose endless problems of an academic nature. But at every turn the research worker finds himself confronted by the greater problems that beset mankind as a whole—the world's economic, political and social problems that can never be entirely dissociated from one another. We are aware that revolution and war stem not infrequently from hunger and dissatisfaction with established systems of land tenure and the economic and social hierarchy. Modest but steady progress in a people's standard of living may be the best guarantee of a nation's internal stability, and to avoid severe discontent at home is to remove at least one temptation to a government to indulge in distracting military adventures abroad. Irrespective of ideological views it should be a matter of common humanity to make every endeavour to provide adequate means of feeding the world's growing population, and any discipline which reveals facts and clarifies relationships likely to advance this cause should be pursued with all possible vigour. Any contribution that agricultural geography can make in this direction is ultimately more important than its academic justification.

Each of the types of agriculture has its own problems, both physical and cultural. Systems of subsistence agriculture are usually carried on with few technical aids and little scientific knowledge. But their disturbance is fraught with danger and should be encouraged only after the most careful study. Plantation agriculture, in the form that Europeans have developed it in tropical lands over four centuries, seems likely for political reasons to be doomed at least in some countries where it is still a major source of economic strength, and alternative forms of organisation will have to be found to take its place. State-operated and collective farms have not measured up to the hopes of Soviet planners, but compromises between these forms and private enterprise practised by a modernised peasantry may yet prove a solution in some areas. Chinese, Cuban, Israeli and other experiments must be closely watched for the lessons they can convey to other societies.

European countries which are advanced technologically are burdened with excessive numbers of small, fragmented and inefficient farms. Here, too, the competition for land is acute as the swelling population demands more and more land for housing, factories, roads, playgrounds, water catchment and other uses. Even in North America, Australia and New Zealand, where land is still relatively plentiful, there are problems of farm size and shape and of technical and climatic difficulties as well as htndrances to the disposal of produce in conditions of impeded international trade.

With production reiarded by physical and institutional obstacles while only a minority of the world's population enjoys a satisfactory diet, the applications of agricultural geography must be added to those of other sciences. Geographical methods can be used advantageously in analysis of farm units, patterns of cropping and livestock, intensity of usage, diffusion of techniques, effects of changed methods and innumerable other aspects of agriculture. Studies of land use and land potential lead to a more comprehensive and more valuable inventory of agricultural resources and their most effective employment. Geographers have no monopoly of any of these approaches and techniques; and advances will be made all the more rapidly if there is appreciation on all sides of the interdependence of the several disciplines that contribute to the solution of any geographical problem. This attempt to write an introduction to agricultural geography will have been justified in spite of some partiality of approach if it helps in spreading appreciation of techniques already available, of their limitations and of the urgent need to develop sharper tools of analysis and synthesis.

It is hoped that the reader will have been stimulated already to refer to some of the works cited in the text. Many of these are 'secondary' sources particularly valuable for taking studies a stage further while being more widely available than many of the papers and monographs that provide for a thorough understanding of the subject. No attempt has been made to include a comprehensive bibliography, but that which follows, comprising essentially the details of works to which reference has been made in this book, provides a guide which will serve as a basis for further study. References and bibliographies in the works quoted open up a vast literature in several languages.

Bibliography

Ableiter, J. K. (1940) 'Productivity ratings of soil types'. *Missouri Agric. Expt. Sta. Bull.*, 421.

Academy of Sciences of the USSR. *See* USSR.

Ahmad, E. (1952) 'Rural settlement types in the Uttar Pradesh (United Provinces of Agra and Oudh)'. *Annals Assoc. American Geographers*, Vol. 42, 223–246.

Baker, O. E. (1925) 'The potential supply of wheat'. *Economic Geography*, Vol. 1, 15–52. (*See also series of articles by this author in subsequent issues of this journal.*)

Beavington, F. (1963) 'The change to more extensive methods in market gardening in Bedfordshire'. *Inst. British Geographers, Trans. and Papers*, Vol. 33, 89–100.

Bell, R. E. (1961) 'How Soviet agriculture compares with ours'. *Foreign Agriculture*, Sept, 1961.

Beresford, M. W., and St. Joseph, J. K. S. (1958) *Medieval England, an aerial survey*. Cambridge.

Berry, B. J. L. (1958). 'A note concerning methods of classification'. *Annals Assoc. American Geographers*, Vol. 48, 300–303.

Best, R. H. (1960) *The major land uses of Great Britain*. Wye College.

Best, R. H., and Coppock, J. T. (1962) *The changing use of land in Britain*, London.

Best, R. H., and Ward, J. T. (1956) *The garden controversy*. Wye College.

Birch, J. W. (1954) 'Observations on the delimitation of farming-type regions, with special reference to the Isle of Man'. *Inst. British Geographers, Trans and Papers*, Vol. 20, 141–158.

Bower, U. G. (1952) *Naga path*. London.

Brade-Birks, S. G. (1944) *Good soil*. London.

British Geomorphological Research Group (1962). Report No. 5 unpublished.

Brockie, W. J. (1958) 'Some aspects of aerial top-dressing in New Zealand'. *Proceedings of the Second New Zealand Geography Conference*, Christchurch, 13–22.

Brookfield, H. C., and Brown, Paula (1963) *Struggle for land. Agriculture and group territories among the Chimbu of the New Guinea Highlands*. Melbourne.

Buchanan, K. M. (1965) 'The people's communes after six years'. *Pacific Viewpoint*, Vol. 6, 52–64.

Buchanan, R. O. (1935) *The pastoral industries of New Zealand*, Inst. British Geographers.

Buchanan, R. O. (1951) 'Approach to economic geography'. *Indian Geographical Journal*, Silver Jubilee Souvenir Volume, 1–8.

Buchanan, R. O. (1959) 'Some reflections on agricultural geography'. *Geography*, Vol. 44, 1–13.

Bunge, W. (1962). *Theoretical geography*, Lund.

Bunting, B. T. (1965) *The geography of soil*. London.

Burley, T. (1961) *Land use research in the Hunter Valley: the land cover survey*. Newcastle, N.S.W.

Carter, G. F., and Pendleton, R. L. (1956) 'The humid soil, process and time'. *Geographical Review*, Vol. 46, 488–507.

Chisholm, M. (1962) *Rural settlement and land use*. London.

Chisholm, M. (1964) 'Problems in the classification and use of farming-type regions'. *Inst. British Geographers, Trans. and Papers*, Vol. 35, 91–103.

Chisholm, M. (1966) *Geography and economics*. London.

Clark, C., and Haswell, M. R. (1964) *The economics of subsistence agriculture*. London.

Clarke, J. G. D. (1952) *Prehistoric Europe: the economic basis*. London.

Coleman, A., and Maggs, K. R. A. (1961) *Land use survey handbook*. (2nd ed.) Isle of Thanet Geographical Association.

Coppock, J. T. (1964a) 'Crop, livestock and enterprise combinations in England and Wales'. *Economic Geography*, Vol. 40, 65–81.

Coppock, J. T. (1964b) *Agricultural atlas of England and Wales*. London.

Coppock, J. T. (1964c) 'Post-war studies in the geography of British agriculture'. *Geographical Review*, Vol. 54, 409–426.

Courtenay, P. P. (1965) *Plantation agriculture*. London.

Cumberland, K. B. (1944) 'The survey and classification of land in New Zealand; a basis for planning'. *Trans. Royal Soc. N.Z.* Vol. 74, 185–195.

Cumberland, K. B., and Fox, J. W. (1962) *New Zealand, a regional view*. Christchurch (1958, 2nd ed. 1962).

Darling, F. F. (ed.) (1955) *West Highland Survey*. London.

de Schlippe, Pierre. *See* Schlippe.

Devon Commission (1847–8) *Digest of evidence taken before H.M. Commissioners of Enquiry into the state of the law and practice in respect of the occupation of land in Ireland* (2 vols.). H.M.S.O. Dublin.

Dexter, K. (1961) *Farming for profits*. Harmondsworth.

Digby, M. (1963) *Co-operative land use, the challenge to traditional co-operation*. Oxford.

Donkin, R. A. (1963) 'The Cistercian Order in medieval England: some conclusions'. *Inst. British Geographers, Trans. and Papers*, Vol. 33, 181–198.

Duchaufour, Ph. (1960) *Précis de pédologie*. Paris.

Duley, F. L., and Hays, O. E. (1932) 'The effect of the degree of slope on runoff and soil erosion'. *Jnl. Agricultural Research*, Vol. 45, 349–360.

Dumont, R. (1954) *Types of rural economy.* Paris, translated by D. Magnin, London, 1957.

Duncan, J. S. (1962) 'The land for the people, land settlement and rural population movements, 1886–1906' in *Land and livelihood, geographical essays in honour of George Jobberns* (ed. M. McCaskill), 170–190. N.Z. Geog. Soc., Christchurch.

Dunn, E. S. (1954) *The location of agricultural production*, Gainesville.

Elliott, F. F. (1933) *Types of farming in the United States.* U.S. Govt. Printing Office.

Ellison, W. (1953) *Marginal land in Britain*, London.

Evans, E. Estyn (1956) 'The ecology of peasant life in western Europe'. in *Man's role in changing the face of the earth* (ed. W. L. Thomas), Chicago, 217–239.

Eyre, S. R. (1963) *Vegetation and soils; a world picture.* London.

Farmer, B. H. (1960) On not controlling subdivision in paddy lands, *Inst. British Geographers, Trans. and Papers*, Vol. 28, 225–235.

Faucher, D. (1949) *Geographie agraire: types de cultures.* Paris.

Fielding, G. J. (1964) 'The Los Angeles milkshed: a study of the political factor in agriculture'. *Geographical Review*, Vol. 54, 1–12.

Fielding, G. J. (1965) 'The role of government in New Zealand wheat growing'. *Annals Assoc. American Geographers* Vol. 55, 87–97.

Florence, P. S. (1944) 'The selection of industries suitable for dispersion into rural areas'. *Jnl. Royal Statistical Soc.*, Vol. 107, 93–107.

Forde, C. D. (1934) *Habitat, economy and society.* London.

Fortes, M., Steel, R. W., and Ady, P. (1948) 'Ashanti survey, 1945–46: an experiment in social research'. *Geographical Jnl.*, Vol. 110, 149–179.

Fox, J. W. (1956) *Land-use survey, general principles and a New Zealand example*, Auckland University College Bull., 49.

Franklin, S. H. (1962). 'Reflections on the peasantry'. *Pacific Viewpoint* Vol. 3, 1–26.

Fullerton, B. (1954) 'The northern margin of grain production in Sweden in the twentieth century'. *Inst. British Geographers, Trans. and Papers*, Vol. 20, 181–191.

Garnett, A. (1937) *Insolation and relief*, Inst. British Geographers. London.

Garrad, G. H. (1954) *A survey of the agriculture of Kent.* London.

George, P. (1962) *L'U.R.S.S.* (2nd ed.). Paris.

Gourou, P. (1961) *The tropical world*, (3rd ed.).

Gregory, S. (1954) 'Accumulated temperature maps of the British Isles'. *Inst. British Geographers, Trans. and Papers*, Vol. 20, 59–73.

Grigg, D. (1965). 'The logic of regional systems'. *Annals Assoc. American Geographers*, Vol. 55, 465–491.

Grist, D. H. (1953) *Rice*, London.

Grotewald, A. (1959) 'Von Thünen in retrospect'. *Economic Geography*, Vol. 35, 346–355.

Haggett, P. (1965) *Locational analysis in human geography*, London.

Halstead, C. A. (1958) 'The climate of the Glasgow region' in *The Glasgow region: a general survey*, eds. R. Miller and J. Tivy, Glasgow, 62–72.

Hartshorne, R., and Dicken, S. N. (1935) 'A classification of the agricultural regions of Europe and North America on a uniform statistical basis'. *Annals Assoc. American Geographers*, Vol. 25, 99–120.

Hartshorne, R. (1939) *The nature of geography*, Lancaster, Pa.

Hartshorne, R. (1959) *Perspective on the nature of geography*, Chicago.

Haystead, L., and Fite, G. C. (1955) *The agricultural regions of the United States*. Norman, Oklahoma.

Heichelheim, F. M. (1956) 'Effects of classical antiquity on the land' in *Man's role in changing the face of the earth* (ed. W. L. Thomas). Chicago, 165–182.

Henderson, J. M. (1957) 'The utilisation of agricultural land: a regional approach', *Papers and Proceedings, Regional Science Association*, Vol. 3, 99–117.

Higbee, E. (1958) *American agriculture*. New York.

Hoover, E. M. (1948) *The location of economic activity*. New York.

Howell, J. P. (1925) *Agricultural atlas of England and Wales*, Southampton.

Hutchinson, Sir Joseph (1965) *Essays on crop plant evolution*. Cambridge.

Institute of Agrarian Affairs (1955) 'Agriculture and forestry; competition or coexistence?' *International Jnl. Agrarian Affairs*, Vol. 2.

International Geographical Union (1952) *Report of the Commission on World Land Use Survey (1949-1952)*. Worcester, U.S.A.

International Institute for Land Reclamation and Improvement (1959) *Land consolidation in Europe*, prepared by E. H. Jacoby (F.A.O.) Waneningen.

Isard, W. (1956) *Location and the space economy*. Cambridge, Mass.

Jacoby, E. H. *See* International Institute for Land Reclamation and Improvement.

Jacks, G. V. (1946) *Land classification for land use planning*. Imperial Bureau of Soil Science, Harpenden.

Jackson, B., Barnard, C., and Sturrock, F. (1963) *The pattern of farming in the eastern counties*. Farm Economics Branch, Cambridge.

Jin-Bee, Ooi. *See* Ooi Jin-Bee.

Johnston, W. B. (1962) 'The fragmentation of farm land in Canterbury' in *Land and livelihood, geographical essays in honour of George Jobberns* (ed. M. McCaskill), 202–223. N.Z. Geog. Soc., Christchurch.

Jonasson, Olof (1925) 'The agricultural regions of Europe'. *Economic Geography*, Vol. 1, 277–314.

Jones, W. D. (1930) 'Ratios and isopleth maps in regional investigations of agricultural land occupance'. *Annals Assoc. American Geographers*, Vol. 20, 177–195.

Kohnke, H., and Bertrand, A. R. (1959) *Soil conservation*. New York.

Konstantinov, O. A. (1962) 'Economic geography' in *Soviet geography, accomplishments and tasks*, trans. by L. Ecker, American Geographical Society, New York.

Kuznetsov, G. A. (1963) 'An economic appraisal of lands in connection with the organisation of lands on state farms of the virgin lands'. *Geografiya i khozyaistyo*, trans. in *Soviet Geography, Review and Translation*, Vol. 4, 10–15.

Lewthwaite, G. R. (1966) Environmentalism and determinism: a search for clarification, *Annals Assoc. American Geographers*, Vol. 56, 1–23.

Lösch, A. (1940) *The economics of location*, Jena, trans. from revised edition, 1954, New Haven.

Lydolph, P. A. (1964) *Geography of the U.S.S.R.* New York.

Macgregor, D. R. (1957) 'Some observations on the geographical significance of slopes'. *Geography*, Vol. 42, 167–173.

McClintock, A. H. (ed.) (1960) *A descriptive atlas of New Zealand*, Wellington.

McHugh, B. J. (1963) 'County Tyrone' in *Land use in Northern Ireland* (ed. L. Symons), London, 252–266.

Marshall, T. J. (1947) *Mechanical composition of soil in relation to field descriptions of texture*, Council for Scientific and Industrial Research, Melbourne.

Maruta, S. (1956) *Memoirs of the Faculty of Agriculture*, Kagoshima University, Japan.

Messer, M. (1932) *Agricultural atlas of England and Wales*, 2nd ed.

Meteorological Office M.O. Form 3300 (1928) *Tables for the evaluation of daily values of accumulated temperature above and below 42 degrees F. from daily values of maximum and minimum temperature*, H.M.S.O. London.

Narr, K. J. (1956) 'Early food producing populations' in *Man's role in changing the face of the earth* (ed. W. L. Thomas) Chicago, 134–151.

New Zealand Department of Scientific and Industrial Research (1962) *Soil survey method*, Soil Bureau bulletin No. 25 by N. H. Taylor and I. J. Pohlen, Wellington.

Newth, J. A. (1961) 'Soviet agriculture: the private sector, 1950–1959'. *Soviet Studies*, Vol. 13, 160–171 and 414–432.

North East Development Association (1950) *A physical land classification of Northumberland, Durham and part of the North Riding of Yorkshire.* Newcastle.

Nye, P. H., and Greenland, D. J. (1960). *The soil under shifting cultivation.* Commonwealth Agricultural Bureaux, Farnham Royal.

Nye, P. H., and Stephens, D. (1960) *Agriculture and land-use in Ghana.*

Ochse, J. J., Soule, M. J. (Jr.), Dijkman, M. J., and Wehlburg, C. (1961) *Tropical and subtropical agriculture*, 2 vols., New York.

Ooi Jin-Bee (1961) The rubber industry of the Federation of Malaya, *Jnl. Tropical Geography*, Vol. 15, 46–65.

Ooi Jin-Bee (1963) *Land, people and economy in Malaya*, London.

Organisation for European Economic Co-operation (1960) *Agricultural regions in the E.E.C.* Paris.

Peattie, R. (1936) *Mountain geography* Cambridge, Mass.

Pedler, F. J. (1955) *Economic geography of West Africa*, London.

Peters, G. H. (1964) 'The "new" agricultural policy'. *Westminster Bank Review*, Nov. 1964, 35–39.

Polish Academy of Sciences (1961) *Problems of applied geography*. Institute of Geography, Warsaw.

Rauch, Georg von (1957) *A history of Soviet Russia* translated by P. and A. Jacobsohn, London.

Renner, G. T. (1935) 'The statistical approach to regions'. *Annals Assoc. American Geographers*, Vol. 25, 137–152.

Romney, D. H. (ed.) (1959) *Land in British Honduras*, H.M.S.O. London.

Sachs, I. (ed.) (1964) *Agriculture, land reforms and economic development.* Warsaw.

Salaman, R. N. (1949) *The history and social influence of the potato*. Cambridge.

Samuelson, P.A. (1964) *Economics*, 6th ed. New York.

Sauer, C. O. (1919) 'Mapping the utilisation of the land'. *Geographical Review*, Vol. 8, 47–54.

Sauer, C. O. (1952) *Agricultural origins and dispersals*. American Geographical Society, New York.

Schlippe, Pierre de (1956) *Shifting cultivation in Africa: The Zande system of agriculture*. London.

Scott, P. (1957) 'The agricultural regions of Tasmania: a statistical definition'. *Economic Geography*, Vol. 33, 109–121.

Sears, P. D. (1962) 'Regional differences in grassland farming practice, New Zealand conditions and some overseas comparisons' in *Land and livelihood, geographical essays in honour of George Jobberns* (ed. M. McCaskill), 191–202. N.Z. Geog. Soc., Christchurch.

Slicher van Bath, B. (1963) *The agrarian history of western Europe AD 500–1850*. London.

Smith, W. (1949) *An economic geography of Great Britain*. London.

Spencer, J. E., and Hale, G. A. (1961) The origin, nature and distribution of agricultural terracing, *Pacific Viewpoint*, Vol. 2, 1–40. Comment by A. C. S. Wright and reply by J. E. Spencer appear in *Pacific Viewpoint*, Vol. 3 (1962), 97–105.

Stamp, L. D. (ed.) (1937–44) *The land of Britain*, the report of the Land Utilisation Survey of Britain.

Stamp, L. D. (1948) *The land of Britain, its use and misuse*. London, 3rd ed. 1962.

Stamp, L. D. (1960) *Applied geography*. Harmondsworth.

Stephens, N. (1963) 'Climate', in *Land use in Northern Ireland* (ed. L. Symons), London, 75–92.

Stewart, O. C. (1956) 'Fire as the first great force employed by man' in *Man's role in changing the face of the earth* (ed. W. L. Thomas). Chicago, 115–133.

Storie, T. E. (1933) 'An index for rating the agricultural value of soils'. *Calif. Expt. Sta. Bull.*, 556.

Sumner, B. H. (1947) *Survey of Russian history*, 2nd ed. 1961. London.

Symons, L. (1955–6) 'Hill land utilisation in Ulster'. *J. Statist. Social Inquiry Soc. Ireland*, Vol. 19, 58–81.

Symons, L. (1959) 'The economic conquest of the hills'. *Scottish Geographical Magazine*, Vol. 75, 18–29.

Symons, L. (1960–61) 'The pastoral economy of New Zealand and some comparisons with Ireland'. *J. Statist. Social Inquiry Soc. Ireland*, Vol. 21, 94–131.

Symons, L. (1961) 'Land development in Southland'. *New Zealand Geographer*, Vol. 17, 87–93.

Symons, L. (ed.) (1963) *Land use in Northern Ireland.* London.

Tagg, J. R. (1957) *Wind data related to the generation of electricity by wind power*, British Electrical and Allied Industries Research Association, Leatherhead.

Tax, S. (1956) Contribution to discussion on subsistence economies in *Man's role in changing the face of the earth* (ed. W. L. Thomas). Chicago, 421.

Taylor, N. H., and Pohlen, I. J. *See* New Zealand Department of Scientific and Industrial Research.

Tempany, A., and Grist, D. H. (1958) *An introduction to tropical agriculture.* London.

Thomas, D. (1963) *Agriculture in Wales during the Napoleonic wars.* Cardiff.

Thomas, D. E. L. (1963) 'Farm types and farm incomes' in *Land use in Northern Ireland* (ed. L. Symons), London, 162–175.

Thomas, W. L. (ed.) (1956) *Man's role in changing the face of the earth.* Chicago.

Thomsen, F. L., and Foote, R. J. (1952) *Agricultural prices*, 2nd ed. New York.

Thornthwaite, C. W. (1948) An approach toward a rational classification of climate, *Geographical Review*, Vol. 38, 55–94.

Thünen, J. von (1826) *Der isolierte Staat in Beziehung auf Landwirtschaft und Nationalökonomie*, Rostock.

Tracy, M. (1964) *Agriculture in western Europe: crisis and adaptation since 1880.* London.

Trow-Smith, R. (1957) *A history of British livestock husbandry to 1700.* London.

Trow-Smith, R. (1959) *A history of British livestock husbandry 1700–1900.* London.

United Nations Food and Agriculture Organisation (1957). 'Shifting cultivation'. *Unasylva*, Vol. 11, No. 1, 9–11, reprinted in *Trop. Agric. Trin.* Vol. 34, 159–164.

U.S.A. Dept. of Agriculture (1951) *Soil survey manual.*

U.S.A. Dept. of Agriculture (1954) *A manual on conservation of soil and water.*

U.S.A. Dept. of Agriculture (1955) *Water*, Washington.

U.S.A. Dept. of Agriculture (1957) *Soil*, Washington.

U.S.A. National Resources Planning Board (1941). *Land classification in the United States.*

U.S.S.R. Academy of Sciences of the (1962). *Soil-geographical zoning of the U.S.S.R.* (*in relation to the agricultural usage of lands*) translated by A. Gourevitch. Jerusalem and London, 1963.

Vavilov, N. I. (ed. and principal author) (1935) *Teoreticheski osnovi selektsi rasteni.* Moscow, 1935. Selected writings translated in 'The origin variation, immunity and breeding of cultivated plants'. *Chronica Botanica,* Vol. 13, 1949–50, Waltham, Mass., 1951, 1–366.

Vilenskii, D. G. (1957) *Soil science.* Moscow, trans. by A. Barron and Z. S. Cole, Jerusalem and London, 1963.

von Rauch. *See* Rauch.

von Thünen. *See* Thünen.

Wadham, S., Wilson, R. and Wood, J. (1957). *Land utilisation in Australia* 3rd edition, Melbourne and London.

Ward, R. G. (1956) 'Land development in the Taupo country'. *New Zealand Geographer,* Vol. 12, 115–132.

Watson, J. A. S., and More, J. A. (1962) *Agriculture.* 11th ed. Edinburgh and London.

Watters, R. F. (1960) 'The nature of shifting cultivation: a review of recent research'. *Pacific Viewpoint,* Vol. 1, 59–99.

Weaver, J. C. (1954) Crop combination regions in the Middle West, *Geographical Review,* Vol. 44, 175–200.

Weber, A. (1909) *Theory of the location of industries,* translated by C. J. Freidrich, Chicago, 1929. 2nd impression, 1957.

Whittlesey, D. (1936) Major agricultural regions of the earth, *Annals Assoc. American Geographers,* Vol. 26, 199–240.

Whittlesey, D. (1954) 'The regional concept and the regional method' in *American geography, inventory and prospect* (eds. P. E. James, C. F. Jones and J. K. Wright) Syracuse.

Winter, E. H. (1956) *Bwamba economy.* East African Inst. of Social Research.

Wycherley, P. R. (1963) Variation in the performance of *Hevea* in Malaya, *Jnl. Tropical Geography,* Vol. 17, 143–171.

Youngblood and Cox (1922) *An economic study of a typical ranching area on the Edwards plateau of Texas,* Bulletin No. 295, Texas Agricultural Experimental Station.

Zobler, L. (1957) 'Statistical testing of regional boundaries'. *Annals Assoc. American Geographers,* Vol. 47, 83–95.

Zuckerman, Sir Solly and others (1958). *Land ownership and resources.* Cambridge.

Zvorykin, K. V. (1963) 'Scientific principles for an agro-production classification of lands'. *Geografiya i khozyaistvo,* trans. in *Soviet Geography, Review and Translation,* Vol. 4, 3–10.

Index